*Elements of Network Synthesis*

*Reinhold Electrical Engineering Sciences Textbook Series*


CONSULTING EDITOR

PROFESSOR SAMUEL SEELY
*Case Institute of Technology*
*Cleveland, Ohio*

## Consulting Editor's Statement

Modern network synthesis has developed into a set of methods by which a special class of functions—the positive real functions—are employed in the realization of one or more networks with the prescribed functional form. For the most part, however, the known techniques have remained independent of one another, each with its own limitations, and none providing very much insight into how to make a logical extension that results in a broader technique allowing the inclusion of a number of methods.

Dr. Hazony provides the first generalization of the problem in "Elements of Network Synthesis"—a book that successfully places the many techniques available in reasonable perspective. In this unique work Dr. Hazony has accomplished a major breakthrough in network synthesis. The text contains numerous examples with the details for carrying out specific problems and is sufficiently developed to permit a complete understanding of its substance. Moreover, the perspective provided by the entire study accomplishes more than the coordination of past methods. The extension of the generalization to $n$-port networks, a matter previously of quite limited success, is a result of major significance. The implications of this generalization have by no means been exhausted within the confines of Dr. Hazony's well-disciplined treatment, and his book should open new vistas for further research.

It is a pleasure to welcome this distinctive book to the REINHOLD ELECTRICAL ENGINEERING SCIENCES TEXTBOOK SERIES—a series dedicated to offering unique contributions to the literature of modern electrical engineering.

SAMUEL SEELY

# ELEMENTS OF
# NETWORK SYNTHESIS

## Dov Hazony

*Associate Professor of Electrical Engineering*
*Case Institute of Technology*
*Cleveland, Ohio*

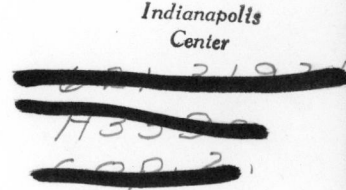
*New York*
**REINHOLD PUBLISHING CORPORATION**
*Chapman & Hall Ltd., London*

*TO MY FATHER AND MOTHER*

# For the Student

SYNTHESIS, in a way, signifies the reverse of analysis. For example, if you turn the steering wheel of your car, you hope that the car will turn also. Let us suppose that the automobile veers, according to your expectation, to the right. An *analysis* of this total action would state that turning the wheel in a clockwise direction moves the car to the right. On the other hand, the design of the steering mechanism would be defined as *synthesis*. That is, synthesis implies the design problem that must be solved to meet a given purpose (here to turn the car when we revolve the wheel). In a similar way, we note that the analysis of the operation of a television set reveals that a signal coming from the antenna produces a picture on the screen. The synthesis problem would be: given a signal at the antenna and a picture on the screen, what should we have inside the television set.

Now let us consider a case more closely related to electrical engineering. An analysis of a transformer shows that the ratio between the steady-state voltage appearing across the primary windings and that appearing across the secondary windings is constant. Our synthesis problem is to construct a mechanism having such a property.

It is clear from these examples that synthesis can be closely related to almost any form of human creativity. However, we shall restrict our discussion in this text to a class of problems encountered in engineering. We elaborate. The steering mechanism of the car is an interconnection of mechanical elements. The television set is an interconnection of mostly electrical elements. An interconnection of elements is called a network. Clearly, a network may be made up of an interconnection of other networks (called subnetworks). We shall be concerned with a special class of networks that obey the following constraints.

They are:

(a) *Lumped*

If we are given a frequency range, then, within the tolerance limits of our measurements, each network may be divided into a finite number of subnetworks, each of which consists of a single kind of element. For example, one such subnetwork is a purely resistive network.

(b) *Linear*

By this we mean that, if we apply in turn a voltage across each element of the network and observe the current passing through it, an increase in the steady-state voltage will produce a proportional increase in the steady-state current. In other words, the proportionality is independent of the magnitude of the current.

(c) *Passive*

The networks do not contain energy sources.

The ordinary transformer has two windings (the primary and the secondary). It is customary to designate this transformer as a 2-port device. Here the term "port" has the meaning of a portal of entry, or an access. Referring to the figure on the cover of the book, we see that the buffer is a $2n$-port device and the terminal box (denoted by $[\zeta]$) is an $n$-port device. The over-all combination is an $n$-port device.

The material in the text is concerned with the range of networks from 1-port to $n$-port.

*Cleveland, Ohio*                                              Dov Hazony
*November, 1962*

# *For the Teacher*

THE RAPID growth of electronics, controls, computers, and related technologies has created an ever-increasing demand for a thorough understanding of the field of networks. Take, for example, a complex network, involving electrical, mechanical, and other elements. If all of the nonlinear and active elements are removed from this network, what remains is a linear passive $n$-port network. Although the analysis of such an $n$-port network is a relatively well-understood science, the synthesis of such a network is not so simple. The synthesis problem would arise, of course, if we first described the behavior of the $n$-port in a mathematical form (subject to some optimal constraints) and then wanted to construct a network to do the job. Once the synthesis is complete, we may reconstitute the desired network behavior by reinstating the nonlinear and active elements in their proper ports.

This book is an attempt to present the problem of network synthesis in a continuous concise manner, the main emphasis being on fundamentals. In an effort to have the book self-contained, all of the necessary tools have been developed within it. However, in the sections on Laplace transformations, functions of a complex variable, and matrices, I have tried to be convincing rather than rigorous, since the emphasis is on review. The textbook is designed primarily for a two semester course for the senior or the graduate student in electrical or in mechanical engineering, and has been class-tested at Case Institute of Technology. Since Chapters 2, 8, and 14 are rather more theoretical in nature than the others, they probably would be less emphasized for the undergraduate student.

Some recent breakthroughs in network synthesis have warranted several departures from the conventional approach developed in previous books. These are as follows:

(a) The area of interest extends from 1-port to $n$-port networks.
(b) Several unifying concepts have been developed. For example, it is shown that the Bott-Duffin, Brune, and cascade synthesis techniques can be arrived at in a natural manner by applying a Darlington-type synthesis to extensions of Richards' theorem. This approach is continued to $n$-port synthesis.

(c) Transformerless transfer function synthesis of two-element-kind networks with arbitrary but bounded gain is presented.

(d) A wide use has been made of nonreciprocal networks (gyrators). This makes it possible to develop some of the theories in a natural manner, thereby resulting in a great deal of simplification. However, in all cases reciprocal representations are also provided.*

The first chapter provides a general background. It is anticipated that some of the students may be familiar with a different notation, and others might even have gone through a program in physics or mathematics rather than in engineering. A review of the material of the first chapter will insure that they all will use the same terms. The chapter also serves as a review of Laplace transform theory and certain parts of circuit analysis which are very important to the text.

In the second chapter the reader is introduced to some of the mathematics of network synthesis. The main purpose of the chapter is to have the student familiarize himself with a set of tools and terms that will be of great use to him later in the course.

The positive real function, which is introduced in the first chapter, is of paramount importance. It is elaborated on in the second chapter, and tests for it are given in the third. In the fourth chapter it is shown that all $RLC$ networks lead to positive real functions, and in Chapter 5, that all positive real functions may be realized as series-parallel combinations of $RLC$ networks. Thus the first five chapters provide the necessary and sufficient conditions for the realization of any positive real function as an $RLC$ network.

In Chapters 6, 7, and 8, the concepts underlying 1-port cascade synthesis are developed. Toward this end the properties of 2-port networks and 2-port elements are studied in Chapter 6, and the Darlington synthesis is covered in Chapter 7. The theory of cascade synthesis is amplified in Chapter 8 through the application of Darlington-type synthesis to extensions of Richards' theorem.

The even part of an impedance function plays a very important role in network synthesis. This is the subject of Chapter 9. The study of even-part synthesis provides a great deal of insight into the problem of network synthesis and clarifies the fundamental rules involved. It is demonstrated through an investigation of the even part that it is possible to link together the cascade, Brune, and Bott-Duffin syntheses.

Various aspects of three-terminal transfer function synthesis are treated in Chapters 10, 11, and 12. Chapter 10 provides a synthesis procedure for transfer functions through the use of constant resistance networks. In Chapter 11 two-element-kind 2-port network synthesis is considered in

---

* Complete synthesis procedures for nonreciprocal networks are beyond the scope of this text.

detail. It is shown that the simplicity of the corresponding realizations yields very useful results in the synthesis of three-terminal transfer functions. The chapter culminates in the synthesis of the double-resistive-terminated lossless networks. Chapter 12 discusses the necessary and sufficient conditions for the realization of the transfer function of three-terminal two-element-kind networks.

The background material necessary for the study of $n$-port synthesis is presented in Chapter 13. This material includes one- and two-element-kind immittance matrices, and singular and reduced matrices (Oono's). The proof of the existence theorem for an $n$-port is concluded by applying the Gewertz-Oono synthesis procedure to the reduced matrices. A detailed study of the Bott-Duffin and the cascade $n$-port synthesis is given in Chapter 14. In Chapter 15 Oono's synthesis procedure is developed by applying a Darlington-type synthesis to the reduced matrices of Chapter 13.

DOV HAZONY

*Cleveland, Ohio*
*November, 1962*

# Acknowledgments

THERE IS ONLY one name on the cover; yet this book is the result of many long hours by many people. The author would like to thank these people. Special thanks are due to Professors R. J. Duffin of Carnegie Institute of Technology and S. Seely of Case Institute of Technology without whose help the book probably would not have been completed. Also the encouragement and guidance of Professor A. Fialkow of the Polytechnic Institute of Brooklyn are very much appreciated.

The author was overwhelmed by the enthusiasm and support of many of his colleagues and students, particularly: Professor J. B. Murdoch (now at the University of New Hampshire), Dr. H. J. Nain, R. D. Joseph, A. A. Clark, K. Prasad, A. D. Warren, and T. Zeren. The author is indebted also to his colleagues, Professors R. E. Collin, J. Miro, R. Plonsey, and J. D. Schoeffler, who shared in so may ways in writing the manuscript. Acknowledgment is also due to Mr. J. Hart of the Reinhold Publishing Corporation for the many hours of very useful discussion and help related to the publication of the material.

The author is very thankful to Professor R. E. Bolz, Head of the Engineering Division, and to Professor Emeritus J. R. Martin, former Acting Chairman of the Electrical Engineering Department, at Case Institute of Technology, for the generous provisions of facilities and encouragement, and to Misses Janet Leonard and Marlene Lewis for eager and cheerful typing of the manuscript.

Special thanks are due to Dr. E. F. Bolinder of the U. S. Air Force Cambridge Research Laboratories, Office of Aerospace Research, United States Air Force.

תושלב״ע

DOV HAZONY

# *Contents*

# *Introduction* | **CHAPTER 1**

## NETWORK SYNTHESIS AND ANALYSIS—GENERAL COMMENT 1.1

Network synthesis is a branch of network theory that deals with the problem of the realization of systems or "black boxes" that satisfy prescribed characteristics. For example, an ideal low-pass filter has the characteristics shown in Fig. 1.1.

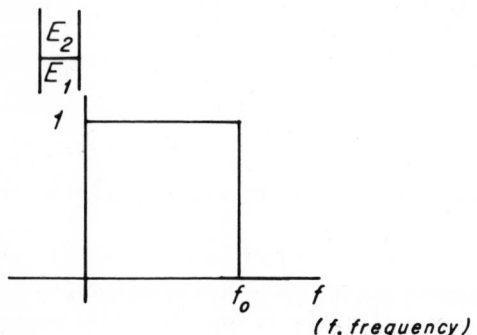

**Fig. 1.1. Characteristics of an ideal low-pass filter**

On the other hand, the box $B$ in a feedback loop may require another set of prescribed frequency-dependent features (Fig. 1.2).

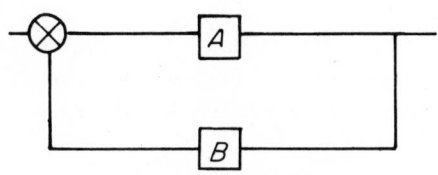

**Fig. 1.2. A feedback loop**

1

In general, the prescribed functions that characterize the "black boxes" are functions of complex frequencies. These latter functions are obtained when the Laplace transformation techniques are applied to the integro-differential equations that describe linear dynamic systems.

The Laplace transformation technique is reviewed briefly in Section 1.2, and is augmented in Section 1.3, where there is a standard development of partial fraction expansion—a technique generally useful in network synthesis. Section 1.4 discusses the effects of the use of the Laplace transforms on network analysis and introduces the type of functions and tools that will be employed throughout the text.

## 1.2. THE LAPLACE TRANSFORMATION

The Laplace transformation is a technique for the solution of linear integro-differential equations subject to prescribed initial conditions. In effect, the method transforms an integro-differential equation into an algebraic one. Then after a certain amount of algebraic manipulation, the result may be written in a form suitable for subsequent interpretation.

The Laplace transformation, written as $\mathcal{L}[f(t)]$, is defined by the integral

$$F(s) \triangleq \mathcal{L}[f(t)] \equiv \int_0^\infty f(t)e^{-st}\, dt \qquad \text{1.2.1}$$

$F(s)$ is called the Laplace transform of $f(t)$, and is an algebraic function of the complex variable $s$.

In linear $RLC$ (resistors, inductors, and capacitors) networks, the resulting $F(s)$ is a rational function of the complex variable $s$ and may be expressed both as the ratio of the polynomials

$$F(s) = \frac{a_n s^n + a_{n-1}s^{n-1} + \cdots + a_0}{b_m s^m + b_{m-1}s^{m-1} + \cdots + b_0}$$

or equivalently as the continued product

$$F(s) = H\frac{\underset{p}{\Pi}\,(s - a_p)}{\underset{q}{\Pi}\,(s - b_q)} \qquad \text{1.2.2}$$

where $H$ is a constant. The constants $a_p$ and $b_q$ are called the zeros and poles of $F(s)$, respectively $f(t)$ may be obtained from $F(s)$ by means of an integral which is written as follows:

$$f(t) = \mathcal{L}^{-1}[F(s)] = \frac{1}{2\pi j}\int_{c-j\infty}^{c+j\infty} F(s)e^{st}\, ds = \frac{H}{2\pi j}\int_{c-j\infty}^{c+j\infty} \frac{\underset{p}{\Pi}(s - a_p)}{\underset{q}{\Pi}(s - b_q)}e^{st}\, ds \qquad \text{1.2.3}$$

where $c$ is a real constant larger than the real part of the largest of the $b$'s. Hence if all the poles are in the left half of the complex $s$ plane (that is, $b_q < 0$), $c$ may be taken as zero.

The operation characterized by Eq. 1.2.3 is called the inverse Laplace transformation. To find the inverse transform by this method involves contour integration in the complex plane. The details seldom need to be carried out, however, because of the availability of tables of transform pairs, which make it easy to obtain the inverse of a given function by inspection. Also, by the technique of partial fraction expansion the form of $F(s)$ can be written in forms available in even limited tables of Laplace transforms (see Table 1.1). These details will be considered in a series of examples.

## Example 1.2.1

Find the Laplace transform of a constant $f(t) = A$.

### Solution

Use the basic definition of $\mathcal{L}[f(t)]$ to write

$$\mathcal{L}[A] = \int_0^\infty A e^{-st}\, dt = -\frac{A e^{-st}}{s}\Big]_0^\infty = \frac{A}{s} \qquad 1.2.4$$

## Example 1.2.2

Find the Laplace transform of $f(t) = e^{-at}$.

### Solution

The result is written directly as

$$\mathcal{L}[e^{-at}] = \int_0^\infty e^{-at} e^{-st}\, dt = \frac{-e^{-(a+s)t}}{(s+a)}\Big]_0^\infty = \frac{1}{s+a} \qquad 1.2.5$$

Observe that if $a = j\omega_0$, the transform of $e^{-j\omega_0 t}$ is $1/(s + j\omega_0)$, and since $\cos \omega_0 t = \operatorname{Re} e^{-j\omega_0 t}$, $\mathcal{L}[\cos \omega_0 t] = \operatorname{Re} 1/(s + j\omega_0) = s/(s^2 + \omega_0^2)$. Similarly $\sin \omega_0 t = -\operatorname{Im} e^{-j\omega_0 t}$, and $\mathcal{L}[\sin \omega_0 t] = \omega_0/(s^2 + \omega_0^2)$. In general, in solving integro-differential equations of the type

$$g(t) = a_n \frac{d^n f(t)}{dt^n} + a_{n-1} \frac{d^{n-1} f(t)}{dt^{n-1}}$$

$$+ + a_1 \frac{df(t)}{dt} + a_0 f(t) + a_{-1} \int^t f(t)\, dt + + \qquad 1.2.6$$

it is also necessary to find the Laplace transforms of derivatives and integrals of $f(t)$. Those can be evaluated in terms of $\mathcal{L}[f(t)] = F(s)$.

### Example 1.2.3

Find the transforms of $df(t)/dt$ and $\int^{t} f(t)\ dt$.

**Solution**

$$\mathcal{L}[f'(t)] = \mathcal{L}\left[\frac{df(t)}{dt}\right] = \int_{0}^{\infty} e^{-st}\frac{d}{dt}\ f(t)\ dt$$

Now integrate by parts to get

$$\mathcal{L}[f'(t)] = f(t)\ e^{-st}\ \Big]_{0}^{\infty} + s\int_{0}^{\infty} f(t)\ e^{-st}\ dt$$

which becomes

$$\mathcal{L}[f'(t)] = -f(0) + sF(s) \tag{1.2.7}$$

Similarly the transform of $\int^{t} f(t)\ dt$ is

$$\mathcal{L}\left[\int^{t} f(t)\ dt\right] = \int_{0}^{\infty}\left[\int^{t} f(t)\ dt\right] e^{-st}\ dt$$

$$= -\frac{1}{s}\left[\int^{t} f(t)\ dt\right] e^{-st}\ \Big]_{0}^{\infty} + \frac{1}{s}\int_{0}^{\infty} f(t)e^{-st}\ dt \tag{1.2.8}$$

$$= +\frac{1}{s}\int^{0} f(t)\ dt + \frac{1}{s}\ F(s)$$

$$= \frac{1}{s}\ F(s) + \frac{f^{-1}(0)}{s}$$

These results may be used now to obtain solutions to some physical problems using the Laplace transformation.

### Example 1.2.4

Find $i(t)$ in the network Fig. 1.3, using the initial conditions $e(0) = 0 = i(0)$ (i.e., the network is said to be in a relaxed condition at $t = 0$) when $e(t) = 1$ for $t > 0$.

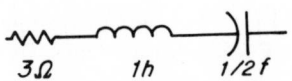

$3\Omega$      $1h$      $1/2 f$

**Fig. 1.3. An RLC network**

**Solution**

The differential equation describing the system is as follows:

$$e(t) = \frac{di(t)}{dt} + 3\ i(t) + 2\int i(t)\ dt \tag{1.2.9}$$

The results of Eqs. 1.2.1, 1.2.7, and 1.2.8, respectively, give

$$E(s) = \frac{1}{s}, \quad \mathcal{L}\left[\frac{di(t)}{dt}\right] = sI(s) + 0 \text{ and } \mathcal{L}[2\int i(t)\, dt] = \frac{2}{s}I(s) + 0$$

Hence

$$\frac{1}{s} = sI(s) + 3\,I(s) + 2\,I(s)/s \qquad \text{1.2.10}$$

which may be solved for $I(s)$ yielding

$$I(s) = \frac{1}{s+1} - \frac{1}{s+2} \qquad \text{1.2.11}$$

Each of these terms is of the form

$$\mathcal{L}[e^{-at}] = \frac{1}{s+a} \qquad \text{1.2.5}$$

which means that $i(t) = \mathcal{L}^{-1}[I(s)]$

$$= e^{-t} - e^{-2t}$$

This example illustrates the philosophy of the method of the Laplace transformation in which the differential equation (Eq. 1.2.9) was transformed into the algebraic equation (Eq. 1.2.10). Algebraic manipulation permitted an expression for $I(s)$ to be obtained. The inverse transform of $I(s)$ was not obtained by the integral definition shown in Eq. 1.2.3. Instead, $I(s)$ was expanded in a partial fraction so that the results of Example 1.2.2 may be utilized. Similar transform pairs are shown in Table 1.1.

**TABLE 1.1. LAPLACE TRANSFORMS**

| $f(t)$ | $F(s)$ | $f(t)$ | $F(s)$ |
|--------|--------|--------|--------|
| 1 | $\dfrac{1}{s}$ | $\displaystyle\lim_{a\to 0}\frac{1}{a}\int_0^a dt = \text{(Dirac }\delta\text{ function)}$ | 1 |
| $t$ | $\dfrac{1}{s^2}$ | $\dfrac{d}{dt}f(t)$ | $sF(s) - f(0)$ |
| $e^{-at}$ | $\dfrac{1}{s+a}$ | $\dfrac{d^2 f(t)}{dt^2}$ | $s^2 F(s) - sf(0) - f'(0)$ |
| $t\,e^{-at}$ | $\dfrac{1}{(s+a)^2}$ | $f^{-1}(t) = \displaystyle\int^t f(t)\, dt$ | $\dfrac{F(s)}{s} + \dfrac{f^{-1}(0)}{s}$ |
| $\cos \omega_0 t$ | $\dfrac{s}{s^2 + \omega_0^2}$ | $f^{-2}(t)$ | $\dfrac{F(s)}{s^2} + \dfrac{f^{-1}(0)}{s^2} + \dfrac{f^{-2}(0)}{s}$ |
| $\sin \omega_0 t$ | $\dfrac{\omega_0}{s^2 + \omega_0^2}$ | | |

## 1.3. PARTIAL FRACTION EXPANSION

In the previous section (Example 1.2.4) it was briefly pointed out that partial fraction expansion of the ratios of two polynomials is useful in the evaluation of the inverse Laplace transforms. The expansion is also very valuable in network synthesis. In particular, the expansion is useful for two-element networks where each term of the expansion might assume physical meaning. The Heaviside approach to partial fraction expansion will be utilized. It will be introduced by a simple example. The more difficult examples will be attacked later.

### Example 1.3.1

Expand $Z(s)$ in a partial fraction expansion:

$$Z(s) = \frac{(s+1)}{s(s+2)} \qquad \textbf{1.3.1}$$

*Solution*

The desired expansion is of the form

$$Z(s) = \frac{A}{s} + \frac{B}{s+2} \qquad \textbf{1.3.2}$$

The coefficients $A$ and $B$ can be evaluated by performing the identity

$$A(s+2) + Bs = s+1 \qquad \textbf{1.3.3}$$

yielding $A + B = 1$, and $2A = 1$, and therefore $A = B = \frac{1}{2}$.

However, these coefficients also can be obtained by the use of another method. Accordingly, multiply both sides of Eq. 1.3.2 by the factor $(s+0)$:

$$Z(s) \times (s+0) = \frac{A(s+0)}{s+0} + \frac{B(s+0)}{s+2} = A + \frac{Bs}{s+2} \qquad \textbf{1.3.4}$$

Note that the right side of the equation reduces to $A$ if $s$ is set to zero. Hence $A$ may be obtained by either deleting the factor $1/s$ from $Z(s)$ and setting $s$ to zero, or by evaluating the expression

$$A = sZ(s) \Big|_{s=0} = \lim_{s \to 0} [sZ(s)] = \frac{1}{2} \qquad \textbf{1.3.5}$$

To deduce the coefficient $B$, both sides of Eq. 1.3.2 are multiplied by $(s+2)$:

$$Z(s)(s+2) = \frac{A(s+2)}{s} + B\frac{(s+2)}{(s+2)} = \frac{A(s+2)}{s} + B \qquad \textbf{1.3.6}$$

Now the right side of the equation reduces to $B$ if $(s+2)$ is set to zero. It follows that the coefficient, $B$, may be obtained by either deleting the pole $(s+2)$ and setting $s+2$ to zero, or by the evaluation of the corresponding expression:

$$B = (s+2)Z(s) \Big|_{(s+2)=0} = \lim_{s \to -2} [(s+2)Z(s)] = \frac{1}{2} \qquad \textbf{1.3.7}$$

The limiting process indicated in Eq. 1.3.5 and 1.3.7 is necessary because, unless the respective pole is deleted, the corresponding expression is indeterminate and L'Hospital's rule must be followed. Henceforth, however, an expression of the type

$$a_p = (s + b_p)Z(s)\Big|_{s+b_p=0} \qquad \text{1.3.8}$$

will be interpreted to say that $a_p$ is obtained by deleting the pole $(s + b_p)$ and setting $s + b_p = 0$.

In trying to formalize the rules governing partial fraction expansions, we find that three distinct cases come into play.

## Case I

The numerator of $Z(s)$ is lower in degree than the denominator, and $Z(s)$ has no high-order poles.

In this case, $Z(s)$ can be written in the form

$$Z(s) = \sum_p \frac{a_p}{s + b_p} \qquad \text{1.3.9}$$

where $a_p$ is given by Eq. 1.3.10.

$$a_p = (s + b_p)Z(s)\Big|_{s+b_p=0} \qquad \text{1.3.10}$$

The proof of this statement may be obtained by observing that in the same way that $B$ drops out of consideration in Eq. 1.3.4 when $s$ is set to zero, the rest of the coefficient will drop out as well and $A$ (or $a_p$) is the only unaffected term.

## Example 1.3.2

Expand $Z(s)$ in a partial fraction expansion:

$$Z(s) = \frac{(s + 1)(s + 3)}{s(s + 2)(s + 4)} \qquad \text{1.3.11}$$

*Solution*

The expansion is of the form

$$Z(s) = \frac{A}{s} + \frac{B}{s + 2} + \frac{C}{s + 4} \qquad \text{1.3.12}$$

where

$$A = Z(s)s\Big|_{s=0} = \frac{1 \times 3}{2 \times 4} = \frac{3}{8}$$

$$B = Z(s)(s + 2)\Big|_{s+2=0} = \frac{(-2 + 1)(-2 + 3)}{(-2)(-2 + 4)} = \frac{1}{4}$$

and

$$C = Z(s)(s + 4)\Big|_{(s+4)=0} = \frac{(-4 + 1)(-4 + 3)}{(-4)(-4 + 2)} = \frac{3}{8}$$

It is sometimes convenient to express Eq. 1.3.10 in the following form:

$$a_p = \frac{P(s)(s + b_p)}{Q(s)}\bigg|_{s+b_p=0} \qquad \text{1.3.13}$$

[$P(s)$ is the numerator and $Q(s)$ the denominator of $Z(s)$.]

Since $Q(s)$ has the factor $s + b_p$, the expression is in an indeterminant form when $s$ approaches $-b_p$. The value of $a_p$ can be obtained by using L'Hospital's rule:

$$a_p = \frac{P + (s + b_p)\, dP/ds}{dQ/ds}\bigg|_{s+b_p=0} = \frac{P}{\dfrac{dQ}{ds}}\bigg|_{s+b_p=0} \qquad \text{1.3.14}$$

## Case II

The numerator of $Z(s)$ is of the same degree or higher than that of the denominator.

The process employed so far would lead into difficulties, for example, if $Z(s)$ is given by

$$Z(s) = \frac{a_4 s^4 + a_3 s^3 + a_2 s^2 + a_1 s + a_0}{b_2 s^2 + b_1 s + b_0} \qquad \text{1.3.15}$$

However, if long division is used, $Z(s)$ may be rewritten as

$$Z(s) = Z_1 + c_0 + c_1 s + c_2 s^2 \qquad \text{1.3.16}$$

where

$$Z_1 = \frac{a_1' s + a_0'}{b_2 s^2 + b_1 s + b_0}$$

where $Z_1$ (sometimes referred to as the principal part) has a numerator of lower degree than that of the denominator.

There is no obvious multiplication factor that will make it possible to isolate the constants $c_0$, $c_1$, or $c_2$ (upon setting this factor to zero), though the process of long division is entirely adequate. On the other hand, $Z_1$ is of the form discussed in Case I, and may be expanded in a partial fraction expansion as has been outlined earlier.

## Case III

$Z(s)$ has high-order poles.

In such cases the higher-order poles must be accounted for in the partial fraction expansion. One way of obtaining the expansion is illustrated by the following example:

## Example 1.3.3

Expand in a partial fraction

$$Z(s) = \frac{(s + 2)}{(s + 1)^2(s + 3)} = \frac{A}{(s + 1)^2} + \frac{B}{s + 1} + \frac{C}{s + 3} \qquad 1.3.17$$

### Solution

The coefficients $A$ and $C$ may be obtained by the usual method

$$A = Z(s)(s + 1)^2 \Big|_{(s+1) = 0} = \frac{(-1 + 2)}{(-1 + 3)} = \frac{1}{2}$$

and

$$C = Z(s)(s + 3) \Big|_{(s+3) = 0} = \frac{(-3 + 2)}{(-3 + 1)^2} = -\frac{1}{4}$$

But $B$ cannot be obtained in this manner because

$$Z(s)(s + 1) \Big|_{(s+1) = 0} = \infty$$

To avoid the difficulty one could resort to differentiation. From Eq. 1.3.17 we have

$$\frac{d}{ds} Z(s)(s + 1)^2 = \frac{dA}{ds}(=0) A + B + C(s + 1)\left[-\frac{(s + 1)}{(s + 3)^2} + \frac{2}{s + 3}\right] \; 1.3.18$$

Thus $B$ can be obtained by setting $(s + 1)$ to zero in the expression $\frac{d}{ds} Z(s)(s + 1)^2$. This yields $B = \frac{1}{4}$.

This result can be extended in the following way. If $Z(s)$ can be expanded in a partial fraction of the form

$$Z(s) = \frac{A_0}{(s + b)^n} + \frac{A_1}{(s + b)^{n-1}} + + + \frac{A_{n-1}}{s + b} + F(s) \qquad 1.3.19$$

then

$$A_0 = Z(s)(s + b)^n \Big|_{s+b = 0}$$

$$A_1 = \frac{d}{ds} Z(s)(s + b)^n \Big|_{s+b = 0}$$

$$\qquad \qquad \qquad \qquad \qquad \qquad \qquad 1.3.20$$

$$\cdot$$
$$\cdot$$
$$\cdot$$

$$A_{n-1} = \frac{1}{n - 1!} \frac{d^{n-1}}{ds^{n-1}} Z(s)(s + b)^n \Big|_{s+b = 0}$$

Sometimes the process of evaluating residues* can be simplified considerably by the use of the following theorem.

### Theorem 1.3.1**

If $Z(s)$ is written as

$$Z(s) = \frac{a_0 s^n + a_1 s^{n-1} + a_2 s^{n-2} + \cdots}{s^{n+r} + b_1 s^{n+r-1} + b_2 s^{n+r-2}} \qquad \text{1.3.21}$$

where $n$ and $r$ are positive integers, the sum of the residues is zero if $r > 1$ and it is equal to $a_0$ if $r = 1$.

*Proof*

Let $Z(s)$ be given by

$$Z(s) = \frac{k_1}{s + c_1} + \frac{k_2}{s + c_2} + \cdots = \sum_i \frac{k_i}{s + c_i} \qquad \text{1.3.22}$$

Bringing the right side of the equation into a common denominator, we get

$$Z(s) = \frac{(\Sigma k_i)\, s^{n+r-1} + (k_1 c_2 + k_2 c_1 + k_1 c_3 + \cdots) s^{n+r-2} + \cdots}{s^{n+r} + b_1 s^{n+r-1} + \cdots} \qquad \text{1.3.23}$$

Equating coefficients of like power of $s$ in the numerators of Eqs. 1.3.21 and 1.3.23, we have

$$\Sigma k_i = a_0 \text{ if } r = 1$$
$$= 0 \text{ if } r > 1$$

where $\Sigma k_i$ is the sum of the residues.

In case of the presence of high-order poles, the problem is more complex, but the results are the same. (Remember that coefficients of high-order poles are not residues).

*Proof completed*

The application of this theorem to Example 1.3.3 gives $B = \frac{1}{4}$, since $C = -\frac{1}{4}$ and since the sum $B + C$ must be zero. Similarly, the sum of the residues is one in Example 1.3.2, as can be easily verified. Hence, the theorem may be used either to check the results or as an aid in the solution of a problem when there are higher-order poles.

* Residues are defined as coefficients of simple poles in a partial fraction expansion. In Eq. 1.3.19 only $A_{n-1}$ is a residue.

** Hazony, D. and Riley, J. C., "Evaluating Residues and Coefficients of High Order Poles," *IRE Trans. on Automatic Control*, AC-4, pp. 132–136, November, 1959.

In concluding this section it is, perhaps, worthwhile to note that the typical term in a partial fraction expansion

$$\frac{a_p}{s + b_p}$$

can be obtained as the impedance function of the network shown in Fig. 1.4 (for zero initial conditions and if $a_p > 0 < b_p$).

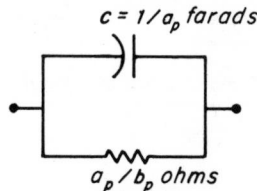

**Fig. 1.4. A network whose impedance function is $a_p/(s + b_p)$**

## IMPEDANCE FUNCTIONS 1.4

Laplace transforms can be used to evaluate the properties of a network (Fig. 1.5) having

**Fig. 1.5. An RLC network**

zero initial conditions. In this case $\dfrac{di(t)}{dt}$ and $\int i\, dt$ become $sI(s)$ and $\dfrac{1}{s}I(s)$, respectively. Then $\dfrac{E(s)}{I(s)} = (R + sL + \dfrac{1}{sC}) = Z(s)$ is called a driving point impedance function.

### Example 1.4.1

Find the impedance function of the network in Fig. 1.6.

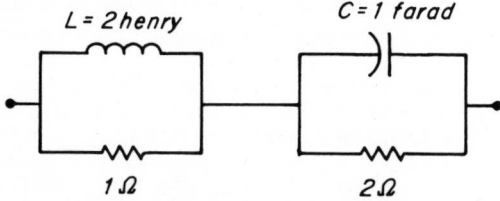

**Fig. 1.6. The network of Example 1.4.1**

*Solution*

To determine $Z(s)$ the network values are rewritten as in Fig. 1.7.

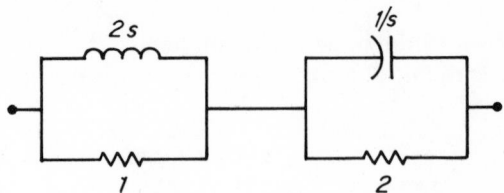

**Fig. 1.7. Modification of network in Fig. 1.6**

It follows that

$$Z(s) = \frac{2s}{2s+1} + \frac{\dfrac{2}{s}}{2 + \dfrac{1}{s}} \qquad \text{1.4.1}$$

$$= \frac{2(s+1)}{2s+1}$$

$Z(s)$ becomes an ordinary impedance when $s$ is set at $j\omega$:

$$Z(j\omega) = \frac{2(j\omega + 1)}{2j\omega + 1} \qquad \text{1.4.2}$$

$Z(j\omega)$ is called $Z(s)$ along the $j\omega$ axis. The real part of $Z(j\omega)$ is the resistive component, and the imaginary part is the reactive component. Thus

$$\text{Re } Z(j\omega) = 2 \times \frac{1 + 2\omega^2}{1 + 4\omega^2} = \text{resistive component}$$

$$\text{Im } Z(j\omega) = -2\omega \frac{1}{1 + 4\omega^2} = \text{reactive component}$$

It will be shown in Chapter 4 (Section 4.1) that if $Z(s)$ is made up of resistors, inductors, and capacitors, $Z(s)$ is a ratio of two rational polynomials of the complex variable $s$. It is useful for our subsequent work to write these polynomials in terms of $m$ and $n$, their even and odd parts, respectively. Thus in a polynomial $P(s)$

$$P(s) = m + n = \text{Ev } P(s) + \text{Od } P(s).$$

In general, however, this may be written as

$$P(s) = \frac{P(s) + P(-s)}{2} + \frac{P(s) - P(-s)}{2}$$

Therefore

$$m = \frac{P(s) + P(-s)}{2}$$

$$n = \frac{P(s) - P(-s)}{2}$$

**1.4.3**

### Example 1.4.2

Find $m$ and $n$ in the following polynomial:

$$P = s^4 + a_1 s^3 + a_2 s^2 + a_3 s + a_4$$

*Solution*

$$P(-s) = s^4 - a_1 s^3 + a_2 s^2 - a_3 s + a_4 \qquad \textbf{1.4.4}$$

Hence

$$\frac{P(s) + P(-s)}{2} = s^4 + a_2 s^2 + a_4 = m$$

and

$$\frac{P(s) - P(-s)}{2} = a_1 s^3 + a_3 s = n$$

These results may be generalized to say that $m$ is the sum of all the even-power terms in $s$ and that $n$ is the sum of all the odd-power terms in $s$. Utilizing these terms in expressing $Z(s)$, we obtain

$$Z(s) = \frac{m_1 + n_1}{m_2 + n_2} \qquad \textbf{1.4.5}$$

The multiplication of both numerator and denominator of $Z(s)$ with $m_2 - n_2$ yields

$$Z(s) = \frac{(m_1 + n_1)(m_2 - n_2)}{(m_2 + n_2)(m_2 - n_2)}$$

$$= \frac{m_1 m_2 - n_1 n_2}{m_2^2 - n_2^2} + \frac{n_1 m_2 - n_2 m_1}{m_2^2 - n_2^2}$$

**1.4.6**

Now, since $m_1 m_2$, $n_1 n_2$, $m_2^2$, and $n_2^2$ are all even functions of $s$, the first term to the right of $Z(s)$ above is an even function of $s$. This term is called Even $Z(s)$ and is designated Ev $Z(s)$:

$$\text{Ev } Z(s) = \frac{m_1 m_2 - n_1 n_2}{m_2^2 - n_2^2} \qquad \textbf{1.4.7}$$

$$\text{(Note that Re } Z(j\omega) = \text{Ev } Z(s) \Big|_{s=j\omega} \text{)}$$

Similarly, the second term is an odd function of $Z(s)$. It is called Odd $Z(s)$ and is designated Od $Z(s)$:

$$\text{Od } Z(s) = \frac{n_1 m_2 - n_2 m_1}{m_2{}^2 - n_2{}^2} \qquad \textbf{1.4.8}$$

(Note that $j\text{Im } Z(j\omega) = \text{Od } Z(s)\Big|_{s=j\omega}$  )

## Example 1.4.3

Find the even and odd parts of the following function:

$$Z(s) = \frac{s^2 + s + 1}{s^2 + s + 4} \qquad \textbf{1.4.9}$$

*Solution*

Note that $m_1 = s^2 + 1$, $m_2 = s^2 + 4$, and $n_1 = n_2 = s$. Hence, by Eq. 1.4.7

$$\text{Ev } Z(s) = \frac{(s^2 + 4)(s^2 + 1) - (s)(s)}{(s^2 + 4)^2 - s^2}$$

$$= \frac{(s^2 + 2)^2}{s^4 + 7s^2 + 16} \qquad \textbf{1.4.10}$$

Similarly, by Eq. 1.4.8

$$\text{Od } Z(s) = \frac{s(s^2 + 4) - s(s^2 + 1)}{(s^2 + 4)^2 - s^2} = \frac{3s}{s^4 + 7s^2 + 16} \qquad \textbf{1.4.11}$$

Along the $j\omega$ axis Ev $Z(s)$ is made up of real quantities only; therefore, it is a real function of $\omega$. On the other hand, Od $Z(s)$ is made up of strictly imaginary components; therefore, it is an imaginary function of $\omega$. These results may be reinterpreted as follows:

Along the $j\omega$ axis Ev $Z(s)$ equals Re $Z(s)$

Along the $j\omega$ axis Od $Z(s)$ equals $j$Im $Z(s)$.

Thus, in Example 1.4.3

$$\text{Re } Z(s)\Big|_{s=j\omega} = \frac{(s^2 + 2)^2}{s^4 + 7s^2 + 1}\Big|_{s=j\omega} \qquad \textbf{1.4.12}$$

$$= \frac{(-\omega^2 + 2)^2}{\omega^4 - 7\omega^2 + 16}$$

$$j\text{Im } Z(s)\Big|_{s=j\omega} = \frac{3s}{s^4 + 7s^2 + 16}\Big|_{s=j\omega} \qquad \textbf{1.4.13}$$

$$= \frac{3j\omega}{\omega^4 - 7\omega^2 + 16}$$

It may be instructive to note that the denominator of Re $Z(s)$ is non-negative for $s = j\omega$. Also the numerator is never negative since it is a square. Then Re $Z(j\omega) \geq 0$ (the equal sign is obtained when $\omega = \sqrt{2}$). This is not an accident. The impedance function $Z(s)$ of Example 1.4.3 may be realized in terms of $RLC$'s (Fig. 1.8). Furthermore, it can be verified that both Eq. 1.4.1 and Eq. 1.4.9 satisfy the constraints

$$Z(s) = \text{real} \qquad \text{when} \qquad s = \text{real}$$

$$\text{Re } Z(s) \geq 0 \qquad \text{when} \qquad \text{Re } s = 0$$

$$\text{Re } Z(s) > 0 \qquad \text{when} \qquad \text{Re } s > 0$$

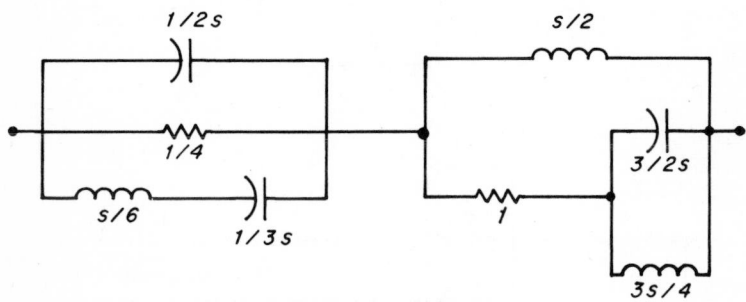

**Fig. 1.8. A network for Z(s)**

Rational functions of $s$ satisfying these constraints are called positive real functions (prf) and are taken up in Chapter 2. Positive real functions play a very important role in network synthesis.

The foregoing discussion raises the question whether all $RLC$ networks yield positive real functions. In Chapter 4 we will find that this is true. The inverse question, that is, whether all positive real functions are realizable as $RLC$ networks, will be answered in the affirmative in Chapter 5.

## PROBLEMS

1.1. Find the solution of $q(t)$ by means of Laplace transforms (zero initial conditions):

(a). $\dfrac{d^2q}{dt^2} + 4\dfrac{dq}{dt} + 3q = 1$

(b). $\dfrac{d^2q}{dt^2} + 5\dfrac{dq}{dt} + 4q = t$ \hfill Use Table 1.1.

1.2.  Find the inverse Laplace transform, $\mathcal{L}^{-1}[F(s)]$:

$$F(s) = \frac{(s-1)(s+3)}{(s+2)(s+4)}$$

Use Table 1.1. (Hint: expand $F(s)$ in partial fractions.)

1.3.  Find the impedance, $Z(s)$, of the following networks.

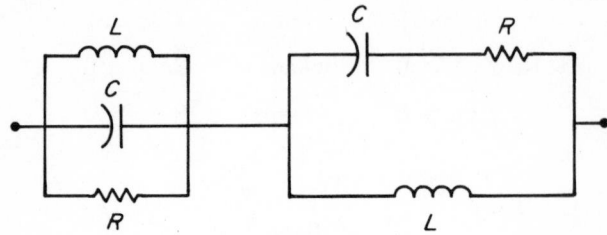

**Fig. P 1.3a**

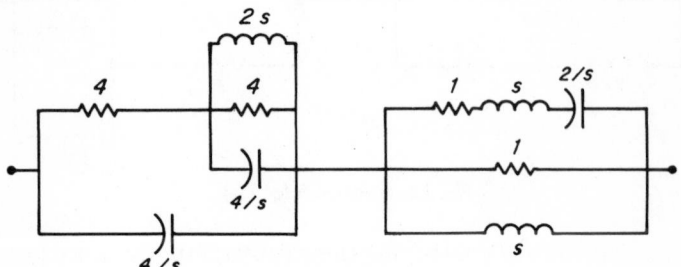

**Fig. P 1.3b**

Answer: $Z(s) = \dfrac{s^2 + 3s + 4}{s^2 + s + 1}$

1.4.  Show that Re $Z(s) > 0$ for Re $s > 0$ in

(a). $Z(s) = \dfrac{s+1}{2s+1}$

(b). $Z(s) = \dfrac{s^2 + s + 1}{s^2 + s + 4}$

by setting $s = \sigma + j\omega$.

1.5.  Show that Re $Z(s) \geq 0$ for Re $s = 0$:

$$Z(s) = \frac{s^2 + s + 2}{2s^2 + s + 1}$$

## FÜRTHER READING

A CLOSE PARALLEL DEVELOPMENT

1.1. Van Valkenburg, M. E., "Circuit Analysis," Chaps. 7 and 10, Prentice Hall, Inc., Englewood Cliffs, N. J., 1955. Especially Chap. 7.

LAPLACE TRANSFORMATION

1.2. Gardner, M. F., and Barnes, J. L., "Transients in Linear Systems," John Wiley & Sons, Inc., New York, 1939.

1.3. Thomson, W. T., "Laplace Transformation," 2nd ed., Prentice Hall Inc., Englewood Cliffs, N. J., 1960.

# CHAPTER 2 | *Positive Real Functions*

## 2.1. ELEMENTARY CONSTRAINTS

A rational polynomial function of $s$ is called a positive real function (abbreviated prf) if it satisfies the constraints

$$
\begin{aligned}
Z(s) &= \text{real} & s &= \text{real} \\
\text{Re } Z(s) &\geqslant 0 & \text{Re } s &= 0 \\
\text{Re } Z(s) &> 0 & \text{Re } s &> 0
\end{aligned}
$$

**2.1.1**

These constraints can be described geometrically. Then we would say that $Z(s)$ maps the right half $(r.h.)$ $s$ plane into a portion of the $r.h.\, Z(s)$ plane. In other words, for any point $s_0$ in the $r.h.\,s$ plane (that is, Re $s_0 > 0$) the corresponding point $Z(s_0)$ is located in the $r.h.\,Z(s)$ plane. To emphasize this property, the complex $s$ plane is superimposed on the corresponding complex $Z(s)$ plane (Fig. 2.1).

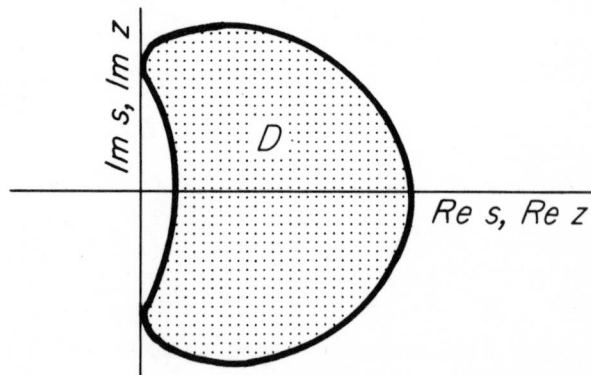

**Fig. 2.1.** Mapping properties of a positive real function

## Example 2.1.1

Map the entire right half $s$ plane into the $Z(s)$ plane for the function

$$Z(s) = \frac{s^2 + s + 1}{s^2 + s + 4}$$

### Solution

Consider first the real part, Re $Z(s)$, and the imaginary part, Im $Z(s)$, as $s$ moves along the $j$ axis. These are given by

$$\left.\frac{\text{Re } Z(s)}{s = j\omega}\right. = \frac{(2 - \omega^2)^2}{(\omega^2 - 4)^2 + \omega^2} \text{ and } \left.\frac{\text{Im } Z(s)}{s = j\omega}\right. = \frac{3\omega}{(\omega^2 - 4)^2 + \omega^2}$$

The plot of these quantities is given in Fig. 2.2. The corresponding points for Re $s > 0$ are in the shaded area.

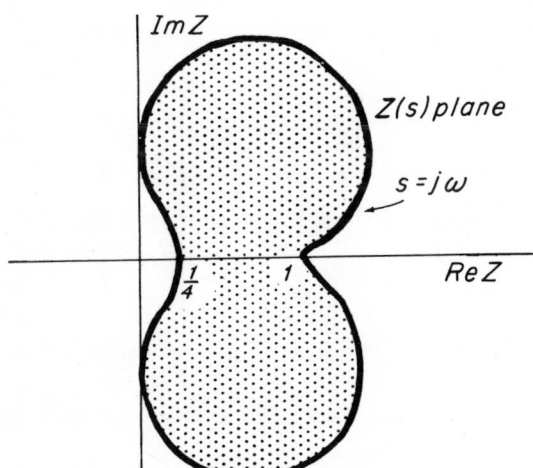

**Fig. 2.2. Map of the r.h.s. plane into the $Z(s)$**
$$= \frac{s^2 + s + 1}{s^2 + s + 4} \text{ plane}$$

## Example 2.1.2

Show that if $Z(s)$ is prf, $1/Z(s)$ is also prf.

### Solution

Let
$$\frac{1}{Z(s)} = U + jV \qquad \text{(U and V are real)} \qquad\qquad \textbf{2.1.2}$$

and
$$Z(s) = x + jy \qquad \text{(x and y are real)} \qquad\qquad \textbf{2.1.3}$$

$$= \frac{U}{U^2 + V^2} - j\frac{V}{U^2 + V^2} \qquad\qquad \textbf{2.1.4}$$

Equating the real parts of Eq. 2.1.3 and Eq. 2.1.4, we get

$$x = \frac{U}{U^2 + V^2}$$

which can be rearranged to demonstrate the properties of a circle for $x = C$:

$$V^2 + \left(U - \frac{1}{2C}\right)^2 = \left(\frac{1}{2C}\right)^2 \qquad \textbf{2.1.5}$$

The radius of the corresponding circle is given by $R = 1/2C$. The lines $x = C$ in the $Z(s)$ plane, and their corresponding circles in the $1/Z(s)$ plane are shown in Fig. 2.3. The whole $r.h.Z(s)$ plane (represented by the area inside the lines $C \to 0$ and $C \to \infty$) is mapped into the $r.h.Z(s)^{-1}$ plane (represented by the area between the smallest circle and the largest one).

Now, since $Z(s)$ maps* the $r.h.s$ plane into a portion of the $r.h.s$ plane, that portion is certainly in the $r.h.1/Z(s)$ plane. Then $1/Z(s)$ is prf.

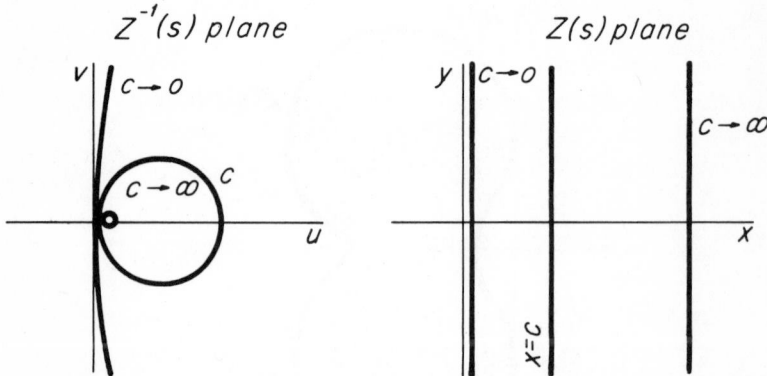

**Fig. 2.3. Map of the line x = C in the Z(s) plane into the 1/Z(s) plane**

In general, given any two functions $f(s)$ and $Z(s)$ which are prf, then $f[Z(s)]$ is also prf. To prove this, observe that the $r.h.s$ plane is mapped into a part of the $r.h.Z(s)$ plane which, in turn, is mapped into a subsequently smaller part of the $f[Z(s)]$ plane. This can be restated as follows:

*A positive real function of a positive real function is also a positive real function.*

## 2.2. POLE ZERO CONFIGURATION IF Z(s) IS PRF

Any polynomial of $s$ of the type

$$P = s^n + as^{n-1} + \cdots + a_{n-1}s + a_n \qquad \textbf{2.2.1}$$

---

* If $Z(s)$ is prf.

can be written as the product

$$P = \prod_{i=1}^{n}(s + C_i) \qquad 2.2.2$$

The $C_i$'s are called the zeros of the polynomials. Now, if $Z(s)$ is given as a ratio of two polynomials $P/Q$, the zeros of $P$ are called the zeros of $Z(s)$. The zeros of $Q$ are called the poles of $Z(s)$.

## Theorem 2.2.1

A positive real function $Z(s)$ cannot have any poles or zeros in the r.h.s plane. $j$ axis poles of $Z(s)$ and $1/Z(s)$ must be simple with real positive residues.

To prove this statement, suppose that $Z(s)$ has a r.h.s plane pole of multiplicity $n$ at $s = s_0$. Expand $Z(s)$ in the following manner:

$$Z(s) = \frac{A}{(s - s_0)^n} + F \qquad 2.2.3$$

where $F$ may contain a pole (of lower multiplicity than $n$) at $s = s_0$.

Suppose that $s$ is now permitted to assume values close to $s = s_0$. In general, this will put the point $s$ in the r.h.s plane. This means, according to Eq. 2.1.1, that if $Z(s)$ is prf, then

$$\text{Re } Z(s) \to \text{Re } \frac{A}{(s - s_0)^n} > 0 \qquad 2.2.4$$

where $F$ of Eq. 2.2.3 is neglected since it is much smaller than $A/(s - s_0)^n$ for $s \sim s_0$. Suppose now that the point $s$ moves around $s_0$ along the circumference of a small circle of radius $\rho$. Then $s - s_0 = \rho e^{-i\theta}$. Now Eq. 2.2.4 assumes the form $(A = |A|e^{i\alpha})$

$$\text{Re } Z(s) \to \text{Re } \frac{|A|}{\rho^n} e^{i\alpha} \times e^{-in\theta} = \frac{|A|}{\rho^n} \cos(\alpha - n\theta) > 0 \qquad 2.2.5$$

Hence $\cos(\alpha - n\theta) > 0$, and therefore its argument must be smaller than $\pi/2$, namely

$$|\alpha \pm n\theta| \leq \pi/2 \qquad 2.2.6$$

The plus minus sign was installed to emphasize the fact that $\theta$ may be negative as well. The equal sign is possible when $s$ is on the $j$ axis. Now, so long as $s$ is in the r.h.s plane, $\theta$ may assume any value up to $\pi$. But then Eq. 2.2.6 cannot be satisfied unless $\alpha$ is zero and $n = 1/2$. Letting $\alpha = 0$ is possible; $n$, however, must be an integer if $Z(s)$ is rational. Then no pole in the r.h.s plane is possible. However, poles may lie on the $j$ axis since then $|\theta|$ may not exceed $\pi/2$ and $n$ may be unity. ($\alpha$ must still be zero.)

Hence the fact that $n = 1$ and $\alpha = 0$ proves that if $s_0$ is along the $j$ axis, the corresponding pole is simple and its residue must be real and positive.

These restrictions are also valid for $1/Z(s)$ since it is also prf (Example 2.1.2). Therefore, the theorem has been proved.

### Example 2.2.1

Show that if $Z(s)$ is prf, the degree of the numerator cannot differ from that of the denominator by more than unity.

### Solution

If the difference of the degrees is $n$, then $Z(s)$ has an $n^{\text{th}}$ order pole or zero at $j\omega = 0$ or $j\omega = \infty$. But these are $j$ axis poles or zeros which must be simple (Theorem 2.2.1). This completes the proof.

## 2.3. ANALYTICITY OF $Z(s)$

The statement, "$Z(s)$ is analytic," implies that the derivative of $Z(s)$ exists throughout a certain domain $D$ and that it is unique, irrespective of the values of $\dfrac{d\omega}{d\sigma}$, for $s = \sigma + j\omega$.

### Example 2.3.1*

Show that $s^n$ is analytic.

### Solution

From the definition of the derivative

$$\frac{df(s)}{d(s)} = \lim_{s \to s_0} \frac{f(s) - f(s_0)}{s - s_0}$$

it follows that

$$\frac{ds^n}{ds} = \lim_{s \to s_0} \frac{s^n - s_0^n}{s - s_0} \qquad 2.3.1$$

By direct division this expression becomes

$$\frac{ds^n}{ds} = \lim_{s \to s_0} (s^{n-1} + s_0 s^{n-2} + s_0^2 s^{n-3} + + + s_0^{n-1}) = n s_0^{n-1} \qquad 2.3.2$$

Thus $s^n$ has a unique derivative for any $s_0$ throughout the complex plane except at the point of infinity (where the function has a pole).

---

\* Also see Copson, E. T., "Theory of Functions of a Complex Variable," Oxford University Press, Section 3.3.2., 1935.

### Example 2.3.2

Show that $Z = \dfrac{s+1}{s-1}$ is analytic everywhere in the complex plane except at the point $s - 1 = 0$ [the pole of $Z(s)$].

*Solution*

From the basic definition of a derivative

$$\frac{dZ(s)}{ds} = \lim_{s \to s_0} \frac{\dfrac{s+1}{s-1} - \dfrac{s_0+1}{s_0-1}}{s - s_0} = \lim_{s \to s_0} \frac{-2}{(s_0 - 1)(s - 1)} = \frac{-2}{(s_0 - 1)^2}$$

This expression is finite and unique for all values of $s_0$ except $s_0 = 1$.

The results of the foregoing example may be extended. Let $Z(s)$ be expressed in the form

$$Z(s) = U(\sigma, \omega) + jV(\sigma, \omega) \qquad\qquad 2.3.3$$

where $U(\sigma, \omega) = \operatorname{Re} Z(\sigma + j\omega)$ and $V(\sigma, \omega) = \operatorname{Im} Z(\sigma + j\omega)$. The derivative of $Z(s)$ now can be expressed in terms of $U(\sigma, \omega)$ and $V(\sigma, \omega)$

$$\frac{dZ(s)}{ds} = \frac{U_\sigma \, d\sigma + jV_\sigma \, d\sigma + U_\omega \, d\omega + jV_\omega \, d\omega}{d\sigma + jd\omega} \qquad\qquad 2.3.4$$

where $U_\sigma = \dfrac{\partial U}{\partial \sigma}$, $V_\sigma = \dfrac{\partial V}{\partial \sigma}$, $U_\omega = \dfrac{\partial U}{\partial \omega}$, and $V_\omega = \dfrac{\partial V}{\partial \omega}$. This expression may be written as follows:

$$\frac{dZ(s)}{ds} = (U_\sigma + jV_\sigma) \frac{1 + \dfrac{V_\omega - jU_\omega}{U_\sigma + jV_\sigma} \dfrac{jd\omega}{d\sigma}}{1 + \dfrac{jd\omega}{d\sigma}} \qquad\qquad 2.3.5$$

and it is independent of $\dfrac{d\omega}{d\sigma}$ if and only if

$$\frac{V_\omega - jU_\omega}{U_\sigma + jV_\sigma} = 1$$

since then the factor $1 + \dfrac{jd\omega}{d\sigma}$ is cancelled from the numerator and the denominator. This gives

$$\begin{aligned} V_\omega - jU_\omega &= U_\sigma + jV_\sigma \\ V_\omega &= U_\sigma \qquad\qquad 2.3.6 \\ -U_\omega &= V_\sigma \end{aligned}$$

These are the Cauchy Riemann differential equations. It follows, since all polynomial functions of $s$ are analytic except at their poles, that they satisfy the Cauchy Riemann differential equations everywhere except at their poles.

## 2.4. INTEGRATION* OF $Z(s)$

Integration of $Z(s)$ is a sum defined as follows:

$$\int_{s_0}^{s} Z(s)\, ds = \lim_{\substack{n \to \infty \\ \|\Delta\| \to 0}} \sum_{i=1}^{n} Z(s_i)(s_i - s_{i-1}) \qquad \textbf{2.4.1}$$

where the quantity $\|\Delta\|$ is called the norm and is defined as the maximum length of the intervals $s_i - s_{i-1}$. That is

$$\|\Delta\| = |s_i - s_{i-1}|_{\max}$$

The fact that a polynomial function of $s$ has unique derivatives has an analogous counterpart in integration, namely, if $Z(s)$ is analytic in a domain $D$ of the complex $s$ plane, then the integral

$$\int_{s_0}^{s} Z(s)\, ds \qquad \textbf{2.4.2}$$

is independent of the path of integration. This may be restated to say that the integral over any closed contour $C(s = s_0)$ in the domain $D$ is zero.

**Example 2.4.1**

Show that $\int_{s_0}^{s} s\, ds = \dfrac{1}{2}(s^2 - s_0^2)$.

*Solution*

From the basic definition of the integral given in Eq. 2.4.1

$$\int_{s_0}^{s} s\, ds = \lim_{\substack{n \to \infty \\ \|\Delta\| \to 0}} \sum_{i=1}^{n} s_i(s_i - s_{i-1}) \qquad \textbf{2.4.3}$$

Note also that this may be evaluated from (since $s_i \sim s_{i-1}$)

$$\int_{s_0}^{s} s\, ds = \lim_{\substack{n \to \infty \\ \|\Delta\| \to 0}} \sum_{i=1}^{n} s_{i-1}(s_i - s_{i-1}) \qquad \textbf{2.4.4}$$

---

* Also see Copson, Section 4.12—reference cited earlier.

Now the last two forms may be summed to give

$$\int_{s_0}^{s} s\,ds = \lim_{\substack{n \to \infty \\ \|\Delta\| \to 0}} \frac{1}{2} \sum_{i=1}^{n} (s_i + s_{i-1})(s_i - s_{i-1}) \qquad \textbf{2.4.5}$$

which reduces to

$$\int_{s_0}^{s} s\,ds = \lim_{\substack{n \to \infty \\ \|\Delta\| \to 0}} \frac{1}{2} \sum_{i=1}^{n} (s_i{}^2 - s_{i-1}{}^2) \qquad \textbf{2.4.6}$$

But in the sum $\dfrac{1}{2} \displaystyle\sum_{i=1}^{n} (s_i{}^2 - s_{i-1}{}^2)$ all terms cancel except the first and the

last. Then

$$\int_{s_0}^{s} s\,ds = \lim_{\substack{n \to \infty \\ \|\Delta\| \to 0}} \frac{s_n{}^2 - s_0{}^2}{2} = \frac{s^2 - s_0{}^2}{2} \qquad \textbf{2.4.7}$$

This result will now be generalized to show that the integral around a closed contour $C$ (enclosing $D$) is zero for any function $Z(s)$ satisfying Cauchy Riemann differential equations in $D$. Expanding $Z(s)$ in terms of its real and imaginary parts gives

$$\oint_C Z(s)\,ds = \oint_C (U\,d\sigma - V\,d\omega + j(U\,d\omega + V\,d\sigma)) \qquad \textbf{2.4.8}$$

This integral may be put in a different form by applying Green's theorem which states that if $M(\sigma, \omega)$ and $N(\sigma, \omega)$ are continuous, single-valued functions over the domain $D$ bounded by $C$, then

$$\oint_C (M\,d\sigma + N\,d\omega) = \iint_D \left( \frac{\partial N}{\partial \sigma} - \frac{\partial M}{\partial \omega} \right) d\sigma\,d\omega \qquad \textbf{2.4.9}$$

As a result

$$\oint_C Z(s)\,d(s) = -\iint_D [(U_\omega + V_\sigma) + j(V_\omega - U_\sigma)]\,d\sigma\,d\omega \qquad \textbf{2.4.10}$$

But since $Z(s)$ satisfies the Cauchy Riemann differential equations, both $(U_\omega + V_\sigma)$ and $(V_\omega - U_\sigma)$ are zero.

From the statement of Green's theorem $D$ must exclude singular points (poles) of $Z(s)$, where Cauchy Riemann differential equations are not satisfied (i.e., where $Z(s)$ is not analytic), and consequently Green's theorem does not apply (Example 2.4.2).

### Example 2.4.2

Show that if $Z(s)$ is analytic inside a closed contour, $C_1$, then

$$Z(s_0) = Z_0 = \frac{1}{2\pi j} \oint_{C_1} \frac{Z(s)}{s - s_0} \, ds \qquad 2.4.11$$

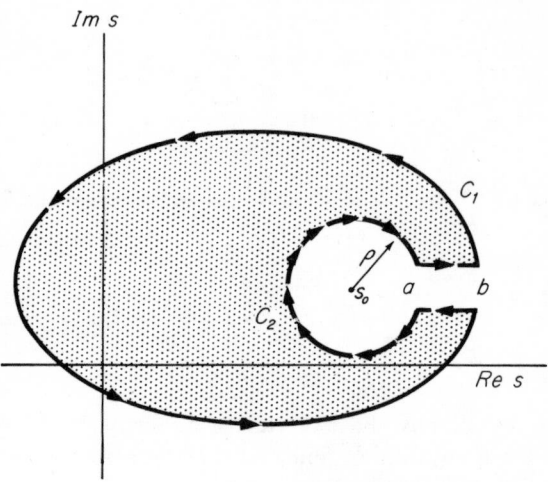

**Fig. 2.4. Modifying D to exclude a pole**

### Solution

The function $\dfrac{Z(s)}{s - s_0}$ has a pole at $s - s_0 = 0$. In Fig. 2.4 this pole is excluded from the domain of integration by constructing a small circle (radius $\rho$). The domain under consideration is shaded. A thin slot connects $C_1$ (the original contour of interest) with the inner circle $C_2$. Inside the shaded domain $\dfrac{Z(s)}{s - s_0}$ is analytic. The value of the integral around the domain is consequently zero.

$$0 = \oint_{C_1} \frac{Z(s) \, ds}{s - s_0} + \int_a^b \frac{Z(s) \, ds}{s - s_0} + \int_b^a \frac{Z(s) \, ds}{s - s_0} + \oint_{C_2} \frac{Z(s) \, ds}{s - s_0} \qquad 2.4.12$$

When the thickness of the slot approaches zero, the integral from $a$ to $b$ is the same as the negative of the integral from $b$ to $a$; hence second and third integrals cancel.

Similarly the integral along $C_2$ can be taken in the same direction as that along $C_1$ if its sign is changed to minus. It follows that

$$\oint_{C_1} \frac{Z(s) \, ds}{s - s_0} = \oint_{C_2} \frac{Z(s) \, ds}{s - s_0} \qquad 2.4.13$$

But $C_2$ is the circumference of a circle of radius $\rho$. Then on the contour

$C_2$, $(s - s_0) = \rho e^{j\theta}$, and therefore $ds = j\rho e^{j\theta} d\theta$. Now make $\rho$ approach zero. The integration around $C_2$ is reduced into an integration with respect to $\theta$ from 0 to $2\pi$.

Then

$$\oint_{C_2} \frac{Z(s)\,ds}{s - s_0} = \lim_{\rho \to 0} \int_0^{2\pi} Z(s_0 + \rho e^{j\theta})j\,d\theta$$

$$= jZ_0 \int_0^{2\pi} d\theta = 2\pi j Z_0$$

2.4.14

yielding

$$Z_0 = \frac{1}{2\pi j} \oint_{C_1} \frac{Z(s)\,ds}{s - s_0}$$

2.4.15

This integral is called Cauchy's integral formula.

## MAXIMUM MODULUS THEOREM 2.5

### Theorem 2.5.1

If $Z(s)$ is analytic in a domain $D$ and along its boundary $C$ in the $s$ plane, $M$ (the maximum value of $|Z(s)|$ in $D$) lies on $C$. This is called the maximum modulus theorem.

### Proof

From the Cauchy integral formula (Eq. 2.4.15)

$$Z_0 = \frac{1}{2\pi j} \oint_{C_1} \frac{Z(s)\,ds}{s - s_0}$$

2.5.1

where $s_0$ is in $D$, $C_1 = C$.

From the basic definition of the integral this may be written as

$$Z_0 = \frac{1}{2\pi j} \lim_{\substack{n \to \infty \\ \|\Delta\| \to 0}} \sum_{i=1}^{n} \frac{Z(s_i)(s_i - s_{i-1})}{s_i - s_0'}$$

2.5.2

The prime over $s_0$ is to emphasize the fact that it is not the same point obtained by setting $i = 1$.

Thus

$$|Z_0| = \frac{1}{2\pi} \left| \oint_C \frac{Z\,ds}{s - s_0} \right| = \frac{1}{2\pi} \lim_{\substack{n \to \infty \\ \|\Delta\| \to 0}} \left| \sum_{i=1}^{n} Z(s_i) \frac{(s_i - s_{i-1})}{(s_i - s_0')} \right|$$

2.5.3

Since the sum of the lengths of two sides of a triangle is larger than the length of the third side, or expressed symbolically

$$|Z_1 + Z_2| \leqslant |Z_1| + |Z_2|$$

in general, therefore

$$\left| \sum Z_i \right| \leqslant \sum |Z_i| \qquad \qquad 2.5.4$$

Thus

$$|Z_0| \leqslant \frac{1}{2\pi} \lim_{\substack{n \to \infty \\ \|\Delta\| \to 0}} \sum_{i=1}^{n} |Z(s_i)| \left| \frac{s_i - s_{i-1}}{s_i - s_0'} \right| \qquad \qquad 2.5.5$$

which simplifies to

$$|Z_0| \leqslant \frac{1}{2\pi} \lim_{\substack{n \to \infty \\ \|\Delta\| \to 0}} M \sum_{i=1}^{n} \left| \frac{s_i - s_{i-1}}{s_i - s_0'} \right|$$

by choosing $M = |Z(s_i)|_{\max}$. Hence*

$$|Z_0| < \frac{M}{2\pi} \oint_C \left| \frac{ds}{s - s_0} \right| \qquad \qquad 2.5.6$$

Letting $s - s_0 = \rho e^{i\theta}$, we get $ds = j\rho e^{i\theta} d\theta$ and $\dfrac{ds}{s - s_0} = jd\theta$. Correspondingly the integration around $C$ becomes an integration with respect to $\theta$ from $\theta = 0$ to $2\pi$. Therefore

$$|Z_0| < \frac{M}{2\pi} \int_0^{2\pi} d\theta = M \qquad \qquad 2.5.7$$

which completes the proof.

**Theorem 2.5.2**  (*The Minimum Real-Value Theorem*)

If $Z(s)$ is analytic in a domain $D$ which includes the entire *r.h.s* plane, the minimum value of Re $Z(s)$ in $D$ is along the $s = j\omega$ axis.

*Proof*

Utilizing the auxiliary function $e^{-Z(s)}$, we observe that

$$|e^{-Z(s)}| = |e^{-\text{Re } Z(s)} \times e^{-j\text{Im } Z(s)}| = e^{-\text{Re } Z(s)} \qquad \qquad 2.5.8$$

and therefore

$$|e^{-Z(s)}|_{\max} = e^{-\text{Re } Z(s)}{}_{\min} \geqslant e^{-\text{Re } Z(s)} \qquad \qquad 2.5.9$$

---

* The equal sign is dropped in Eq. 2.5.6 since it is obeyed only for the special case of $Z(s) =$ constant. This can be verified by analyzing Eq. 2.5.4 carefully.

Also, in the *r.h.s* plane $Z(s)$ is analytic and Re $Z(s) > 0$; hence $e^{-Z(s)}$ is also analytic there. Therefore by applying the maximum modulus theorem, we obtain

$$|e^{-Z(s)}|_{\max} > |e^{-Z(s)}| \qquad\qquad \textbf{2.5.10}$$
$$\text{Re } s=0 \qquad\qquad \text{Re } s>0$$

or by Eq. 2.5.9, we have

$$|e^{-Z(s)}|_{\max} = e^{-\text{Re } Z(s)}{}_{\min}|_{\text{Re } s=0} > e^{-\text{Re } Z(s)}|_{\text{Re } s>0} \qquad \textbf{2.5.11}$$

and consequently

$$\text{min. Re } Z(s)|_{\text{Re } s=0} < \text{Re } Z(s)|_{\text{Re } s>0} \qquad \textbf{2.5.12}$$

## Corollary 2.5.1

If $Z(s)$ is prf and Re $Z(s) \geqq r_0$ $(r_0 > 0)$ on the $j$ axis, then $Z(s)$ can be written as a sum $Z(s) = Z_0(s) + r_0$. $Z_0(s)$ is prf since Re $Z_0(s) \geqq 0$ on $j$ axis and therefore also throughout the *r.h.s* plane. $Z_0(s)$ is called a minimum resistive positive real function. It follows that any nonminimum resistive impedance function may be expressed as a sum of a minimum resistive impedance function plus a constant $r_0$ (a resistive term).

## Corollary 2.5.2

If $Z(s)$ is prf and has a $j$ axis pole, the pole and its conjugate may be removed leaving a positive real function.

### Proof

Utilizing Theorem 2.2.1* and remembering that $Z(s)$ must be real for real $s$, we can write $Z(s)$ as

$$Z(s) = Z_1(s) + \frac{A}{s + j\omega_0} + \frac{A}{s - j\omega_0} = Z_1(s) + Z_2(s) \qquad \textbf{2.5.13}$$

where $A$ is a real positive constant. The $j$ axis pole is removed along with its conjugate to insure the constraint that $Z(s)$ is real for real $s$. On the $j$ axis Re $Z(s) = 2A$ Re $s/(s^2 + \omega_0{}^2) = 0$ (except precisely at the pole); therefore, Re $Z_1(j\omega) = $ Re $Z(j\omega) \geq 0$. Thus removing the $j$ axis pole and its conjugate (henceforth the statement "removing a $j$ axis pole" will mean removing the conjugate as well) leaves a function $Z_1(s)$ which has a positive real part on the $j$ axis. Also $Z_1(s)$ cannot have any singularities in the *r.h.s* plane as

$$Z_1(s) = Z(s) - \frac{2As}{s^2 + \omega_0{}^2} \qquad \textbf{2.5.14}$$

---

* Theorem 2.2.1 states that $j$ axis poles are simple with positive real residues ($A = $ real $> 0$).

and subtraction of two positive real functions cannot introduce poles in the $r.h.s$ plane. It follows, by Theorem 2.5.2, that $Z_1(s)$ is prf.

Observe that Fig. 2.5 has the impedance function $Z_2(s) = 2As/(s^2 + \omega_0{}^2)$. Thus the removal of a $j$ axis pole may be associated with the removal of an $LC$ tank circuit.

Similarly, if $Z(s)$ has a $j$ axis zero, $1/Z(s)$ has a removable $j$ axis complex pole pair. Correspondingly, $Z(s)$ can be expressed in terms of two functions $Z_1'(s)$ and $Z_2'(s)$ in parallel, where $Z_1'(s)$ is positive real function and $Z_2'(s)$ is an inductor and a capacitor in series.

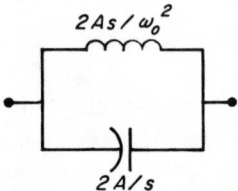

**Fig. 2.5. A network for
$Z(s) = 2As/(s^2 + \omega_0{}^2)$**

## 2.6. MAPPING THE R.H.S. PLANE INTO THE UNIT CIRCLE

Certain aspects of positive real functions seem more evident if the $r.h.s$ plane is mapped into a unit circle of the $W$ plane. The mapping function needed for the purpose is

$$W = \frac{s - 1}{s + 1} \qquad \textbf{2.6.1}$$

To show this, evaluate $s$ in terms of $W$:

$$s = \frac{1 + W}{1 - W} \qquad \textbf{2.6.2}$$

Let $s = \sigma + j\omega$, $W = U + jV$ in Eq. 2.6.2. This gives

$$\sigma + j\omega = \frac{1 + U + jV}{1 - U - jV} \qquad \textbf{2.6.3}$$

Equating real parts of both sides of Eq. 2.6.3 results in the following:

$$\sigma = \frac{1 - U^2 - V^2}{(1 - U)^2 + V^2} \qquad \textbf{2.6.4}$$

This expression is rewritten in the form

$$\left(U - \frac{\sigma}{\sigma + 1}\right)^2 + V^2 = \left(\frac{1}{\sigma + 1}\right)^2 \qquad \textbf{2.6.5}$$

This is the equation of a circle the radius of which is $R = \dfrac{1}{\sigma + 1}$. We note that $R$ approaches zero or unity when $\sigma$ approaches infinity or zero respectively. This shows that all the area between the two lines $\sigma \to 0$ and $\sigma \to \infty$ is mapped into the area between the two circles $R \to 0$ (centered at unity) and $R \to 1$ (centered at the origin) in the $W$ plane (Fig. 2.6). The $j\omega$ axis is mapped along the circumference of the unit circle.

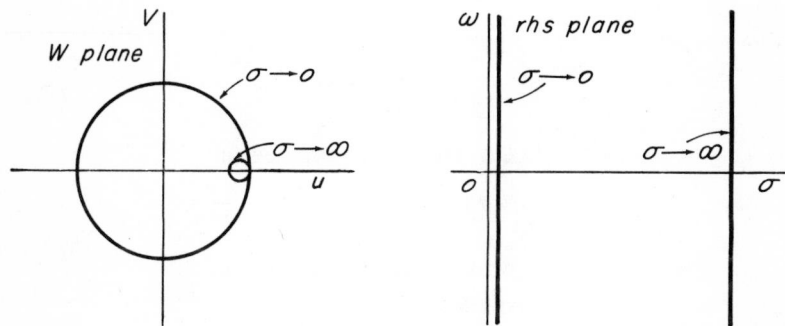

Fig. 2.6. Mapping the r.h.s. plane into the unit circle of $W = \dfrac{s - 1}{s + 1}$ plane

A positive real function maps the $r.h.s$ plane into a portion of the $r.h.Z(s)$ plane. Also this portion of the $Z(s)$ may be represented as a part of the unit circle in the $W$ plane, that is if $W$ is defined as

$$W = \frac{Z(s) - 1}{Z(s) + 1} \qquad \text{2.6.6}$$

and if Re $Z(s) \geqslant 0$ for Re $s = 0$ and Re $Z(s) > 0$ for Re $s > 0$, then

$$|W| \leqslant 1 \text{ for Re } s = 0$$

and

$$|W| < 1 \text{ for Re } s > 0 \qquad \text{2.6.7}$$

Also, since $Z(k)$ is real and positive for positive $k$ when $Z(s)$ is prf (Eq. 2.1.1), $Z(s)/Z(k)$ is also prf for positive $k$, and $W$ may be modified slightly

$$W = \frac{Z(s) - Z(k)}{Z(s) + Z(k)} \qquad \text{2.6.8}$$

without violating the constraints of Eqs. 2.6.7.

### Theorem 2.6.1

For prf $Z(s)$, define $m_1$ and $n_1$ as the even and odd part respectively of the numerator of $Z(s)$, and $m_2$ and $n_2$ as the corresponding parts of the denominator. $\Sigma$ which is formed by interchanging the even parts of the numerator and denominator is also prf.

*Proof*

Write

$$Z(s) = \frac{m_1 + n_1}{m_2 + n_2} \qquad\qquad \textbf{2.6.9}$$

and

$$\Sigma(s) = \frac{m_2 + n_1}{m_1 + n_2} \qquad\qquad \textbf{2.6.10}$$

In the $W$ plane (Eq. 2.6.6) these functions become

$$W_1 = \frac{Z(s) - 1}{Z(s) + 1} = \frac{(m_1 - m_2) + (n_1 - n_2)}{m_1 + n_1 + m_2 + n_2}$$

$$W_2 = \frac{\Sigma(s) - 1}{\Sigma(s) + 1} = \frac{m_2 - m_1 + n_1 - n_2}{m_1 + n_1 + m_2 + n_2} \qquad\qquad \textbf{2.6.11}$$

Along the $j$ axis $(m_1 - m_2)^2 = (m_2 - m_1)^2$ and therefore $|W_2| = |W_1| \leqslant 1$. Furthermore, $W_2$ is analytic in the *r.h.s* plane since it has the same denominator as $W_1$. Then $|W_2| < 1$ for Re $s > 0$ (by the maximum modulus theorem). This means, according to Eq. 2.6.7, that $\Sigma(s)$ is prf.

### Theorem 2.6.2

Given $W = \dfrac{Z(s) - Z(k)}{Z(s) + Z(k)}$ and $P = \dfrac{s - k}{s + k}$, $k$ is a positive real constant, and $Z(s)$ is prf, then $|W| \leqslant |P|$ for Re $s = 0$, and $|W| < |P|$ for Re $s > 0$.

*Proof*

$W = 0$ when $s = k$, which means that $W$ has the factor $s - k$. Then

$$\frac{W}{P} = \frac{\dfrac{Z(s) - Z(k)}{Z(s) + Z(k)}}{\dfrac{s - k}{s + k}}$$

is analytic in the *r.h.s* plane. On the $j$ axis $|W| \leqslant 1$ (Eqs. 2.6.7

and 2.6.8) and $|(s - k)/(s + k)| = 1$ yields $\left|\dfrac{W}{P}\right| \leqslant 1$. Then, by the maximum modulus theorem (Theorem 2.5.1) $|W| < |P|$ for Re $s > 0$. This completes the proof.

### THE R.H.Z(s) PLANE 2.7

It is of interest to establish additional properties of $Z(s)$ in the r.h.s plane. Note that Theorem 2.6.2 can be restated to say that

$$|W|^2 = \left|\frac{\dfrac{Z(s)}{Z(k)} - 1}{\dfrac{Z(s)}{Z(k)} + 1}\right|^2 \leqslant \left|\frac{\dfrac{s}{k} - 1}{\dfrac{s}{k} + 1}\right|^2 = |P|^2 \text{ for Re } s = 0 \qquad 2.7.1$$

$$|W|^2 < |P|^2 \qquad \text{for Re } s > 0$$

Since $k$ is perfectly arbitrary, the inequality must be obeyed for the worst set of conditions. Consider the case when any value of the left side of the inequality 2.7.1 is smaller than the minimum value of $|P|^2$

$$|P|^2 = \left|\frac{\dfrac{s}{k} - 1}{\dfrac{s}{k} + 1}\right|^2 \qquad 2.7.2$$

for all possible values of $\left|\dfrac{s}{k}\right|$. Now let

$$\frac{s}{k} = \left|\frac{s}{k}\right| e^{j\alpha}, \quad \frac{Z(s)}{Z(k)} = \left|\frac{Z(s)}{Z(k)}\right| e^{j\theta}$$

With these substitutions Eq. 2.7.1 may be rewritten as

$$-1 + 2\frac{\left|\dfrac{Z(s)}{Z(k)}\right|^2 + 1}{\left|\dfrac{Z(s)}{Z(k)}\right|^2 + 1 + \left|\dfrac{Z(s)}{Z(k)}\right| 2 \cos \theta} \leqslant -1 + 2\frac{\left|\dfrac{s}{k}\right|^2 + 1}{\left|\dfrac{s}{k}\right|^2 + 1 + 2\left|\dfrac{s}{k}\right| \cos \alpha} \qquad 2.7.3$$

where the equal sign is dropped for $|\alpha| < \pi/2$ (that is, Re $s > 0$). It follows that

$$\frac{\cos \theta}{\left|\dfrac{Z(s)}{Z(k)}\right| + \left|\dfrac{Z(k)}{Z(s)}\right|} \geqslant \frac{\cos \alpha}{\min\left(\left|\dfrac{s}{k}\right| + \left|\dfrac{k}{s}\right|\right)} = \frac{\cos \alpha}{2} \qquad 2.7.4$$

$$\left(\min\left(\left|\frac{s}{k}\right| + \left|\frac{k}{s}\right|\right) = 2\right)$$

The minimization here is in respect to $k$; i.e., for each point $s$ we take $|k| = |s|$. Thus

$$\frac{\cos \theta}{\cos \alpha} \geqslant \frac{1}{2}\left(\left|\frac{Z(s)}{Z(k)}\right| + \left|\frac{Z(k)}{Z(s)}\right|\right) \qquad 2.7.5$$

However, since $k$ was chosen to yield $\left|\dfrac{s}{k}\right| + \left|\dfrac{k}{s}\right| = \text{minimum} = 2$, $k$ is no longer arbitrary. Then

$$\left|\frac{Z(s)}{Z(k)}\right| + \left|\frac{Z(k)}{Z(s)}\right|$$

may never reach its minimum (two). This means that Eq. 2.7.5 degenerates into

$$\frac{\cos \theta}{\cos \alpha} \geqslant \frac{1}{2}\left(\left|\frac{Z(s)}{Z(k)}\right| + \left|\frac{Z(k)}{Z(s)}\right|\right) \geqslant 1 \qquad \textbf{2.7.6}$$

yielding

$$\cos \theta \geqslant \cos \alpha \qquad \text{for } |\alpha| = \pi/2 \qquad \textbf{2.7.7}$$

and

$$\cos \theta > \cos \alpha \qquad \text{for } |\alpha| < \pi/2$$

from Eq. 2.7.1. (Also note that on the real axis again $\cos \theta = \cos \alpha = 0$.)

### Example 2.7.1

Investigate $Z(s) = (s^2 + s + 1)/(s^2 + s + 4)$ for $s = re^{i\alpha}$ with $-\dfrac{\pi}{4} \leqslant \alpha \leqslant \dfrac{\pi}{4}$.

This problem is investigated graphically (Fig. 2.7) and is the same problem as was plotted in Fig. 2.2. In that figure the whole $r.h.s$ plane $\left(-\dfrac{\pi}{2} < \alpha < \dfrac{\pi}{2}\right)$ was plotted into the $r.h.Z(s)$ plane. At two points the $j$ axis of the $Z(s)$ plane touched the $j$ axis of the $s$ plane. This means that Eq. 2.7.7 is obeyed with the equal sign ($\cos \theta_0 = \cos \alpha_0$). In Fig. 2.7, however, Eq. 2.7.7 is never satisfied with the equal sign.

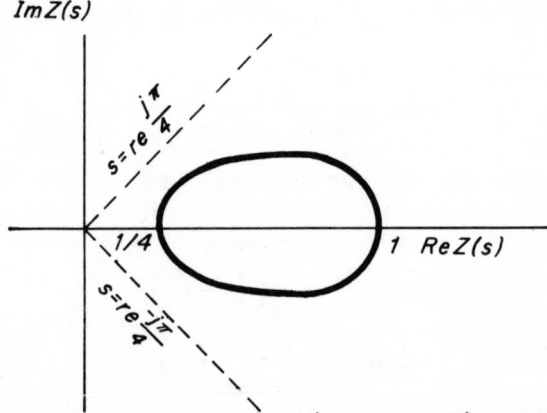

**Fig. 2.7. Map of the plane $re^{i\alpha}$ $\left(-\dfrac{\pi}{4} \leq \alpha \leq \dfrac{\pi}{4}\right)$ into the r.h. plane of $Z(s) = \dfrac{s^2 + s + 1}{s^2 + s + 4}$**

## NUMBER OF ZEROS IN THE R.H. s PLANE 2.8

A great deal of information is obtainable concerning the properties of a function by measuring its properties along the boundaries of a certain domain in the complex plane. Suppose $Z(s)$ is a polynomial $Z(s) = (s - a)^m(s - b)^n$. $D$ is a domain in the complex $s$ plane containing $a$ but not $b$.

Let the point $s$ traverse along $C$ (the boundary of $D$), starting at $s_0$ counterclockwise and returning to $s_0$. The angle $\beta$ is defined by the root $a$ and $s$ and $s_0$ (Fig. 2.8). The angle $\alpha$ is similarly defined for root $b$ outside of the contour $C$. During the traverse of $s$ from $s_0$ around the contour, $\beta$ increases continuously from the value of 0 to $2\pi$, while $\alpha$ oscillates and returns to its original value without a net gain. The total increase in the argument of $Z(s)$ is

$$\Delta \arg. Z(s) = n\Delta\alpha + m\Delta\beta = 2\pi m \qquad 2.8.1$$

Similarly, if $m$ is negative [$(s - \alpha)$ is a pole], the change in argument of $P$ would be $-2\pi m$ as the point $s$ completed a trip around $C$. These results may be generalized.

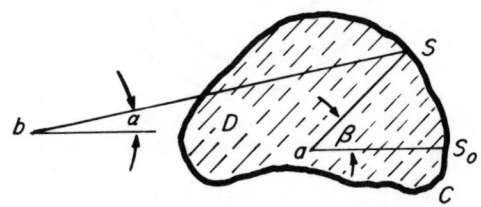

**Fig. 2.8. Increase of the argument of P(s) as s moves along C**

If $Z(s)$ has $N$ zeros and $P$ poles (both counted with their multiplicities) inside a domain $D$ in the complex $s$ plane, the net change in argument $Z(s)$ as $s$ traverses counterclockwise along $C$, is

$$\Delta \arg. Z(s) = 2\pi(N - P) \qquad 2.8.2$$

A direct consequence of these results is known as Rouche's theorem.

### Theorem 2.8.1

If $P(s)$ and $Q(s)$ are analytic interior to a closed curve $C$, and if they are continuous on $C$ and $|P(s)| < |Q(s)|$ on $C$, then the function

$F(s) = P(s) + Q(s)$ has the same number of zeros interior to $C$ as does $Q(s)$.

*Proof*

$$F = P(s) + Q(s) = (1 + P/Q)Q$$
$$\text{arg. } F = \text{arg. } Q(s) + \text{arg. } (1 + P/Q)$$

**2.8.3**

Since $\left|\dfrac{P(s)}{Q(s)}\right| < 1$ on $C$, the point $(1 + P/Q)$ describes a closed curve $C_1$ inside $C$ as $s$ completes a trip along $C$ (Fig. 2.9). Now as $C_1$ does not encircle the origin, the net change in argument of $(1 + P/Q)$ is zero. Thus, Eq. 2.8.3 shows that the net change of argument $F$ equals that of argument $Q(s)$. This means, according to Eq. 2.8.2, that $F$ has as many zeros inside $C$ as $Q(s)$. This completes the proof.

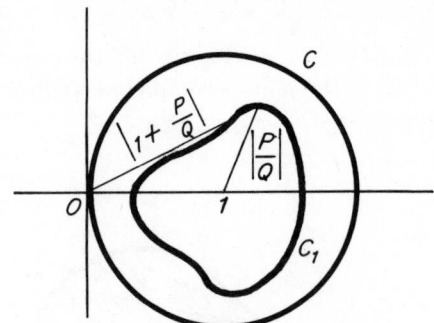

**Fig. 2.9. The variation in argument
(1 + P/Q) as s describes the close contour C**

The same argument can be advanced to show that Rouche's theorem is valid when $|P(s)| \leqslant |Q(s)|$ if $F(s) \neq 0$ on $C$.

## Example 2.8.1

Show that if $Z(s)$ is prf and Re $Z(s) > 0$ on $j$ axis, both $kZ(s) - sZ(k)$ and $kZ(k) - sZ(s)$ have only óne zero each in the *r.h.s* plane.

*Solution*

Let $Q(s) = \dfrac{s - k}{s + k}$. $k$ is a positive real constant, $\left|\dfrac{s - k}{s + k}\right| = 1$ on $j$ axis, and $P(s) = \dfrac{Z - Z(k)}{Z + Z(k)}$. $|P(s)| < 1$ on $j$ axis as Re $Z(s) > 0$ there. Then

$$F(s) = \frac{Z(s) - Z(k)}{Z(s) + Z(k)} + \frac{s + k}{s + k}$$
$$= \frac{2(sZ(s) - kZ(k))}{(Z(s) + Z(k))(s + k)}$$

and, by Rouche's theorem, has only one zero in the right-half plane [the zero of $Q(s)$]. Similarly, it can be shown by choosing $Q(s) = \dfrac{k - s}{k + s}$ that also $[sZ(k) - kZ(s)]$ has only one zero in the *r.h.s* plane.

## PROBLEMS

2.1. Show that $Z(s)$ has a unique derivative at $s_0$ in the *r.h.s* plane:

$$Z = \frac{s^2 + as + b}{s^2 + cs + d} \qquad a, b, c, \text{ and } d \text{ are positive}$$

2.2. Use the definition of the integral (Eq. 2.4.1) to show that

$$\int_{s_0}^{s} s^2 \, ds = \frac{1}{3} \left( s^3 - s_0^3 \right)$$

following Example 2.4.1.

2.3. Apply maximum modulus theorem (Theorem 2.5.1) to $W = \dfrac{Z(s) - 1}{Z(s) + 1}$ to show that if $Z(s)$ is prf and if Re $Z(\omega_0) = 0$ where $\omega_0$ is some point on $j$ axis, then

$$\text{Re } Z(s) \min < \text{Re } Z(s)$$
$$s = j\omega \qquad \text{Re } s > 0$$

2.4. Map the lines $\sigma = \omega$ and $\sigma = 2\omega$ of the $s$ plane onto the $W = \dfrac{s - 1}{s + 1}$ plane.

2.5. Map the *r.h.s* plane into the $Z$ plane (see, for example, Fig. 2.1)

$$Z = \frac{s^2 + s + 2}{2s^2 + s + 1}$$

Use the same $Z(s)$ to map the segment enclosed between the lines $re^{j\pi/4}$ and $re^{-j\pi/4}$ $(0 < r < \infty)$ in the *r.h.s* plane. (See Fig. 2.7.)

2.6. The conditions $\cos \theta \geqslant \cos \alpha$ for $|\alpha| = \pi/2$ and $\cos \theta > \cos \alpha$ for $|\alpha| < \pi/2$ may be reinterpreted to say that

$$\left| \frac{\text{Re } Z(s)}{\text{Im } Z(s)} \right| \geqslant \frac{\sigma}{\omega} \text{ for } \sigma = 0$$

$$\left| \frac{\text{Re } Z(s)}{\text{Im } Z(s)} \right| > \frac{\sigma}{\omega} \text{ for } \sigma > 0$$

Use this to show that if $Z(s)$ is prf

$$\frac{aZ(a) - bZ(b)}{aZ(b) - bZ(a)} > 0 \qquad \text{for } a = \bar{b}$$

$$\text{Re } a = \sigma > 0$$

$$\text{Im } a = \omega$$

2.7. Use Rouche's theorem to show that if $Z(s)$ is prf and $\operatorname{Re}Z(s) > 0$ on $\jmath$ axis, and if $m + n$ is a Hurwitz polynomial of degree $d$ ($m$ even, $n$ odd), both $mZ - n$ and $m - nZ$ have $d$ r.h.s plane zeros each. (See Example 2.8.1.)

## FURTHER READING

COMPLEX VARIABLES

2.1. Churchill, R. V., "Introduction to Complex Variables and Applications," 2nd ed., McGraw-Hill Book Co., Inc., New York, 1960.

2.2. Copson, E. T., "Theory of Functions of a Complex Variable," Oxford University Press, England, 1935.

2.3. LePage, W. R., "Complex Variables and the Laplace Transform for Engineers," McGraw-Hill Book Co., Inc., New York, 1961.

2.4. Marden, M., "The Geometry or the Zeros of a Polynomial in a Complex Variable," The American Math. Soc., 1949, Chapter 1.

NETWORK SYNTHESIS

2.5. Balabanian, N., "Network Synthesis," Prentice-Hall, Inc., Englewood Cliffs, N. J., 1958, Chapter 3.

2.6. Guillemin, E. A., "Synthesis of Passive Networks," John Wiley & Sons, New York, 1957, Chapter 1.

2.7. Storer, J. E., "Passive Network Synthesis," McGraw-Hill Book Co., Inc., New York, 1957, Chapter 2.

2.8. Tuttle, D. F., Jr., "Network Synthesis," John Wiley & Sons, New York, 1958, Chapter 5.

2.9. Van Valkenburg, M. E., "Introduction to Modern Network Synthesis," John Wiley & Sons, New York, 1960, Chapters 3 and 4.

# Tests for Positive Real Functions | CHAPTER 3

## TESTS FOR POSITIVE REALNESS OF Z(s) 3.1

If $Z(s)$ is a rational polynomial function of $s$, then the necessary and sufficient conditions for the positive realness of $Z(s)$ have been given in Section 2.1, and are as follows:

$$Z(s) = \text{real} \qquad \text{if } s = \text{real}$$
$$\text{Re } Z(s) \geq 0 \qquad \text{if Re } s = 0 \qquad\qquad 3.1.1$$
$$\text{Re } Z(s) > 0 \qquad \text{if Re } s > 0$$

In general, a point-by-point test of the function is required before the positive realness is verified. However, it was demonstrated in Section 2.2 that if $Z(s)$ is prf, it has no zeros or poles in the *r.h.s* plane. This means that $Z(s)$ is analytic in the *r.h.s* plane. Therefore, in accordance with the minimum real value theorem (Theorem 2.5.2), in any test for positive realness a check of whether Re $Z(s)$ $\geq 0$ on the $j$ axis is sufficient if $Z(s)$ is analytic in the *r.h.s* plane and all $j$ axis poles are simple with positive residues (Theorem 2.2.1). Hence, this can be elaborated as three relatively simple checks for positive realness.

(1). Test for the analyticity of $Z(s)$ in the *r.h.s* plane—polynomials that have all their zeros in the *l.h.s* (left half) plane are called Hurwitz polynomials; it follows that both the numerator and the denominator of $Z(s)$ must be Hurwitz polynomials.
(2). Verify whether Re $Z(s) \geq 0$ on the $j$ axis.
(3). Examine to see if all $j$ axis poles are simple with positive residues.

In practice, step (1) also reveals if there are any $j$ axis poles. Thus test (3) may not be necessary if $j$ axis poles are absent. On the other hand, the fact that either one of these tests is separately satisfied does not guarantee positive realness.

### Example 3.1.1

Check for positive realness of the following functions:

$$Z(s) = \frac{s^2 + s + 6}{s^2 + s + 1}$$

The poles and zeros of $Z(s)$ are at $s = -1 \pm j\sqrt{3}/2$ and $s = -1 \pm j\sqrt{23}/2$, respectively. These are in the *l.h.s* plane which satisfies requirement (1). However, on the $j$ axis Re $Z(j\omega)$ is

$$\text{Re } Z(j\omega) = \frac{(\omega^2 - 3)^2 - 3}{(\omega^2 + 1)^2 + \omega^2}$$

which is negative for $\omega^2 < 3 + \sqrt{3}$. Thus condition (2) is not satisfied, and $Z(s)$ is not prf.

### Example 3.1.2

Test if the following $Z(s)$ is prf:

$$Z(s) = \frac{s^2 - s - 8}{s^2 + 2s - 2}$$

$Z(s)$ has one pole and one zero in the *r.h.s* plane. Both the numerator and the denominator are not Hurwitz polynomials. Yet, computing Re $Z(j\omega)$, we obtain

$$\text{Re } Z(j\omega) = \frac{(\omega^2 + 4)^2}{(\omega^2 + 2)^2 + 4\omega^2} > 0 \text{ for all } \omega$$

These examples were included to emphasize the need to satisfy both conditions (1) and (2). The next section will be devoted to the study of Hurwitz polynomials. The last section of this chapter presents the Sturm test for verifying whether Re $Z(s) \geq 0$ on $j$ axis.

## 3.2. HURWITZ POLYNOMIALS

One necessary condition for a function to be prf is that all its poles and zeros lie in the *l.h.s* plane (our definition includes the $j$ axis). Polynomials having all their zeros in the *l.h.s* plane are called Hurwitz polynomials. No complex coefficients are to be considered.

Let $P(s) = (s + s_1)(s + s_2)(s + \bar{s}_2) = m + n$ ($m$ even, $n$ odd) be a Hurwitz polynomial (Fig. 3.1).

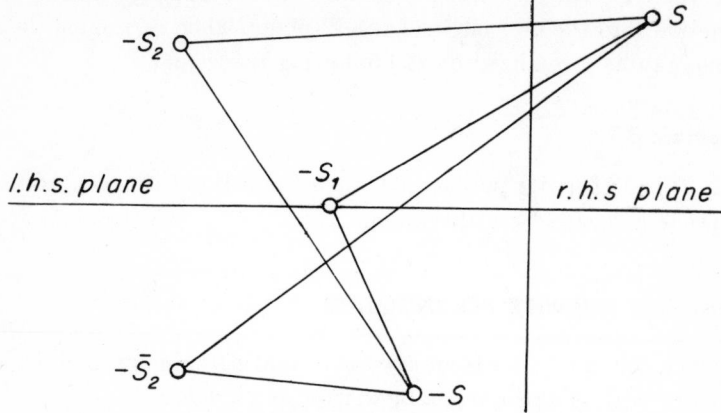

**Fig. 3.1. A polynomial with l.h.s. plane zeros**

Evaluating $|P(s)|$ and $|P(-s)|$ in the factored form, we get for Re $s > 0$

$$|P(s)| = |s + s_1|\,|s + s_2|\,|s + \bar{s}_2|$$
$$|P(-s)| = |s - s_1|\,|s - s_2|\,|s - \bar{s}_2| \qquad \textbf{3.2.1}$$

in which graphical consideration shows that for Re $s > 0$

$$|s + s_1| > |s - s_1|$$
$$|s + s_2| > |s - \bar{s}_2|$$
$$|s + \bar{s}_2| > |s - s_2| \qquad \textbf{3.2.2}$$

Consequently, $|P(s)| > |P(-s)|$ for Re $s > 0$. Similarly, because of symmetry, $|P(s)| = |P(-s)|$ for Re $s = 0$. Hence the quantity $P(-s)/P(s)$, defined as $W$, has the following properties:

$$|W| = \frac{|P(-s)|}{|P(s)|} = \frac{|m - n|}{|m + n|} < 1 \text{ Re } s > 0$$

$$|W| = \frac{|P(-s)|}{|P(s)|} = \frac{|m - n|}{|m + n|} = 1 \text{ Re } s = 0 \qquad \textbf{3.2.3}$$

or

$$|W| = \frac{\left|\dfrac{m}{n} - 1\right|}{\left|\dfrac{m}{n} + 1\right|} < 1 \text{ Re } s > 0$$

$$\qquad \textbf{3.2.4}$$

$$|W| = \frac{\left|\dfrac{m}{n} - 1\right|}{\left|\dfrac{m}{n} + 1\right|} = 1 \text{ Re } s = 0$$

But these are the precise set of conditions for mapping a positive real function into the unit circle of the $W$ plane. Then $m/n$ must be prf. This may be formalized by the following theorem.

**Theorem 3.2.1**

If $P$ is a Hurwitz polynomial, then the ratio of its even and odd parts is a positive real function.

## 3.3. TESTING FOR HURWITZ POLYNOMIALS

Since the ratio $m/n$ is an even over odd polynomial, and since it must be real for $s$ real, it can be written as a product

$$\frac{m}{n} = \frac{\prod_p (s^2 + a_p{}^2)}{s\prod_p (s^2 + b_p{}^2)} \qquad \textbf{3.3.1}$$

where both the zeros and the poles lie symmetrically about the real axis.

The zeros of the denominator are along the $j$ axis if $b_p{}^2 > 0$. Furthermore, if any $b_p{}^2$ is negative, at least one root lies in the $r.h.s$ plane. This case must be ruled out, since $m/n$ is prf and cannot have poles in the $r.h.s$ plane. Similarly, $r.h.s$ plane poles will be present if $b_p{}^2$ is complex, as the location of the pole is given by

$$s_1 = \pm\sqrt{-\text{Re } b_p{}^2 - j \text{ Im } b_p{}^2}$$

$$= \pm\sqrt{|b_p{}^2|}\sin\theta \pm j\sqrt{|b_p{}^2|}\cos\theta$$

$$\theta = \frac{1}{2}\text{ arg. } b_p{}^2$$

Hence the poles lie in the $r.h.s$ plane unless $\theta = \frac{1}{2}\text{arg.} b_p{}^2 = 0$ which means that $b_p{}^2$ must be positive. The same conclusion is reached for $a_p{}^2$ if the zeros of $m/n$ are considered. Thus it is seen that all the zeros and poles of $m/n$ lie on the $j$ axis.

**Example 3.3.1**

Ascertain whether the following polynomial is Hurwitz:

$$P(s) = s^5 + s^4 + 6s^3 + 4s^2 + 8s + 3 \qquad \textbf{3.3.2}$$

Formation of the even over odd ratio gives

$$\frac{m}{n} = \frac{s^4 + 4s^2 + 3}{s(s^4 + 6s^2 + 8)} = \frac{(s^2 + 1)(s^2 + 3)}{s(s^2 + 2)(s^2 + 4)} \qquad \textbf{3.3.3}$$

$$= \frac{3}{8s} + \frac{1}{8(s + j\sqrt{2})} + \frac{1}{8(s - j\sqrt{2})} + \frac{3}{16(s + j2)} + \frac{3}{16(s - j2)} \qquad \textbf{3.3.4}$$

$$= \frac{3}{8s} + \frac{2 \times \frac{1}{8} s}{s^2 + 2} + \frac{2 \times \frac{3}{16} s}{s^2 + 4} \qquad \textbf{3.3.5}$$

The coefficients $3/8$, $1/8$, and $3/16$ are the residues at the poles of $m/n$.

Each of the three terms of Eq. 3.3.5 are positive real functions. To prove this let $s = j\omega + \epsilon$, where $\epsilon$ is a real number. Then the first term becomes

$$\text{Re} \frac{1}{s} \to \frac{\epsilon}{\omega^2 + \epsilon^2} \geq 0 \qquad \text{for all } \omega \text{ and } \epsilon \qquad \textbf{3.3.6}$$

the second and third are of the form

$$\text{Re} \frac{s}{s^2 + a^2} \to \frac{\epsilon(\omega^2 + a^2 + \epsilon^2)}{(-\omega^2 + a^2 + \epsilon^2)^2 + 4\omega^2\epsilon^2} \geq 0 \qquad \text{for all } \omega \text{ and } \epsilon \quad \textbf{3.3.7}$$

Thus the real part of each of the terms of Eq. 3.3.5 is positive throughout the r.h.s plane, since their coefficients are positive. Hence $m/n$ is prf and $P(s)$ is Hurwitz.

Incidentally, the network in Fig. 3.2 has the same impedance function as Eq. 3.3.5.

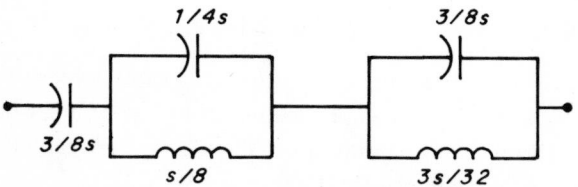

**Fig. 3.2. A network with an impedance function given by Eq. 3.3.5**

### RESIDUE CRITERIA 3.4

In testing for Hurwitz polynomials, the ratios $m/n$ or $n/m$ may be expanded in a partial fraction expansion as follows:

$$\frac{m}{n} = a_0 s + \frac{a'_1}{s} + \sum_p \frac{2b_p s}{s^2 + c_p^2} \qquad \textbf{3.4.1}$$

$a_0$, $a'_1$, and $b_p$ are the residues of $m/n$ at the poles at infinity, at zero, and at $\omega = c_p$, respectively. Moreover, it was shown earlier (Theorem 2.2.1) that since $m/n$ is prf, all the $j$ axis poles have a real positive residue. Then $a_0$, $a'_1$, and all the $b_p$'s are positive and real. The fact that each one of the terms of Eq. 3.4.1 is positive real may be shown by setting $s = j\omega + \epsilon$, and then proceeding as in Eqs. 3.3.6 and 3.3.7. Thus, one way to test whether a polynomial is Hurwitz is to expand either its $m/n$ or $n/m$ functions in a partial fraction of the form of Eq. 3.4.1 and to verify whether all the residues are positive real constants.

## 3.5. STIELJES CONTINUED FRACTION

The method for testing Hurwitz polynomials discussed in the previous section depends on a knowledge of either the zeros or the poles of $m/n$. However, it is possible to obtain expansions of $m/n$ which do not require a knowledge of the location of its poles and zeros. One such method is called Stieljes continued fraction expansion and may be arrived at as follows.

Let $\phi_1(s)$ be defined as

$$\frac{1}{\phi_1(s)} = \frac{m}{n} - a_0 s = \frac{a'_1}{s} + \sum_p \frac{2b_p s}{s^2 + c_p^2} \qquad \text{3.5.1}$$

$\phi_1(s)$ is prf since it is made up of positive real functions. Also, since $\dfrac{1}{\phi_1(s)}$ goes to zero when $s$ goes to infinity, and since the degrees of the numerator and the denominator cannot differ by more than 1, it follows that the degree of the numerator of $\phi_1(s)$ must be 1 higher than the degree of the denominator. Then $\phi_1(s)$, too, can be expanded by removing the pole at infinity

$$\phi_1(s) = a_1 s + \frac{1}{\phi_2(s)} \qquad \text{3.5.2}$$

where $\phi_2(s)$ also has a pole at infinity. This process may be continued as follows

$$\frac{m}{n} = a_0 s + \cfrac{1}{a_1 s + \cfrac{1}{a_2 s + 1}} \qquad \text{3.5.3}$$

until the last term is of degree 1.

Note that the network of Fig. 3.3 gives an impedance function of the form of Eq. 3.5.3.

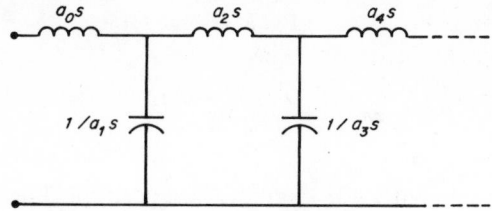

**Fig. 3.3. A network having Eq. 3.5.3 as its impedance function**

The network of Fig. 3.2 is referred to as a Foster canonic form; that of Fig. 3.3 is known as a Cauer canonic form, where the term canonic means that the network for the given impedance function, $Z(s) = m/n$, contains the minimum possible number of elements.

## FINAL REMARKS ON TESTING HURWITZ POLYNOMIALS 3.6

A necessary condition for a polynomial to be Hurwitz is that $m/n$, the ratio of its even and odd parts, is a positive real function. But we have already seen that the ratio $m/n$ is a positive real function if the following constraints are satisfied:

(1). All the zeros and poles are simple and lie along the $j$ axis.
(2). The residues of $m/n$ are real and positive.
(3). [Alternative to (2.)] The residues of $n/m$ are real and positive.
(4). [Alternative to (2.)] The coefficients of the Stieljes continued fraction expansion are real and positive.

Actually, these conditions are necessary but not sufficient, since $m$ and $n$ may have common factors of the form $s^2 - a^2$ ($a$ real). On the other hand, factors of the form $s^2 + a^2$ ($j$ axis zeros) *are* acceptable.

Less severe tests for a Hurwitz polynomial are also available. For example, a Hurwitz polynomial may not have missing or negative coefficients. This may be shown by expressing $P(s)$ as a product, say of the form

$$P(s) = a(s + b) \prod_p (s^2 + A_p s + B_p) = \sum_q c_q s^q$$

where $c_q$ is the sum and product of the $b$, $A_p$'s and $B_p$'s. If one of the $c_q$'s is zero or negative at least one of the $b$, $A_p$'s and $B_p$'s is negative. This means that at least one of the roots is in the $r.h.s$ plane, and the polynomial is not Hurwitz.

### 3.7. TEST FOR POSITIVE REALNESS ON $j$ AXIS

Once the poles and zeros of $Z(s)$ have been found in the $l.h.s$ plane, it remains for us to ascertain that Re $Z(s) \geq 0$ for Re $s = 0$. We recall that on the $j$ axis Re $Z(j\omega) = $ Ev $Z(j\omega)$

$$\text{Re } Z(j\omega) = \frac{m_1 m_2 - n_1 n_2}{m_2{}^2 - n_2{}^2}\bigg|_{s \, = \, j\omega} \qquad\qquad \textbf{3.7.1}$$

and on the $j$ axis both $-n_2{}^2$ and $m_2{}^2$ are positive. Then, essentially, we must investigate whether

$$f(j\omega) = m_1 m_2 - n_1 n_2|_{s=j\omega} \geq 0 \qquad\qquad \textbf{3.7.2}$$

This is an even function of $\omega$ and can be written as

$$f(x) = \sum_{p=0}^{n} a_p x^p \geq 0 \ (x = \omega^2, \, a_p = real) \qquad\qquad \textbf{3.7.3}$$

which means that for $Z(s)$ to be prf, $f(x) \geq 0$ for all $0 \leq x \leq \infty$. This statement does not preclude that some of the $a_p$'s may be negative.

#### Example 3.7.1

Show that $f(x) = x^2 - 2x + 4 \geq 0$ for $0 \leq x \leq \infty$ ($x$ = real).

#### Proof

$f(x) = x^2 - 2x + 4 = (x - 1)^2 + 3$. It is positive since it is a sum of a square (always positive) and a constant.

Observe that $a_1$ is $-2$. This shows that a negative coefficient does not rule out the possibility of $f(x) \geq 0$ for $x$ in the interval $0 \leq x \leq \infty$. On the other hand, if all the coefficients are positive, $f(x)$ in Eq. 3.7.3 is a sum of positive numbers and is definitely positive for all positive $x$. When some of the coefficients are negative, and it is not obvious whether $f(x)$ is positive, a convenient further check is allowed by the Sturm test.

### 3.8. STURM'S TEST

Sturm's test is defined in terms of a set of functions $(f_0, f_1, f_2 \cdots f_n)$ (known as Sturm's functions) obtained in the following manner: The first two are $f_0 = f(x)$ and $f_1 = \dfrac{df(x)}{dx}$, respectively. The third function $f_2$ is defined in terms of the two-term quotient of $f_0/f_1$. More precisely, $f_2/f_1 = b_0x + c_0 - f_0/f_1$ [the term $(bx + c)$ is not relevant to the actual sign test under consideration]. This may be written as $f_0 = (b_0x + c_0)f_1 - f_2$. Now Sturm's set of functions can be presented as a sequence:

$$f_0 = (b_0x + c_0) f_1 - f_2$$
$$f_1 = (b_1x + c_1) f_2 - f_3$$
$$f_2 = (b_2x + c_2) f_3 - f_4$$
$$\cdot \qquad \cdot \qquad \cdot$$
$$\cdot \qquad \cdot \qquad \cdot \qquad \text{3.8.1}$$
$$f_p = (b_px + c_p) f_{p+1} - f_{p+2}$$
$$\cdot \qquad \cdot \qquad \cdot$$
$$\cdot \qquad \cdot \qquad \cdot$$
$$f_n = \text{constant}$$

The set of equations (3.8.1) is known as the Euclidean Algorithm. If $f_0$ has a factor of higher multiplicity, $f_1$ must have that factor too. For if

$$f_0 = (x + d)^r f_{01} \qquad [(x + d) \text{ is the factor}] \qquad \text{3.8.2a}$$

then

$$f_1 = \frac{d}{dx} f_0 = (x + d)^{r-1}[rf_{01} + (x + d)f'_{01}]_{(r \geq 2)} \qquad \text{3.8.2b}$$

and therefore

$$f_2 = -f_0 + (b_0x + c_0)f_1$$
$$= -(x + d)^{r-1}[(x + d)f_{01} - (b_0x + c_0)(rf_{01} + (x + d)f'_{01})] \qquad \text{3.8.3}$$

Similarly it can be deduced that the factor $(x + d)^{r-1}$ is present in all of the Sturm's functions $(f_0, f_1, f_2 \cdots f_{n-r+1})$.

## Example 3.8.1

Find whether $f(x) \geq 0$ for $x$ in $0 \leq x \leq \infty$, where $f_0 = f(x) = x^4 - x^3 - x + 1$.

### Solution

Differentiation gives $f_1 = \dfrac{df(x)}{dx} = 4x^3 - 3x^2 - 1$. The function $f_0/f_1$ can be expressed as

$$\frac{f_0}{f_1} = \frac{x^4 - x^3 - x + 1}{4x^3 - 3x^2 - 1} = \frac{1}{4}x - \frac{1}{16} - \frac{\left(\frac{3}{16}x^2 + \frac{3}{4}x - \frac{15}{16}\right)}{4x^3 - 3x^2 - 1}$$

yielding $f_2 = \left( \dfrac{3}{16} x^2 + \dfrac{3}{4} x - \dfrac{15}{16} \right)$. Formation of the ratio $f_1/f_2$ gives

$$\frac{f_1}{f_2} = \frac{4x^3 - 3x^2 - 1}{\dfrac{3}{16} x^2 + \dfrac{3}{4} x - \dfrac{15}{16}} = \frac{64}{3} x - \frac{19 \times 16}{3} + \frac{96(x - 1)}{\dfrac{3}{16} x^2 + \dfrac{3}{4} x - \dfrac{15}{16}}$$

producing $f_3 = -96(x - 1)$. The ratio

$$\frac{f_2}{f_3} = \frac{\dfrac{3}{16} x^2 + \dfrac{3}{4} x - \dfrac{15}{16}}{-96(x - 1)} = -\frac{3}{16 \times 96} (x + 5)$$

This yields $f_4 = 0$ (no remainder). Thus, the set of Sturm functions is the following:

$$f_0 = x^4 - x^3 - x + 1$$
$$f_1 = 4x^3 - 3x^2 - 1$$
$$f_2 = \frac{3}{16} x^2 + \frac{3}{4} x - \frac{15}{16} \qquad\qquad \textbf{3.8.4}$$
$$f_3 = -96(x - 1)$$

A comparison of Eq. 3.8.4 with Eq. 3.8.1 shows that the last term $f_n = f_4$ is missing. Actually it is zero, and the sequence is truncated prematurely. This results from the fact that the factor $(x - 1)$ is a factor of $f_2$, and because of the nature of the set $(x - 1)$ is also a factor in $f_0$ and $f_1$. It follows from Eq. 3.8.2 that $(x - 1)^2$ is a factor of $f_0$. Factoring $(x - 1)^2$ in $f_0$, we get

$$f_0 = (x - 1)^2(x^2 + x + 1)$$

Since both factors are positive for all $x$'s in $0 \leq x \leq \infty$, $f(x) \geq 0$ throughout the interval.

This example shows that eventually the common factor becomes very conspicuous by becoming the last function of the set $(f_{n-r+1})$.

In trying to determine whether $f(x) \geq 0$ in $0 \leq x \leq \infty$, we find that factorization is a great help, since then the problem reduces to the determination of the sign of the individual factors. Toward this end, the construction of the Sturm set affords a good method for discovering zeros of higher multiplicity which can then be factored out. Eventually, however, the polynomial under consideration is reduced to a function without high-order zeros. To test whether this function is positive in the interval under consideration, construct the set of Sturm functions (Eq. 3.8.1) again. However, now it is assumed that $f(x)$ has no zeros of higher multiplicity.

Before stating Sturm's theorem, we will present another example in order to familiarize us with the terms of the theorem.

## Example 3.8.2

Verify that $f(x) = x^2 - 2x + 4 \geq 0$ for $0 \leq x \leq \infty$ (Example 3.7.1).

*Solution*

Construction of the Sturm's set (Eq. 3.8.1) gives

$$f_0 = x^2 - 2x + 4$$

$$f_1 = 2x - 2$$

The third term is obtained from $f_0/f_1$

$$\frac{f_0}{f_1} = \frac{x^2 - 2x + 4}{2x - 2} = \frac{1}{2} x - \frac{1}{2} - \frac{-3}{f_1}$$

giving $f_2 = -3$.

Now construct Sturm's sign table (Table 3.1).

TABLE 3.1. STURM'S SIGN TABLE

| | Sign of the function | | | Total variation in sign |
|---|---|---|---|---|
| | $f_0$ | $f_1$ | $f_2$ | $V$ |
| $x = 0$ | $+$ | $-$ | $-$ | 1 |
| $x = \infty$ | $+$ | $+$ | $-$ | 1 |
| | | | | $V_\infty - V_0 = 0$ |

The fact that $V_\infty - V_0$ is zero in the table means that $f(x)$ does not go through any zero as $x$ moves from zero to infinity. Then $f(x)$ never changes sign and must be positive for $0 \leq x \leq \infty$.

The preceding result arises from Sturm's theorem, which is now stated formally:

The total number of zeros that $f(x)$ has in the interval $\alpha \leq x \leq \beta$, equals $V_\beta - V_\alpha$. $V_\alpha$ and $V_\beta$ are the number of sign changes in the set $(f_0, f_1, f_2 \cdots f_n)$ evaluated at $x = \alpha$ and $x = \beta$, respectively.

## PROOF OF STURM'S THEOREM 3.9

Before proving the theorem, we make the following observations (Eqs. 3.9.1, 3.9.2, 3.9.3):

$$f_p = (b_p x + c_p)f_{p+1} - f_{p+2}$$

$$= -f_{p+2} \qquad \text{when } f_{p+1} = 0 \text{ (by 3.8.1)}$$

**3.9.1**

Since $f(x)$ is assumed to have only simple zeros, $f_1 = \dfrac{df}{dx}$ has
at least one zero between any two consecutive zeros of $f(x)$.

**3.9.2**

Furthermore, since $f(x)$ is assumed to have only simple zeros, no two consecutive functions have the same zero. To prove this, observe that since $f_p = (b_p x + c_p) \times f_{p+1} - f_{p+2}$, then if $f_{p+1}$ and $f_{p+2}$ have the same zero, $f_p$ must also have the same zero. Hence all these functions have the same zero which must be a high-order zero of $f(x)$, and this is a contradiction.

**3.9.3**

Suppose the sign of each one of the set of functions $f_0 \cdots f_n$ is established at a particular value of $x$, say $x = \alpha$. In particular, assume that $f_5$ is the last term of the sequence and that it is negative. Now examine Table 3.2 which shows the variations in sign of each of the set of Sturm functions as $x$ moves along the real axis from $x = \alpha$ (row 1) to $\beta$ (row 6).

**TABLE 3.2. BEHAVIOR OF STURM FUNCTIONS**

|  | Sign of $(f_0, f_1, \cdots f_n)$ | | | | | | Number of sign variations $V$ |
|---|---|---|---|---|---|---|---|
|  | $f_0$ | $f_1$ | $f_2$ | $f_3$ | $f_4$ | $f_5$ |  |
| 1. $(x = \alpha)$ | + | − | − | − | + | − | 3 |
| 2. $f_1$ passed a zero | + | + | − | − | + | − | 3 |
| 3. $f_0$ passed a zero | − | + | − | − | + | − | 4 |
| 4. $f_2$ passed a zero | − | + | + | − | + | − | 4 |
| 5. $f_1$ passed a zero | − | − | + | − | + | − | 4 |
| 6. $f_0$ passed a zero $(x = \beta)$ | + | − | + | − | + | − | 5 |

Let $x$ increase slowly. No element of the set changes sign unless it becomes zero first. Also, no one of the set ($f_{p+1}$) may go through zero unless it is between two functions ($f_p$ and $f_{p+2}$) opposing each other in sign ($f_p = -f_{p+2}$). This is required by Eq. 3.9.1. The possibility that two consecutive functions go to zero simultaneously is excluded by Eq. 3.9.3. Accordingly, only $f_1$ and $f_3$ in the first row of Table 3.2 satisfy this requirement. But if $f_1$ changes sign (row 2), the total number of sign variations does not change ($V_2 = V_1 = 3$). The same result would be obtained if $f_3$ changed sign. It follows that as $x$ increases no change in the total number of sign variations can be produced by sign changes in ($f_1, f_2, \cdots f_n$). The only change in $V$ can be produced when $f_0$ goes through zero.

To complete the proof of Sturm's theorem, it is still necessary to show that when $f_0$ goes through several zeros the number of sign

variations changes correspondingly. Suppose that $f_0$ goes through a
zero and changes sign (row 3); $f_0$ cannot change sign again until $f_1$
changes sign (Eq. 3.9.2). But $f_1$ is between two negative functions
and, therefore, cannot change sign before $f_2$ does (Eq. 3.9.1). Then
in row 4, $f_2$ becomes plus. Now $f_1$ may change to minus (row 5)
which permits $f_0$ to pass through its second zero (row 6). The total
number of variations in sign in row 6 is 5. Then, $V_\beta - V_\alpha$ and the
change in number of variations as $f_0$ passes through two zeros is
$5 - 3 = 2$. This process may be formalized by use of induction
techniques to show that $V_\beta - V_\alpha$ equals the number of zeros passed
by $f(x)$ as $x$ increases from $\alpha$ to $\beta$.

### Example 3.9.1

Given $f(x) = x^3 - x^2 - 4x + 6$. Verify whether $f(x) \geq 0$ for $0 \leq x \leq \infty$.
Verification by Sturm's test:

$$f_0 = x^3 + x^2 - 4x + 6$$
$$f_1 = 3x^2 + 2x - 4$$
$$f_2 = \frac{26}{9} x - \frac{58}{9}$$
$$f_3 = - \frac{1601}{169}$$

The Sturm's sign table gives

|           | $f_0$ | $f_1$ | $f_2$ | $f_3$ | $V$ |
|-----------|-------|-------|-------|-------|-----|
| $x = 0$   | $+$   | $-$   | $-$   | $-$   | 1   |
| $x = \infty$ | $+$ | $+$   | $+$   | $-$   | 1   |

$$V_\infty - V_0 = 0$$

Thus $f(x)$ does not pass through any zeros as $x$ moves from zero to infinity.
Consequently the function $f(x)$ cannot change sign and is positive throughout
the interval.

### PROBLEMS

3.1. Which of the following polynomials are Hurwitz?

$$P_1 = s^2 + as + b \qquad a > 0 < b$$
$$P_2 = s^3 - s^2 + s + 1$$
$$P_3 = s^3 + s^2 + s + 1$$
$$P_4 = s^4 + s^3 + s^2 + s + 1$$
$$P_5 = 2s^3 + s^2 + s + 6$$
$$P_6 = s^4 + 1$$

3.2. Check whether the following polynomials are Hurwitz:

(a) $P_1 = s^3 + s^2 + s + 0.9$

(b) $P_2 = s^3 + 2s^2 + 2s + 3.9$

(c) $P_3 = s^3 + 60s^2 + 120s + 8000$

(d) $P_4 = 50s^3 + 150s^2 + 149.5s + 49.5$

(e) $P_5 = P_1 + P_2$

(f) $P_6 = P_3 + P_4$

(g) $P_7 = (s + 1)(s + 2)(s + 3) + (s + 4)(s + 5)(s + 6)$

3.3. Test for Hurwitz polynomials using partial fraction expansion:

(a) $P_1 = s^7 + 4s^6 + 6s^5 + 18s^4 + 11s^3 + 22s^2 + 6s + 6$

(b) $P_2 = s^7 + 2s^6 + 6s^5 + 10s^4 + 11s^3 + 16s^2 + 6s + 6$

(c) $P_3 = P_1 + P_2$

3.4. Use Stieljes continued fraction expansion to check whether the following polynomial is Hurwitz:

$$P = 60s^7 + 107s^6 + 177s^5 + 295s^4 + 186s^3 + 260s^2 + 120s + 120$$

3.5. Test for positive realness.

(a) $Z(s) = (s^2 + 2s + 2)/(s^2 + 2s + 1)$

(b) $Z(s) = (s^2 + 2s + 5)/(s^2 + 2s + 2)$

(c) $Z(s) = (3s^3 + 6s^2 + 14s + 7)/(3s^3 + 6s^2 + 10s + 11)$

(d) $Z(s) = (3s^3 + 6s^2 + 8s + 4)/(3s^3 + 6s^2 + 7s + 5)$

Use Sturm's test for (c) and (d).

3.6. Obtain the maximum value of the constant $\alpha$ such that the following functions are prf.

(a) $Z(s) = (s^2 + s + 4)/(2s^2 + 2s + 5) - \alpha_1$

(b) $Z(s) = (s^2 + s + 2)/(3s^2 + 2s + 3) - \alpha_2$

3.7. Given a Hurwitz polynomial

$$P(s) = a_0 s^n + a_1 s^{n-1} + \cdots + a_n$$

$$= \sum_0^n a_p s^{n-p} \qquad n \text{ even}$$

find the first three elements in a Cauer expansion.

## FURTHER READING

3.1. Balabanian, N., "Network Synthesis," Prentice Hall, Inc., Englewood Cliffs, N. J., 1958, Chapter 3.
3.2. Guillemin, E. A., "Synthesis of Passive Networks," John Wiley & Sons, New York, 1957, Chapter 1.
3.3. Tuttle, D. F., Jr., "Network Synthesis," John Wiley & Sons, New York, 1958, Chapter 5.
3.4. Van Valkenburg, M. E., "Introduction to Modern Network Synthesis," John Wiley & Sons, New York, 1960, Chapter 4.

# CHAPTER 4

# *Immittance of RLC Networks*

## 4.1. RATIONAL PROPERTIES OF Z(s)

You will recall that in Chapter 3, the properties of a driving point impedance function $Z(s)$ were investigated in detail and that $Z(s)$ was assumed to be rational and prf. In this chapter, however, we will examine a particular $Z(s)$. This one is assumed to be an *RLC* (resistance, inductance, and capacitance, coupling permitted) driving point impedance function. We will show in the course of this chapter that all such impedance functions are prf, but this will be done by first demonstrating that $Z(s)$ is rational and analytic except at its poles.

At this point, let the network under consideration (Fig. 4.1) be restricted to lumped, passive, linear networks. In other words, the network is made up of *RLC* elements (coupling between loops is permitted). The elements are discrete, linear, and passive (no energy sources except in the first loop $E_1$). To compute $Z(s)$, we use the Laplace transformation and assume that the network is initially relaxed; that is, that all initial current and voltage values are zero.

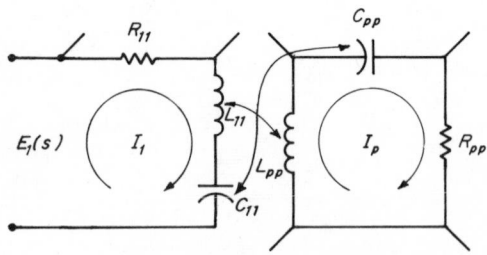

**Fig. 4.1. A possible network**

54

All parallel networks are further divided into loops so that no single loop contains parallel elements. Writing the loop equations in the Laplace transformed notation, we get

$$E_1(s) = \sum_{p=1}^{n} a_{1p} I_p(s) \qquad (n = \text{number of loops})$$

$$0 = \sum_{p=1}^{n} a_{2p} I_p(s)$$

$$\cdot$$
$$\cdot$$

$$0 = \sum_{p=1}^{n} a_{qp} I_p(s)$$

$$\cdot$$
$$\cdot$$

$$0 = \sum_{p=1}^{n} a_{np} I_p(s)$$

4.1.1

where the coefficients $a_{qp}$ are the coefficients of impedance appropriate to each loop.

Since each loop contains no parallel elements $a_{qp}$, the general loop impedance equals

$$a_{qp} = R_{qp} + s L_{qp} + \frac{1}{sC_{qp}} \qquad \text{4.1.2}$$

Coupling terms do not change the character of $a_{qp}$, though some of the coefficients may be negative owing to negative couplings.

Equation 4.1.1 is a typical set of $n$ linear algebraic equations. To examine the properties of the driving point impedance function, $[E_1(s)]/[I_1(s)]$, we solve for $I_1(s)$. Thus by Cramer's rule

$$I_1(s) = E_1(s) \frac{\begin{vmatrix} a_{22} & a_{23} & a_{24} & \cdot \\ a_{32} & a_{33} & a_{34} & \cdot \\ a_{42} & a_{43} & a_{44} & \cdot \\ \cdot & \cdot & \cdot & \end{vmatrix}}{\begin{vmatrix} a_{11} & a_{12} & a_{13} & a_{14} & \cdot \\ a_{21} & a_{22} & a_{23} & a_{24} & \cdot \\ a_{31} & a_{32} & a_{33} & a_{34} & \cdot \\ a_{41} & a_{42} & a_{43} & a_{44} & \cdot \\ \cdot & \cdot & \cdot & \cdot & \end{vmatrix}} \equiv E_1(s)/Z(s) \qquad \text{4.1.3}$$

Thus $Z(s)$ is made up of sums and products of functions of the form $a_{qp}$ (Eq. 4.1.2). All of these terms are rational functions of $s$ (no irrational roots of $s$). Therefore $Z(s)$ is a rational function of $s$. Furthermore, since the final result would be in a ratio of polynomials, then $Z(s)$ is also an analytic function of $s$ throughout the complex $s$ plane except at the poles.

## 4.2. PROPERTIES OF $Z(s)$—THE ENERGY FUNCTIONS

As we continue the work of the previous section, you will recall that the system was passive. This means that the total instantaneous energy stored or dissipated by the network is always positive or zero. This additional constraint is hidden in some of the interrelationships between the coefficients $a_{qp}$. These interrelationships will be brought to light by studying the energy functions of the network. These are defined in Eq. 4.2.4. Refer to Eqs. 4.1.1 and multiply both sides of each member of the set of equations by $\bar{I}_q(s)$:

$$E_1(s)\bar{I}_1(s) = \sum_{p=1}^{n} a_{1p}I_p(s)\bar{I}_1(s)$$

$$0 = \sum_{p=1}^{n} a_{2p}I_p(s)\bar{I}_2(s)$$

$$\cdot$$
$$\cdot$$

$$0 = \sum_{p=1}^{n} a_{qp}I_p(s)\bar{I}_q(s)$$

$$\cdot$$
$$\cdot$$

$$0 = \sum_{p=1}^{n} a_{np}I_p(s)\bar{I}_n(s)$$

4.2.1

These equations can be added and the result written in more compact form:

$$E_1(s)\bar{I}_1(s) = \sum_{q=1}^{n}\sum_{p=1}^{n} a_{qp}I_p(s)\bar{I}_q(s) \equiv \sum_{qp} a_{qp}I_p\bar{I}_q$$

Collecting like terms in $s$, we get

$$E_1(s)\bar{I}_1(s) = \sum_{qp}^{n} R_{qp}I_p\bar{I}_q + s\sum_{qp}^{n} L_{qp}I_p\bar{I}_q + \frac{1}{s}\sum_{qp}^{n} \frac{1}{C_{qp}} I_p\bar{I}_q \qquad \textbf{4.2.2}$$

This is written in the abbreviated form

$$E_1(s)\bar{I}_1(s) = 2F + 2sT + \frac{2V}{s} \qquad \textbf{4.2.3}$$

where

$$F = \frac{1}{2}\sum_{qp}^{n} R_{qp}I_p\bar{I}_q,$$

$$\qquad \textbf{4.2.4}$$

$$T = \frac{1}{2}\sum_{qp}^{n} L_{qp}I_p\bar{I}_q,$$

and

$$V = \frac{1}{2}\sum_{qp}^{n} \frac{1}{C_{qp}} I_p\bar{I}_q$$

The quantities $F$, $T$, and $V$ are defined as energy functions. In the following section it will be shown that conservation of energy restricts the coefficients of the energy functions ($R_{qp}$, $L_{qp}$, and $1/C_{qp}$) in such a way that the energy functions themselves ($F$, $T$, and $V$) are never negative for all possible values of $I_p$ and $I_q$. This is true in spite of the fact that the energy functions do not represent energy in the usual sense, since $I_p$ and $I_q$ are not currents (they are the Laplace transforms of the currents).

## THE POSITIVE REALITY OF THE ENERGY FUNCTIONS 4.3

The energy functions will now be examined critically. Rewritten for convenience, they are

$$F(s) = \frac{1}{2}\sum_{pq}^{n} R_{pq}I_p\bar{I}_q$$

$$T(s) = \frac{1}{2}\sum_{pq}^{n} L_{pq}I_p\bar{I}_q \qquad \textbf{4.3.1}$$

$$V(s) = \frac{1}{2}\sum_{pq}^{n} \frac{1}{C_{pq}} I_p\bar{I}_q$$

As already noted, $I_p$ and $I_q$ are not functions of time, and therefore the terms above do not represent energy in the usual sense. Note, for example, that the instantaneous energy stored in the inductors is given by

$$T(t) = \frac{1}{2} \sum_{pq}^{n} L_{pq} i_p(t) i_q(t) \qquad \textbf{4.3.2}$$

$T(t)$ is very similar to $T(s)$. Furthermore, $T(t)$ is positive, since the total energy stored in the inductors cannot be negative. (This is another way of saying that the system is passive.) But this can only be true if a certain relation is maintained among the $L_{pq}$'s. (More precisely, in fact, the energy functions must be a quadratic form.) As an example, let the $p^{\text{th}}$ and $q^{\text{th}}$ loop be coupled magnetically. Any uncoupled coil would manifest itself in a stronger deviation from a perfect coupling (that is $\beta$ below would differ from unity). Thus in Fig. 4.2

$$L_{qp} = \beta \sqrt{L_{qq} L_{pp}} = L_{pq}$$

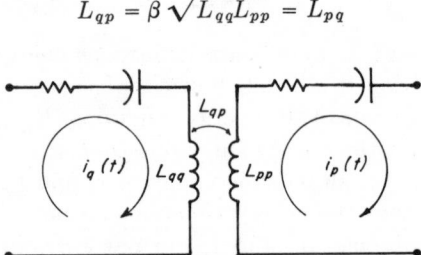

**Fig. 4.2. Magnetic coupling between two loops**

The total magnetic energy stored in the two loop system is

$$T_{pq}(t) = \frac{1}{2} L_{qq} i_q^2(t) + \frac{1}{2} L_{pp} i_p^2(t) + \frac{1}{2} L_{qp} i_p(t) i_q(t) + \frac{1}{2} L_{pq} i_p(t) i_q(t)$$

resulting in

$$T_{pq}(t) = \frac{1}{2} L_{qq} i_q^2(t) + \frac{1}{2} L_{pp} i_p^2(t) + \beta \sqrt{L_{qq} L_{pp}}\, i_p(t) i_q(t) \qquad \textbf{4.3.3}$$

which can be written as a sum of squares:

$$T_{pq}(t) = \frac{1}{2} \left( \sqrt{L_{qq}}\, i_q(t) + \beta \sqrt{L_{pp}}\, i_p(t) \right)^2 + \frac{1}{2} (1 - \beta^2) L_{pp} i_p^2(t) \qquad \textbf{4.3.4}$$

Conservation of energy requires that $T_{pq}(t) \geq 0$ for all possible values of $i_q(t)$ and $i_p(t)$. This can only be true in Eq. 4.3.4 if

$1 - \beta^2 \geq 0$. Then it may be contended that conservation of energy requires that

$$1 - \beta^2 \geq 0 \qquad\qquad \textbf{4.3.5}$$

in the two corresponding loops.

Now, suppose that $T(s)$ (Eq. 4.3.1) is computed for the same two loops. Towards this end, let

$$I_p(s) = a_p + jb_p$$
$$I_q(s) = a_q + jb_q \qquad\qquad \textbf{4.3.6}$$

$$(a_p, a_q, b_p, \text{ and } b_q \text{ are real})$$

Then

$$T(s) = \frac{1}{2} L_{pp}(a_p - jb_p)(a_p + jb_p) + \frac{1}{2} L_{pq}(a_q - jb_q)(a_p + jb_p)$$

$$\qquad\qquad \textbf{4.3.7}$$

$$+ \frac{1}{2} L_{qp}(a_p - jb_p)(a_q + jb_q) + \frac{1}{2} L_{qq}(a_q - jb_q)(a_q + jb_q)$$

which can be expanded to give

$$T(s) = \frac{1}{2} L_{pp}(a_p{}^2 + b_p{}^2) + \frac{1}{2} L_{pq}((a_q a_p + b_q b_p) - j(b_q a_p - b_p a_q))$$

$$\qquad\qquad \textbf{4.3.8}$$

$$+ \frac{1}{2} L_{qp}((a_p a_q + b_p b_q) - j(b_p a_q - b_q a_p)) + \frac{1}{2} L_{qq}(a_q{}^2 + b_q{}^2)$$

whereas the substitution $L_{pq} = L_{qp} = \beta \sqrt{L_{pp}L_{qq}}$ yields

$$T(s) = \frac{1}{2} L_{pp}(a_p{}^2 + b_p{}^2) + \beta \sqrt{L_{pp}L_{qq}} (a_q a_p + b_q b_p) + \frac{1}{2} L_{qq}(a_q{}^2 + b_q{}^2)$$

which may be grouped into squares

$$T(s) = \frac{1}{2} (\sqrt{L_{pp}} a_p + \beta \sqrt{L_{qq}} a_q)^2 + (1 - \beta^2) \frac{1}{2} L_{qq} a_q{}^2$$

$$\qquad\qquad \textbf{4.3.9}$$

$$+ \frac{1}{2} (\sqrt{L_{pp}} b_p + \beta \sqrt{L_{qq}} b_q)^2 + (1 - \beta^2) \frac{1}{2} L_{qq} b_q{}^2$$

Then, since the $a$'s and $b$'s are real, $T(s)$ is real. Furthermore, $T(s)$ is made up of a sum of squares, and since conservation of energy requires that $1 - \beta^2 \geq 0$ (Eq. 4.3.5), it follows that $T(s) \geq 0$.

These results were obtained by choosing two arbitrary loops. They may be extended to include all the loops of the network. Thus the fact that $T(t) \geq 0$ in Eq. 4.3.2 for all possible values of $i_q(t)$ and $i_p(t)$ constrains $T(s)$ in Eq. 4.3.1 to be real* and positive (or zero).

---

* $T(s)$ is real primarily due to the fact that $L_{qp} = L_{pq}$. However, this also is a requirement of conservation of energy, discussed in Chapter 6, Eq. 6.4.9.

Similar considerations show that $F(s)$ and $V(s)$ in Eq. 4.3.1 are also real and positive (or zero). This completes the proof of the positive reality of the energy functions.

### Example 4.3.1

Find the energy functions of the circuit in Fig. 4.3 and use them to determine $Z(s)$.

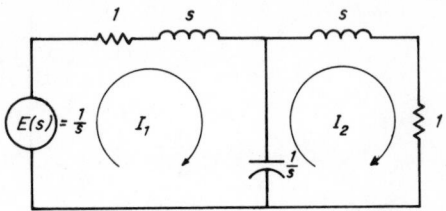

**Fig. 4.3. An RLC two-loop network**

### Solution

Summing voltages around each loop, we get

$$\frac{1}{s} = \left(1 + s + \frac{1}{s}\right) I_1(s) - \frac{1}{s} I_2(s)$$

and

$$0 = -\frac{1}{s} I_1(s) + \left(1 + s + \frac{1}{s}\right) I_2$$

$\qquad$ 4.3.10

Therefore

$$I_1(s) = \frac{\frac{1}{s}\left(1 + s + \frac{1}{s}\right)}{\left(1 + s + \frac{1}{s}\right)^2 - \frac{1}{s^2}} = \frac{(s^2 + s + 1)}{s(s + 1)(s^2 + s + 2)}$$

and

$$I_2(s) = \frac{1}{s(s + 1)(s^2 + s + 2)}$$

$\qquad$ 4.3.11

Then

$$F = \frac{1}{2}\left(|I_1(s)|^2 + |I_2(s)|^2\right), \qquad T = \frac{1}{2}\left(|I_1(s)|^2 + |I_2(s)|^2\right)$$

and

$$V = \frac{1}{2}|I_1(s) - I_2(s)|^2$$

$\qquad$ 4.3.12

---

* $E(s)$ is taken as $\frac{1}{s}$ for the sake of simplicity. It may be left in symbolic form.

It follows that

$$F = \frac{1}{2}\left(\left|\frac{s^2 + s + 1}{s(s+1)(s^2 + s + 2)}\right|^2 + \left|\frac{1}{s(s+1)(s^2 + s + 2)}\right|^2\right) = T$$

and

$$V = \frac{1}{2}\left|\frac{1}{s^2 + s + 2}\right|^2$$

$$\left.\right\} \quad \text{4.3.13}$$

Now

$$Z(s) = E_1(s)\bar{I}_1(s)/|I_1(s)|^2 = \frac{2}{|I_1|^2}\left(F + sT + \frac{V}{s}\right)$$

These give

$$Z(s) = (1 + s)\frac{|I_1(s)|^2 + |I_2(s)|^2}{|I_1(s)|^2} + \frac{1}{s}\frac{|I_1(s) - I_2(s)|^2}{|I_1(s)|^2} \qquad \text{4.3.14}$$

Substituting values for $I_1(s)$ and $I_2(s)$ as obtained in Eq. 4.3.11, we get

$$Z(s) = (1 + s)\left(1 + \frac{1}{|s^2 + s + 1|^2}\right) + \frac{1}{s}\left|\frac{s(s+1)}{s^2 + s + 1}\right|^2 \qquad \text{4.3.15}$$

which reduces to

$$Z(s) = 1 + s + \frac{(1 + s) + \frac{1}{s}|s(s+1)|^2}{|s^2 + s + 1|^2} \qquad \text{4.3.16}$$

yielding

$$Z(s) = 1 + s + \frac{(s+1)((\bar{s})^2 + \bar{s} + 1)}{|s^2 + s + 1|^2} = \frac{(s+1)(s^2 + s + 2)}{s^2 + s + 1} \qquad \text{4.3.17}$$

## UTILIZATION OF THE ENERGY FUNCTIONS 4.4

It is possible to arrive at an expression for a driving point impedance function in terms of the energy functions. Repeating Eq. 4.2.3, we get

$$E_1(s)\bar{I}_1(s) = 2F + 2sT + \frac{2V}{s} \qquad \begin{array}{l}\text{4.2.3}\\\text{4.4.1}\end{array}$$

If both sides of this equation are divided by $|I_1|^2$, there results

$$Z(s) = \frac{E_1}{I_1} = \frac{2}{|I_1|^2}\left(F + sT + \frac{V}{s}\right) \qquad \text{4.4.2}$$

It follows that $Z(s)$ equals a positive constant times $F + sT + \frac{V}{s}$.
For the sake of convenience, let the energy functions be normalized accordingly:

$$Z(s) = F + sT + \frac{V}{s} \qquad \text{4.4.3}$$

A similar development in terms of node voltages would lead to

$$Y(s) = \frac{1}{Z(s)} = F_1 + sT_1 + \frac{V_1}{s}$$

where

$$F_1 = \frac{1}{|E_1|^2} \sum_{pq} \frac{1}{R_{pq}} E_p \bar{E}_q$$

$$T_1 = \frac{1}{|E_1|^2} \sum_{pq} C_{pq} E_p \bar{E}_q$$

**4.4.4**

and

$$V_1(s) = \frac{1}{|E_1|^2} \sum_{pq} \frac{1}{L_{pq}} E_p \bar{E}_q$$

These expressions, Eqs. 4.4.3 and 4.4.4, can be used to show that $Z(s)$ is prf. This will be done in three steps. (1). It will be shown that $Z(s)$ is analytic in the *r.h.s* plane. (2). It will be demonstrated that Re $Z(s) \geq 0$ for Re $s \geq 0$. (3). It will be shown that if $Z(s)$ has $j$ axis poles, they are simple and have positive residues.

(1). The approximate location of the zeros of $Z(s)$ can be computed by solving the quadratic equation (Eq. 4.4.2). This gives

$$s = -\frac{F}{2T} \pm \sqrt{\left(\frac{F}{2T}\right)^2 - \frac{V}{T}}$$

**4.4.5**

The precise value of $s$ cannot be determined since the energy functions are functions of $s$. However, they are always positive. Also the magnitude of the term with the radical sign is smaller than $\frac{F}{2T}$. It follows that no solution of Eq. 4.4.5 may exist for $s$ in the *r.h.s* plane. Then all the zeros of $Z(s)$ are in the *l.h.s* plane. The same argument may be applied to $Y(s)$ in Eq. 4.4.4 showing that $Y(s)$ cannot have *r.h.s* plane zeros. Then $Z(s)$ is analytic in the *r.h.s* plane.

(2). We now wish to obtain the real part of $Z(s)$ in Eq. 4.4.2. Write $s = \sigma + j\omega$. Then

$$\text{Re } Z(s) = F + \sigma T + \frac{\sigma V}{\sigma^2 + \omega^2} \geq 0$$

**4.4.6**

where

$$\sigma = \text{Re } s \geq 0$$

$$\omega = \text{Im } s$$

The fact that the energy functions are positive guarantees that the real part of $Z(s)$ is positive throughout the *r.h.s* plane, and therefore it is certainly positive along the $j$ axis. This disposes of part (2). However, it is not too clear what happens at the origin or, for that matter, at any possible $j$ axis pole of $Z(s)$. This will be answered in part (3).

(3). $j$ axis poles of $Z(s)$ are simple and their residues are positive.

The proof can be done along the lines set forth in Section 2.2. The bases for the proof are as follows: (I). $Z(s)$ is a ratio of rational polynomials (Section 4.1), and (II). Re $Z(s) \geq 0$ for Re $s \geq 0$ by Eq. 4.4.6. Hence in the neighborhood $(s \sim s_0)$ where $Z(s)$ has a pole

$$\text{Re } Z(s) \sim \text{Re } \frac{A}{(s - s_0)^n} \geq 0 \qquad\qquad \textbf{4.4.7}$$

$$\text{for Re } s \geq 0$$

where $A$ is the coefficient of the $j$ axis pole in a partial fraction expansion. Now let $s - s_0 = \rho e^{j\theta}$ and $A = |A| e^{j\alpha}$ in Eq. 4.4.7, which yields

$$\text{Re } Z(s) \sim \frac{|A|}{\rho^n} \cos (\alpha - n\theta) \geq 0 \qquad\qquad \textbf{4.4.8}$$

$$\text{for } -\frac{\pi}{2} \leq \theta \leq \frac{\pi}{2}$$

But the cosine may not assume any negative values in Eq. 4.4.8. Then

$$|\alpha - n\theta| \leq \frac{\pi}{2} \qquad -\frac{\pi}{2} \leq \theta \leq \frac{\pi}{2} \qquad\qquad \textbf{4.4.9}$$

and since $n$ must be an integer (by I above) it must be unity. This means that all $j$ axis poles are simple. To show that the residues are positive, observe that $\alpha$ must be zero (and the residues are positive), since otherwise the inequality

$$\left| \alpha \pm \frac{\pi}{2} \right| \leq \frac{\pi}{2} \qquad\qquad \textbf{4.4.10}$$

may not be satisfied.

In conclusion, all the tests are satisfied: (1). $Z(s)$ is analytic in the *r.h.s* plane; (2). Re $Z(s) \geq 0$ for Re $s = 0$, and (3). $j$ axis poles of $Z(s)$ are simple and have positive residues. Hence we may apply the minimum real part theorem to show that Re $Z(s) > 0$ for Re $s > 0$ and $Z(s)$ is prf. This completes the proof.

## 4.5. ENERGY FUNCTIONS—LOSSLESS NETWORKS

An $RLC$ driving point impedance function can be written in terms of the normalized energy functions

$$Z(s) = F + sT + \frac{V}{s} \qquad \begin{matrix} \textbf{4.4.3} \\ \textbf{4.5.1} \end{matrix}$$

If no dissipative elements are present, $F$ is zero. In this case, $Z(s)$ is called a reactance function. $Z(s)$ now has the form

$$Z(s) = sT + \frac{V}{s} \qquad \textbf{4.5.2}$$

Similarly, the admittance function has the form

$$Y(s) = \frac{1}{Z(s)} = sT_1 + \frac{V_1}{s} \qquad \textbf{4.5.3}$$

Equations 4.5.2 and 4.5.3 are of the same type as Eq. 4.4.3 of the previous section except that the term $F$ is missing. Thus, proceeding along the lines of the previous section, we may show that both $Z(s)$ and $Y(s)$ have simple poles on the $j$ axis with positive residues and that they are prf. No poles or zeros are possible off of the $j$ axis. To show this note that the location of zeros of both $Z(s)$ and $Y(s)$ can be determined from Eqs. 4.5.2 and 4.5.3, respectively, yielding

$$s = \pm j \sqrt{V/T} \quad \text{[zeros of } Z(s)] \qquad \textbf{4.5.4}$$

and

$$s = \pm j \sqrt{V_1/T_1} \quad \text{[zeros of } Y(s)] \qquad \textbf{4.5.5}$$

Again, it is noted that the precise location of the zeros cannot be determined, as $V$ and $T$ are functions of $s$. But, since both $V$ and $T$ are real and positive, the ratio $V/T$ is positive and the zeros of $Z(s)$ and $Y(s) = 1/Z(s)$ lie on the $j$ axis. This can be stated formally:

If $Z(s)$ is made up of lossless elements, all the poles of $Z(s)$ and of $Y(s)$ are simple, lie on the $j$ axis, and have positive residues.*

This suggests that $Z(s)$ can be expanded in a partial fraction expansion and that all the residues are positive and real. Then $Z(s) = sT + V/s$ can be written as

$$Z(s) = a_0 s + \frac{a_1}{s} + \sum_p \left( \frac{b_p}{s + jC_p} + \frac{b_p}{s - jC_p} \right) \qquad \textbf{4.5.6}$$

---

* For a discussion on positive residues, see the previous section.

or

$$Z(s) = a_0 s + \frac{a_1}{s} + \sum_p \frac{2b_p s}{s^2 + C_p^2} \qquad \textbf{4.5.7}$$

$(a, a_0, b_p, \text{ and } C_p \text{ are positive})$

(Each term is accompanied by its conjugate as $Z(s)$ is *real* for *s real*).*

Careful observation of Eq. 4.5.7 shows that $Z(s)$ is the ratio of even over odd polynomials if $a_1 \neq 0$ and odd over even polynomials if $a_1 = 0$.

Attention is called to the fact, that $Z(s)$ (of a reactance function) has been proven identical with the type of functions obtained by taking the ratio of the even over odd (or odd over even) of a Hurwitz polynomial (Section 3.2). Observe that the technique of synthesizing these functions, as outlined briefly in Sections 3.3 and 3.5 (*LC* elements were identified with terms in the partial fraction and the continued partial expansions), can be applied in general to synthesize reactance functions.

The expansion of $Z(s)$ of a lossless network (given in Eq. 4.5.7) was arrived at by postulating that $Z(s)$ is prf and that all its poles lie on the $j$ axis. These postulates are, therefore, the necessary and sufficient conditions for the realizability of a reactance function. However an equivalent set of necessary and sufficient conditions are given by the following.

### Theorem 4.5.1

*If $Z(s)$ is prf, it is a reactance function if and only if all its poles and zeros are simple and lie on the $j$ axis interlacing each other.*

The theorem will be proved in two parts: Part 1. If $Z(s)$ is a reactance function, its poles and zeros are simple and they interlace each other. Part 2. If $Z(s)$ is real when $s$ is real, and if all the poles and zeros are simple and interlace each other, $Z(s)$ is a reactance function. This theorem is from Foster.

### Proof (Part 1)

The proof of Part 1 may be achieved by first proving that the slope of $Z(s)$ is positive along the $j$ axis.

---

* Expansion 4.5.7 is called the Foster Canonic Expansion.

### Lemma 4.5.1

If $Z(s)$ is a reactance function, then

$$\frac{\partial \text{Im } Z(j\omega)}{\partial \omega} \geqslant 0 \qquad\qquad 4.5.8$$

between poles.

The lemma may be proved by showing that the slope of each term in Eq. 4.5.7 is independently positive. However, an independent proof will be given by the use of the energy functions.

### Proof

Along the $j$ axis (except at the poles) $Z(s)$ is imaginary and of the form

$$Z(s) = j\omega T + \frac{V}{j\omega} \qquad\qquad 4.5.9$$

Now perform the differentiation

$$\frac{\partial[\text{lm } Z(s)]}{\partial \omega} = T + \frac{V}{\omega^2} + \omega \frac{\partial T}{\partial \omega} - \frac{1}{\omega}\frac{\partial V}{\partial \omega} \qquad\qquad 4.5.10$$

Here we cannot say that the slope is positive since one of the terms of Eq. 4.5.10 is negative. The situation can be reexamined if Cauchy Riemann differential equations are used (Eq. 2.3.6). Accordingly

$$\left.\frac{\partial \text{Im } Z(s)}{\partial \omega}\right|_{\sigma \to 0} = \left.\frac{\partial \text{Re } Z(s)}{\partial \sigma}\right|_{\sigma \to 0} = \left.\frac{\partial}{\partial \sigma}\left(\sigma T + \frac{\partial \sigma V}{\sigma^2 + \omega^2}\right)\right|_{\sigma \to 0} = T + \frac{V}{\omega^2} \quad 4.5.11$$

$$\geqslant 0$$

*r oof completed*

### Corollary 4.5.1

If $Z(s)$ is a reactance function, then

$$Z'(s) \pm \frac{Z(s)}{s} \geq 0 \qquad\qquad 4.5.12$$

on the $j$ axis.

### Proof

Equation 4.5.9 shows that $\dfrac{Z(s)}{s} = T - V/\omega^2$ along the $j$ axis, whereas Eq. 4.5.11 gives $Z'(s) = T + V/\omega^2$. Hence $Z'(s) \pm Z(s)/s$ equals either $2T$ or $2V/\omega^2$ and must be positive.

*Proof completed*

Thus a reactance function increases between poles along the $j$ axis. Furthermore, all poles and zeros are along the $j$ axis (Eqs. 4.5.4

and 4.5.5). This requires that between any two consecutive poles there must be a zero (Fig. 4.4).

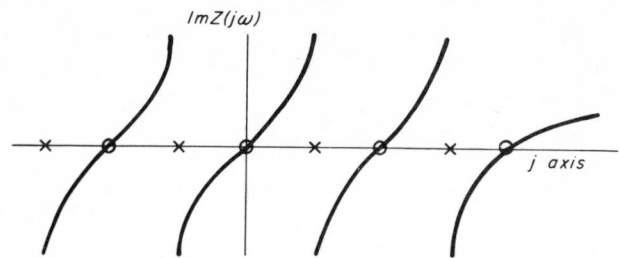

**Fig. 4.4. A plot of a reactance function along the j axis**

Then the poles and the zeros are simple and they interlace each other. This completes the proof of Part 1 (Theorem 4.5.1).

Now the question comes up concerning the points at the origin and infinity. We have not used the fact that $Z(s)$ is real for $s$ real (see Fig. 4.4). This insures that at $s = 0$, $Z(s)$ will not be imaginary. Hence, $Z(s)$ must have either a zero or a pole at the origin, and likewise at infinity.

Before we attempt to prove Part 2 of the same theorem, the following example is given to familiarize us with the terms of the proof.

## Example 4.5.1

Demonstrate that $Z(s) = (s^2 + 1)/s(s^2 + 2)$ is prf.

### Solution

According to Part 1 $Z(s)$ may be prf since all its zeros lie on the $j$ axis and they interlace each other. The fact that $Z(s)$ is prf can be shown by expanding $Z(s)$ in a partial fraction of the type of Eq. 4.5.7 and by showing that each of the residues is positive. This may be done by first expanding $Z(s)/s$ and then multiplying through by $s$:

$$f(x) = \frac{Z(s)}{s} = \frac{(s^2 + 1)}{s^2(s^2 + 2)} = \frac{x + 1}{x(x + 2)} \qquad 4.5.13$$

$$\text{where } (x = s^2)$$

which yields

$$f(x) = \frac{A}{x} + \frac{B}{x + 2}$$

$$\text{where } A = f(x)x \Big|_{x=0} = \frac{x + 1}{x + 2}\Big|_{x=0} = \frac{+1}{+2} \qquad 4.5.14$$

$$\text{and } B = f(x)(x + 2)\Big|_{x+2=0} = \frac{x + 1}{x}\Big|_{x=-2} = \frac{-1}{-2}$$

Thus

$$\frac{Z(s)}{s} = \frac{1/2}{s^2} + \frac{1/2}{s^2 + 2}$$

4.5.15

Multiplying both sides by $s$ we get

$$Z(s) = \frac{1}{2s} + \frac{s}{2(s^2 + 2)}$$

4.5.16

This is of the form of Eq. 4.5.7. The residues are positive, and therefore $Z(s)$ is a reactance function.

$Z(s)$ may be realized by the $LC$ network in Fig. 4.5.

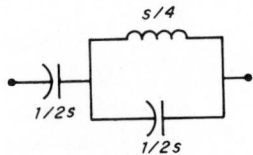

**Fig. 4.5. Realization of $Z(s)$**
$$= \frac{(s^2 + 1)}{s(s^2 + 2)}$$

## Proof (Part 2)

The proof will proceed along the lines of this example by representing $Z(s)$ in a partial fraction of the form of Eq. 4.5.7 and showing that the residues are positive.

Observe that to satisfy the requirements of Part 2, $Z(s)$ or its inverse must have the following form ($\omega_p$ is real):

$$Z(s) = \frac{(s^2 + \omega_1{}^2) \cdots (s^2 + \omega_p{}^2) \cdots (s^2 + \omega_{2n+1}{}^2)}{s(s^2 + \omega_2{}^2) \cdots (s^2 + \omega_{p+1}{}^2) \cdots (s^2 + \omega_{2n+2}{}^2)}$$

4.5.17

where $\omega_p < \omega_{p+1} < \omega_{p+2}$ $(p = \text{odd})$

and $\omega_1 \geq 0$

Write $\dfrac{Z(s)}{s} [= f(x)]$

$$\frac{Z(s)}{s} = \frac{(x + \omega_1{}^2)(x + \omega_3{}^2) \cdots (x + \omega_{2n+1}{}^2)}{x(x + \omega_2{}^2)(x + \omega_4{}^2) \cdots (x + \omega_{2n+2}{}^2)}$$

4.5.18

This is now expanded in the form

$$\frac{Z(s)}{s} = \frac{A_0}{x} + \frac{A_2}{x + \omega_2{}^2} + \frac{A_4}{x + \omega_4{}^2} + + +$$

4.5.19

$(x = s^2)$

The quantities $A_0$, $A_2$, $A_4$ are found directly. $A_0$ is given by

$$A_0 = f(x)x\bigg|_{x=0} = \frac{\omega_1^2\omega_3^2\omega_5^2 \cdots}{\omega_2^2\omega_4^2\omega_6^2 \cdots} \qquad \textbf{4.5.20}$$

This shows that $A_0 > 0$ as $\omega_p^2 > 0$. Now the coefficient $A_2$ is given by

$$A_2 = f(x)(x + \omega_2^2)\bigg|_{x=-\omega_2^2} \qquad \textbf{4.5.21a}$$

yielding

$$A_2 = \frac{-(\omega_2^2 - \omega_1^2)(\omega_3^2 - \omega_2^2) \cdots}{-\omega_2^2(\omega_4^2 - \omega_2^2) \cdots} \qquad \textbf{4.5.21b}$$

Note that $A_2 > 0$ as the negative terms are paired, and all the other factors are positive. Similarly, we have

$$
\begin{aligned}
A_4 &= f(x)(x + \omega_4^2)\bigg|_{x=-\omega_4^2} \\
&= \frac{(-1)(\omega_4^2 - \omega_1^2)(-1)(\omega_4^2 - \omega_3^2) \cdots}{(-1)\,\omega_4^2(-1)(\omega_4^2 - \omega_2^2) \cdots}
\end{aligned}
\qquad \textbf{4.5.22}
$$

and $A_4$ is positive as the negative terms are paired again. This procedure may be continued formally by using mathematical induction to show that all the residues have an even number of negative signs and that they are all positive.

*Proof completed*

## Example 4.5.2

Show that $Z(s) = (s^2 + 1)(s^2 + 3)/s(s^2 + 2)$ is a reactance function (observe that poles and zeros interlace).

## Proof

The desired expansion can be achieved by putting

$$\frac{1}{sZ(s)} = \frac{s^2 + 2}{(s^2 + 1)(s^2 + 3)} \qquad \textbf{4.5.23}$$

Write this

$$f(x) = \frac{x + 2}{(x + 1)(x + 3)} \qquad \textbf{4.5.24}$$

which then is expanded into

$$\frac{1}{sZ(s)} = \frac{1/2}{x + 1} + \frac{1/2}{x + 2} \qquad \textbf{4.5.25}$$

Therefore

$$\frac{1}{Z(s)} = \frac{s}{2(s^2 + 1)} + \frac{s}{2(s^2 + 3)}$$

4.5.26

$Z(s)$ may be realized by the network in Fig. 4.6.

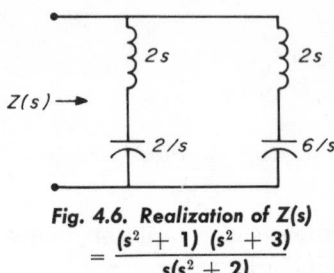

**Fig. 4.6. Realization of Z(s)**
$$= \frac{(s^2 + 1) \ (s^2 + 3)}{s(s^2 + 2)}$$

This geometrical form is called a Foster *canonic* network of the second (or the $Y$) form. The term *canonic* means that the realization contains the minimum possible number of elements. Another form—the Cauer canonic form—was discussed in Section 3.5.

## 4.6. *RL* AND *RC* NETWORKS

*RL* and *RC* networks have similar properties in many respects. For the sake of comparison they will be studied simultaneously. The terms $Z_{RL}$ and $Y_{RL}$ will denote *RL* immittance functions, whereas $Z_{RC}$ and $Y_{RC}$ will be used with *RC* immittance functions.

Two-element-kind (*RC* and *RL*) networks lack one type of energy storage term. Consequently, one term will be absent in the normalized impedance:

$$Z(s) = F + sT + \frac{V}{s}$$

4.4.1
4.6.3

to give

$$Z_{RL} = F + sT, \qquad Z_{RC} = F + \frac{V}{s}$$

4.6.2

For the same reason

$$Y(s) = F_1 + sT_1 + \frac{V_1}{s}$$

4.4.4
4.6.3

is reduced to

$$Y_{RL} = F_1 + \frac{V_1}{s}, \qquad Y_{RC} = F_1 + sT_1$$

4.6.4

Equations 4.6.2 may be interpreted to show that both the zeros of $Z_{RL}$ and $Z_{RC}$ (located at $s = -\dfrac{F}{T}$ and $s = -\dfrac{V}{F}$, respectively) are located along the negative real axis. The same is also true for the poles of these functions as can be verified from Eqs. 4.6.4. Thus $RC$ and $RL$ networks have some properties in common with lossless $(LC)$ networks, namely the zeros and poles of the respective impedance functions lie along one axis of the complex $s$ plane. This similarity goes even further. It will be shown now that for $RL$ (or $RC$) impedance functions the poles and zeros interlace along the negative real axis in the same way that they do along the $j$ axis for $LC$ impedance functions. This can be shown by methods that parallel the proof that reactance functions have their poles and zeros interlacing each other. First it will be shown that the slope of $Z_{RL}$ is never negative along the real axis (between the poles), whereas that of $Z_{RC}$ is never positive along the real axis (between the poles).

**Lemma 4.6.1**

For two-element-kind networks

$$\left.\frac{\partial\ \mathrm{Re}\ Z_{RL}}{\partial\sigma}\right|_{\omega\to 0} \ge 0 \qquad\qquad \textbf{4.6.5a}$$

and

$$\left.\frac{\partial\ \mathrm{Re}\ Z_{RC}}{\partial\sigma}\right|_{\omega\to 0} \le 0 \qquad\qquad \textbf{4.6.5b}$$

along the real axis.

*Proof*

By Cauchy Riemann differential equations

$$\left.\frac{\partial\ \mathrm{Re}\ Z_{RL}}{\partial\sigma}\right|_{\omega\to 0} = \left.\frac{\partial\ \mathrm{Im}\ Z_{RL}}{\partial\omega}\right|_{\omega\to 0} = \frac{\partial}{\partial\omega}\ \omega T = T \qquad\qquad \textbf{4.6.6a}$$

Thus the slope is never negative, since $T$ is never negative.
A similar development for $Z_{RC}$ shows that

$$\left.\frac{\partial\ \mathrm{Re}\ Z_{RC}}{\partial\sigma}\right|_{\omega\to 0} = \left.\frac{\partial}{\partial\omega}\left(\frac{-\omega V}{\omega^2 + \sigma^2}\right)\right|_{\omega\to 0} = -\frac{V}{\sigma^2} \qquad\qquad \textbf{4.6.7b}$$

This quantity is never positive along the real axis, as both $V$ and $\sigma^2$ are never negative. This completes the proof.

The fact that $Z_{RL}$ increase monotonically between two consecutive poles is sufficient to show that $Z_{RL}$ has only simple poles and one zero between consecutive poles (Fig. 4.7a). Similarly, the fact that $Z_{RC}$ decreases monotonically along the real axis also constrains all its poles and zeros to interlace (Fig. 4.7b).

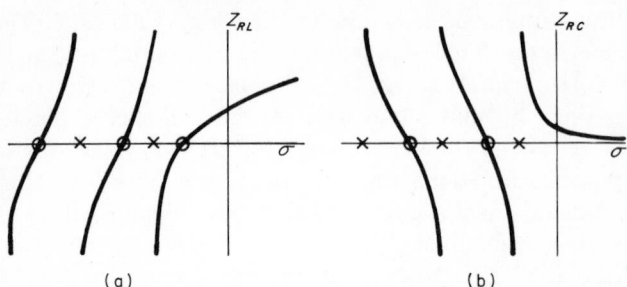

**Fig. 4.7. Plot of RL and RC impedance functions along the real axis**

Observe in Fig. 4.7 that since $Z(0)$ must be real and positive, $Z_{RL}$ must have a zero which is nearest to the origin, whereas $Z_{RC}$ must have a pole there. This is the only conspicuous distinction between the two types of networks in so far as the pole zero geometry is concerned. It follows that $Y_{RL}$ has a pole which is nearest to the origin and therefore it behaves graphically like $Z_{RC}$ in Fig. 4.7b. Likewise $Y_{RC}$ and $Z_{RL}$ are alike graphically. It follows that if $\varphi(s)$ is an immittance function (as given in Fig. 4.7b), $\varphi(s)$ may be either $Z_{RC}$ or $Y_{RL}$, whereas in Fig. 4.7a it would represent either $Z_{RL}$ or $Y_{RC}$.

It has so far been shown that $RL$ and $RC$ impedance functions have simple poles and zeros interlacing along the negative real axis. It will be demonstrated now that the converse is true as well.

**Theorem 4.6.1**

If the poles and zeros of $Z(s)$ are simple, interlacing each other along the negative real axis, and if $Z(s)$ is real for $s$ *real*, then $Z(s)$ can be realized in terms of either $RL$ or $RC$ networks.

*Proof*

The proof may be obtained first for $Z(s)$, where a pole is closer to the origin than the nearest zero. Let $Z(s)$ be expanded as follows:

$$Z(s) = a_0 + \frac{a_1}{s} + \sum_p \frac{b_p}{s + C_p} \qquad \textbf{4.6.7}$$

$C_p$ is positive since the poles lie along the negative real axis. $a_0$ is real and positive since $Z(\infty)$ is positive. To obtain $b_p$, write $Z(s)$ in terms of its poles and zeros:

$$Z(s) = a_0 \frac{(s + C_2)(s + C_4) \cdots (s + C_p) \cdots (s + C_{2n})}{(s + C_1)(s + C_3) \cdots (s + C_{p+1}) \cdots (s + C_{2n+1})} \qquad 4.6.8$$

where $C_p < C_{p+1}$ ($C_1$ might be zero) and $p = $ even. Therefore

$$b_1 = Z(s)(s + C_1)\Big|_{(s+C_1)=0} = a_0 \times \frac{(C_2 - C_1) \times (C_4 - C_1) \cdots}{(C_3 - C_1) \cdots}$$

$b_1$ is positive since all the terms are positive (as $C_1 < C_2$ etc.). Similarly $b_3$ is given

$$b_3 = a_0 \frac{-(C_3 - C_2) \times (C_4 - C_3) \cdots}{-(C_3 - C_1) \cdots \cdots} \qquad 4.6.9$$

This term is positive since it has a pair of negative terms and the rest of the terms are positive. This process may be continued to show that all the negative terms occur in pairs, and therefore the corresponding residues are positive.

Observe that each term in Eq. 4.6.7 can be realized by means of $RC$ networks (Fig. 4.8).

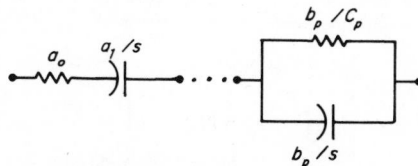

**Fig. 4.8. A realization of Eq. 4.6.7**

Consequently any impedance function whose poles and zeros lie along the negative real axis interlacing each other (and whose first pole is nearer the origin than the first zero) can be realized by means of $RC$ networks as given in Fig. 4.8. Thus $Z(s) = Z_{RC}$ (If the function were an admittance function then $Y(s) = Y_{RL}$).

If $Z(s)$ has a zero nearest to the origin $\dfrac{Z(s)}{s}$ has a pole nearest the origin and it can be expanded in the form of Eq. 4.6.7, yielding

$$\frac{Z(s)}{s} = a_0 + \frac{a_1}{s} + \sum_p \frac{b_p}{s + C_p} \qquad 4.6.10$$

where all the coefficients are positive as was shown for Eq. 4.6.7.

It follows that $\dfrac{Z(s)}{s}$ can be realized by means of the network of Fig. 4.8. Correspondingly, $Z(s)$ can be realized by multiplying each term of Fig. 4.9 by $s$.

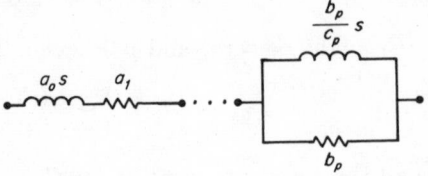

**Fig. 4.9.  A realization of Z(s) in Eq. 4.6.10**

Thus if the poles and zeros of $Z(s)$ lie along the negative real axis interlacing each other, $Z(s)$ is either an $RC$ or an $RL$ network. This completes the proof of Theorem 4.6.1.

Incidentally, since $Z(s)$ in Eq. 4.6.10 has a zero nearest to the origin, $Y(s)$ has a pole nearest to the origin. Then $Y(s)$ can be expanded in the form of Eq. 4.6.7. It follows that $Z(s)$ can be realized in Fig. 4.10 (also see Example 4.6.1, Eqs. 4.6.16 and 4.6.17). The respective coefficients are usually not the same in the two networks. This is called the Foster canonic realization for an $RL$ network—the second form. In Fig. 4.8 we have the first form.

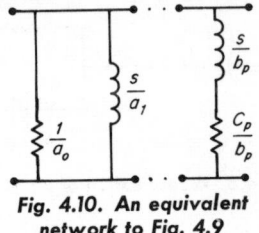

**Fig. 4.10.  An equivalent network to Fig. 4.9**

**Example 4.6.1**

Realize $Z(s)$

$$Z(s) \;=\; \frac{s(s+2)}{(s+1)(s+3)} \tag{4.6.11}$$

Expanding this in the form of Eq. 4.6.10, we get

$$\frac{Z(s)}{s} \;=\; \frac{(s+2)}{(s+1)(s+3)} \;=\; \frac{1}{2(s+1)} + \frac{1}{2(s+3)} \tag{4.6.12}$$

and therefore

$$Z(s) \;=\; \frac{s}{2(s+1)} + \frac{s}{2(s+3)} \tag{4.6.13}$$

This can be realized as in Fig. 4.11, which is similar to the realization of Fig. 4.9.

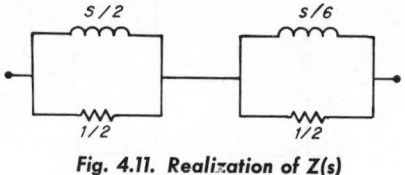

Fig. 4.11. Realization of Z(s)
$$= \frac{s(s+2)}{(s+1)(s+3)}$$

On the other hand, $Z(s)$ can be expressed in the $Y$ form

$$Z(s) = \frac{1}{Y(s)} = \frac{1}{\dfrac{(s+1)(s+3)}{s(s+2)}} \qquad \text{4.6.14}$$

in which the denominator is expanded further to give

$$Z(s) = \frac{1}{1 + \dfrac{3}{2s} + \dfrac{1}{2(s+2)}} \qquad \text{4.6.15}$$

which is realized in Fig. 4.12.

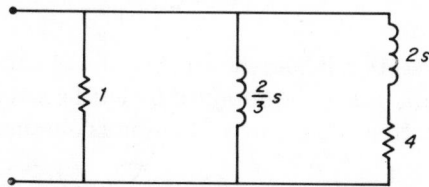

Fig. 4.12. An equivalent network to Fig. 4.11

This example also can be realized by means of continued fraction expansion. To achieve this, first remove the zero at the origin; this gives

$$Z(s) = \frac{1}{\dfrac{3}{2s} + \dfrac{2s+5}{2(s+2)}} \qquad \text{4.6.16}$$

Now remove the minimum resistance of $2(s+2)/(2s+5)$ which is 4/5. This gives

$$Z(s) = \frac{1}{\dfrac{3}{2s} + \dfrac{1}{\dfrac{4}{5} + \dfrac{2s}{5(2s+5)}}} = \frac{1}{\dfrac{3}{2s} + \dfrac{1}{\dfrac{4}{5} + \dfrac{1}{5 + \dfrac{25}{2s}}}} \qquad \text{4.6.17}$$

and since all the coefficients are positive, it can be realized in Fig. 4.13.

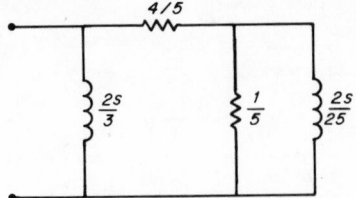

**Fig. 4.13. An equivalent network to
Fig. 4.11**

This is the Cauer *canonic* form for $RL$ networks.

## 4.7. RL AND RC NETWORKS—STIELJES CONTINUED FRACTION

This expansion was used in Section 3.5 to synthesize the odd over even part (or even over odd) of a Hurwitz polynomial. It now will be demonstrated that the expansion can be used for synthesis of $RC$ and $RL$ networks as was briefly shown in Example 4.7.1, Eq. 4.6.17.

Suppose the function under consideration is $Z_{RC}$. Let it be given by

$$Z_{RC} = a_0 + \frac{a_1}{s} + \sum_p \frac{b_p}{s + C_p} \qquad \begin{matrix} \textbf{4.6.7} \\ \textbf{4.7.1} \end{matrix}$$

In the previous section it was shown that all the constants are positive. The constant $a_0$ may be obtained by letting $s$ approach infinity. If $a_0$ is removed from $Z_{RC}$, a new function is obtained:

$$\frac{1}{\varphi_1} = Z_{RC} - a_0 = \frac{a_1}{s} + \sum_p \frac{b_p}{s + C_p} \qquad \textbf{4.7.2}$$

$\varphi_1$ has a pole at infinity as $1/\varphi_1$ is zero there. Also $\varphi_1$ can be synthesized as an $RL$ network (since $1/\varphi_1$ as given by Eq. 4.7.2 is an $RC$ impedance function).

It follows that $\varphi_1$ can be expressed in terms of expansion 4.6.10

$$\frac{\varphi_1}{s} = a_0' + \frac{a'_1}{s} + \sum_p \frac{b'_p}{s + C'_p} \qquad \begin{matrix} \textbf{4.6.10} \\ \textbf{4.7.3} \end{matrix}$$

Again $a'_0$ may be obtained by setting $s = \infty$ and is subsequently removed, yielding

$$\frac{1}{\varphi_2} = \varphi_1 - sa'_0 = a'_1 + \sum_p \frac{b'_p s}{s + C'_p} \qquad \textbf{4.7.4}$$

Now $1/\varphi_2$ is an $RL$ network and therefore $\varphi_2$ is an $RC$ network. This is precisely the same point of the cycle as given by Eq. 4.7.1. The cycle can now continue until the expansion is completed:

$$Z_{RC} = a_0 + \cfrac{1}{a'_0 s + \cfrac{1}{\varphi_2}} \qquad 4.7.5$$

It still remains to show that $\varphi_2$ is reduced in degree.* This can be done by observing that $\varphi_1(\infty) = 0$, and therefore its numerator is reduced in degree. Similarly, the numerator of $\varphi_2$ is 1 less in degree than the denominator of $\varphi_1$. Then $\varphi_2$ is 1 less in degree than $Z(s)$. $Z_{RC}$ in Eq. 4.7.5 can be realized as in Fig. 4.14.

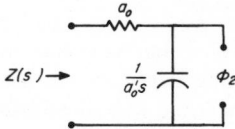

**Fig. 4.14. One stage in the development of the Cauer canonic form**

A similar development may be achieved by removing the pole at zero of Eq. 4.7.1. This would lead to the second Cauer form where the shunting elements are resistors and the series elements are capacitors.

The Cauer form for $RL$ networks can be obtained in a similar fashion. It also can be generated by synthesis of $Z_{RL}/s$ as an $RC$ impedance function, in which each term is later multiplied by $s$.

## PROBLEMS

4.1. Derive the energy functions for the following circuit and utilize them to find $Z(s)$.

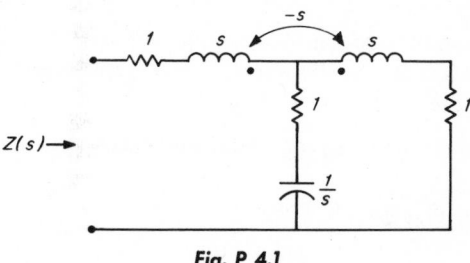

**Fig. P 4.1**

---

* The degree of $Z(s)$ is defined as the highest of the degrees of the numerator and the denominator. Also see page 80 for more elaboration.

4.2. Obtain the energy functions for the following circuit and use them to show that all the zeros of $Z(s)$ lie on the $j$ axis.

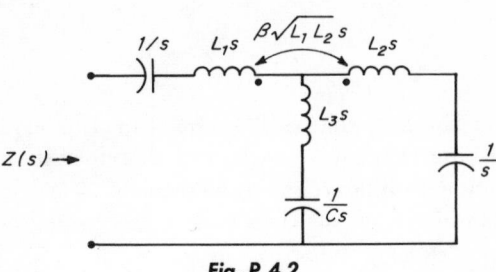

Fig. P 4.2

4.3. Obtain the two Foster canonic networks and the two Cauer canonic networks of the following impedane functions [the second Cauer form may be obtained by realizing $Z(1/s')$ and then replacing $s'$ by $1/s$].

(a). 
$$Z(s) = \frac{s(s^2 + 1)(3s^2 + 1)}{(2s^2 + 1)(4s^2 + 1)}$$

(b). 
$$Z(s) = \frac{(2s^2 + 1)(4s^2 + 1)s}{(s^2 + 1)(3s^2 + 1)(5s^2 + 1)}$$

4.4. Construct two canonic forms for each one of the following, two-element-kind, impedance functions.

(a). 
$$\frac{(s + 1)(3s + 1)(5s + 1)}{s(2s + 1)(4s + 1)}$$

(b). 
$$\frac{s(2s + 1)(4s + 1)}{(s + 1)(3s + 1)(5s + 1)}$$

(c). 
$$\frac{s(5s^2 + 6)(3s^2 + 4)}{(s^2 + 1)(4s^2 + 5)(2s^2 + 3)}$$

(d). 
$$\frac{(s^2 + 1)(4s^2 + 5)(2s^2 + 3)}{s(5s^2 + 6)(3s^2 + 4)}$$

4.5. If $P(s)$ has all its zeros on the negative real axis, show that $P'(s)/P(s)$ is an $RC$ impedance function (from Reza). Explain why $(P(s) + P'(s))$ has negative real axis zeros only.

4.6. If $P(s)/Q(s)$ is an $RC$ impedance function, show that $Q(s)/sP(s)$ is also $RC$.

4.7. Show that if $Z(s)$ is prf

$$\frac{Z(s)}{s} \pm Z'(s) \geqslant 0$$

on the positive real axis. (Hint: See Corollary 4.5.1)

## FURTHER READING

BOOKS

4.1. Balabanian, N., "Network Synthesis," Prentice Hall, Inc., Englewood Cliffs, N. J., 1958, Chapters 1 and 2.

4.2. Cauer, W., "Synthesis of Linear Communication Networks," McGraw-Hill Book Co., Inc., New York, 1958, Chapter 5.

4.3. Guillemin, E. A., "Synthesis of Passive Networks," John Wiley & Sons, New York, 1957, Chapters 2 and 3.

4.4. Kuh, E. S., and Pederson, D. O., "Principles of Circuit Synthesis," McGraw-Hill Book Co., Inc., New York, 1959, Chapters 6 and 10.

4.5. Tuttle, D. F., Jr., "Network Synthesis," John Wiley & Sons, New York, 1958, Chapters 4, 5, 6, and 7 (this is probably the most comprehensive treatment of the subject today).

4.6. Van-Valkenburg, M. E., "Introduction to Modern Network Synthesis," John Wiley & Sons, New York, 1960, Chapters 5 and 6.

A RELATED PAPER

4.7. Bello, P., "Extension of Brune's Energy Function Approach to the Study of LLF Networks," *IRE Trans. on Circuit Theory*, Vol. CT-7, pp. 270–280, Sept., 1960.

| *Series-Parallel Realization*

## 5.1. INTRODUCTION

The fact that all $RLC$ driving point impedance functions are prf was demonstrated in the previous chapter. The opposite is also true, namely:

### Theorem 5.1.1

All positive real impedance functions are realizable in terms of $RLC$ networks without mutual coupling.

A partial proof of this theorem was given in the last chapter, where it was shown that all positive real impedance functions whose poles and zeros are simple and alternating along either the $j$ axis or the negative real axis may be realized in terms of two-element-kind networks. The general proof of the theorem will be done by showing that any positive real function can be realized by means of other positive real functions of reduced degree.

The degree* of $Z(s)$ (denoted as $\delta Z(s)$) is defined as the *highest degree of the numerator and the denominator,* that is, if $Z(s)$ is given by $P/Q$ where $P$ and $Q$ are polynomials in $s$, and if $\delta P$ and $\delta Q$ are the respective degrees then

$$\delta Z(s) = \delta P \qquad \text{if } \delta P \geqslant \delta Q$$
$$\delta Z(s) = \delta Q \qquad \text{if } \delta Q \geqslant \delta P$$

5.1.1

Now suppose, for example, that $Z(s)$ is given by

$$Z(s) = \frac{s^3 + 2s^2 + 5s + 1}{s(s^2 + s + 1)}$$

5.1.2

---

* Bott, R., and Duffin, R. J., in "Impedance Synthesis Without Use of Transformers," *J. Appl. Phys.*, Vol. 20, p. 816, Aug., 1949 defined an impedance rank as the sum of the degrees of the numerator and the denominator. We chose the term "degree" instead of rank to avoid confusion with the term matrix rank necessary in later work.

This function has a pole at the origin with a residue of unity which is now removed, leaving a remainder $Z_1(s)$

$$Z_1(s) = Z(s) - \frac{1}{s} = \frac{s^2 + s + 4}{s^2 + s + 1} \qquad \qquad 5.1.3$$

Hence the degree of $Z(s)$ was reduced by 1 by removing the pole at the origin (the degree would not be reduced if only a partial pole is removed). These results may be generalized to say that a removal of any pole or zero would reduce the degree of $Z(s)$. However, only $j$ axis poles and zeros may always be removed with a positive real remainder (Section 2.5). The removal of the minimum resistance or the minimum conductance may or may not lead to the reduction of the degree of $Z(s)$ (Example 5.2.2).

The proof of Theorem 5.1.1 will be done by first reducing the degree of the impedance function through the removal of $j$ axis poles and zeros and the minimum resistance (or conductance). Other methods will be developed in the course of the chapter to handle cases where the simple methods fail.

Sooner or later during the course of synthesis it becomes clear that there may be several (or many) networks that have the same impedance function. For example, the network in Fig. 5.1 has a unique realization for $Z(s) = 1$ for any positive value of the arbitrary constant $k$.

### Example 5.1.1

Synthesize $Z(s) = 1$.

*Solution*

Let $Z(s)$ be expressed as follows:

$$Z(s) = 1 = \frac{s + k}{s + k} = \frac{s}{s + k} + \frac{k}{s + k} \qquad \qquad 5.1.4$$

Each element on the right of Eq. 5.1.4 can be realized by means of two elements (Fig. 5.1).

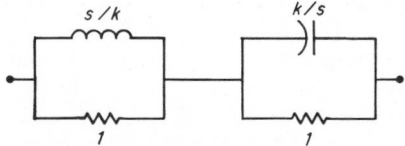

*Fig. 5.1. Realization of Z(s) = 1*

This abundance of solutions may be utilized in many ways. One might strive to achieve a minimum number of elements or a ceiling on element size; one might utilize a prescribed inductor, and so on. However, it is usually assumed that the reduction in the number of elements is a primary objective. Towards this end, and following historical development in network synthesis, the "chop-chop" method will be discussed first.

## 5.2. THE "CHOP-CHOP" METHOD

This method consists of investigating $Z(s)$ very closely and observing whether it has any poles or zeros on the $j$ axis. If such poles or zeros are found they can be removed (it was shown in Section 2.5 that the reduced impedance function is prf), resulting in a reduced impedance function and a reactance function. Once the function is stripped of all its $j$ axis poles and zeros, it is still possible that a minimum resistance or a minimum conductance removal would produce a $j$ axis zero which would permit the continuation of the process. This process also can be described as the "if-if-if" method: namely, if a $j$ axis pole is available, a certain reactance function is removable; if a $j$ axis zero is available, another reactance is removable; whereas if Re $Z(j\omega) > 0$, a minimum resistance is removable and so on.

### Example 5.2.1

Synthesize $Z(s) = (2s^2 + 2s + 1)/s(s^2 + s + 1)$.

### Solution

This function has a pole at the origin suggesting that a capacitor may be removed in series with another positive real function of lower degree. Let $a_0$ be the value of the residue of the pole at the origin. Then

$$Z_1(s) = Z(s) - \frac{a_0}{s} \qquad\qquad \textbf{5.2.1}$$

resulting in

$$Z_1(s) = \frac{2s^2 + 2s + 1}{s(s^2 + s + 1)} - \frac{1}{s} = \frac{s + 1}{s^2 + s + 1} \qquad\qquad \textbf{5.2.2}$$

Now $Z_1(s)$ is zero at infinity. This suggests that the pole of $Y_1(s)$ may be removed now. Then

$$Y_2(s) = Y_1(s) - b_1 s$$

where $b_1$ is the residue of the pole at infinity. Thus

$$Y_2(s) = \frac{s^2 + s + 1}{s + 1} - s = \frac{1}{s + 1} \qquad\qquad \textbf{5.2.3}$$

It follows that $Z(s)$ can be rewritten as

$$Z(s) = \frac{1}{s} + \cfrac{1}{s + \cfrac{1}{s + 1}}$$

5.2.4

with the realization in Fig. 5.2.

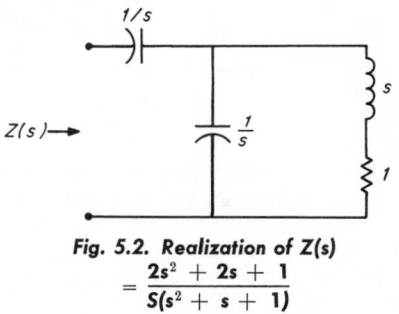

**Fig. 5.2. Realization of $Z(s)$**
$$= \frac{2s^2 + 2s + 1}{S(s^2 + s + 1)}$$

If a minimum resistance is to be removed, a choice is available since the minimum value can be removed from either $Z(s)$ or $Y(s)$. Both values might be tried if one fails to produce the desired simplification.

## Example 5.2.2

Investigate the effects of removal of either the minimum resistance or conductance of the following function:

$$Z(s) = \frac{s^2 + s + 1}{s^2 + 2s + 2}$$

5.2.5

*Solution*

The real part of $Z(s)$ equals

$$\left. \frac{(s^2 + 1)(s^2 + 2) - 2s^2}{(s^2 + 2)^2 - 4s^2} \right|_{s=j\omega} = \left. \frac{s^4 + s^2 + 2}{s^4 + 4} \right|_{s=j\omega}$$

5.2.6

yielding

$$\frac{\omega^4 - \omega^2 + 2}{\omega^4 + 4}$$

5.2.7

This function is plotted in Fig. 5.3.

Thus $Z(s)$ has a minimum of $(3 - \sqrt{2})/4$. Once this value is removed, $Z(s)$ becomes

$$Z_1(s) = \frac{s^2(\sqrt{2} + 1) + s2(\sqrt{2} - 1) + 2(\sqrt{2} - 1)}{4(s^2 + 2s + 2)}$$

5.2.8

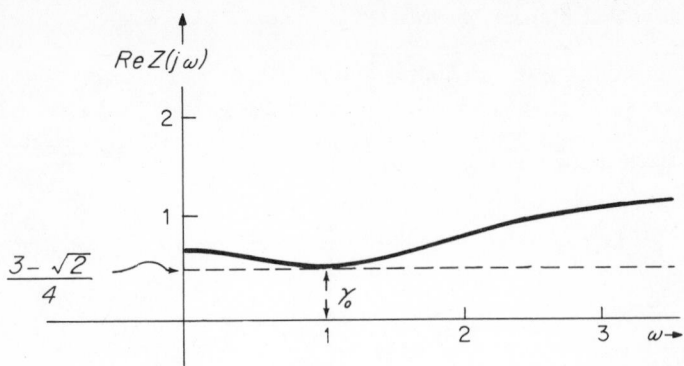

**Fig. 5.3. Plot of Re $Z(j\omega)$ of Eq. 5.2.5 vis $\omega$**

$Z_1(s)$ is minimum resistive, yet its degree is the same as that of $Z(s)$ in Eq. 5.2.5. On the other hand, the removal of a minimum conductance from $Y(s) = 1/Z(s)$ gives

$$Y_1(s) = Y(s) - 1 = \frac{s + 1}{s^2 + s + 1} \qquad \textbf{5.2.9}$$

This expression has a zero at infinity. Removing this zero will reduce the degree.

Thus, sometimes a removal of the minimum conductance may make it possible to continue the process, whereas a minimum resistance removal would not.

The opposite may also be true. On the other hand, if $Z(s)$ is minimum resistive, the inverse function is also minimum resistive, and no obvious additional advantage is obtained by working with the $Y(s)$ form.

For example, $Z(s)$ in Eq. 5.2.10 is minimum resistive:

$$Z(s) = \frac{s^2 + s + 1}{s^2 + s + 4} \qquad \textbf{5.2.10}$$

Since Ev $Z(j\omega) = 0$ for $\omega = \sqrt{2}$, which may be verified by computing Ev $Z(s)$

$$\text{Ev } Z(s) = \frac{(s^2 + 2)^2}{(s^2 + 4)^2 - s^2} \qquad \textbf{5.2.11}$$

Observe that Ev $Y(s)$ is also zero for the same $\omega$:

$$\text{Ev } Y(s) = \frac{(s^2 + 2)^2}{(s^2 + 1)^2 - s^2} \qquad \textbf{5.2.12}$$

Furthermore, the degree of $Z(s)$ of Eq. 5.2.10 cannot be reduced by a removal of either a pole or a zero along the $j$ axis. This function may be synthesized by a technique which will be developed in the following sections (the Bott-Duffin synthesis).

## AN ARBITRARY EXPANSION FOR $Z(s)$ 5.3

If $Z(s)$ is stripped of all its $j$ axis poles and zeros and of its minimum resistance, the "chop-chop" method ceases to be useful. Essentially this means that the function can no longer be expressed as a sum of two other impedance functions of lower degree. At this point the question might be raised as to whether $Z(s)$ could be expressed as a sum of two other impedance functions with a certain degree of arbitrariness. Reconsidering Example 5.1.1

$$Z(s) = 1 = \frac{s}{s+k} + \frac{k}{s+k} \qquad \begin{matrix} \textbf{5.1.4} \\ \textbf{5.3.1} \end{matrix}$$

one might marvel at the fact that both terms on the right of Eq. 5.3.1 are prf for all positive $k$. Fortunately this result has a sequel in the expansion of any positive real function in terms of two others (also prf) with an arbitrary positive constant $k$. This expression is as follows:*†

$$Z(s) = k\,\frac{kZ(s) - sZ(k)}{k^2 - s^2} + s\,\frac{kZ(k) - sZ(s)}{k^2 - s^2} \qquad \textbf{5.3.2}$$

It is abbreviated to

$$Z(s) = Z_1(s) + Z_2(s) \qquad \textbf{5.3.3}$$

This identity may be verified by bringing $Z_1(s)$ and $Z_2(s)$ into a common denominator. To prove that $Z_1(s)$ is prf, observe that its real part is given by $k^2 \operatorname{Re} Z(j\omega)/(k^2 + \omega^2)$, whereas the real part of $Z_2(s)$ is $\omega^2 \operatorname{Re} Z(j\omega)/(k^2 + \omega^2)$ on the $j$ axis. Thus the real parts of both $Z_1(s)$ and $Z_2(s)$ are positive on the $j$ axis if $Z(s)$ is prf. Furthermore, both terms are analytic in the $r.h.s$ plane. This can be shown by observing that each term has a built-in zero at $s = k$, cancelling the only possible $r.h.s$ plane zero of the respective denominator. Consequently each term on the right of Eq. 5.3.2 is analytic in the $r.h.s$ plane, and its real part is positive along the $j$ axis. Also, $Z_1(s)$ and $Z_2(s)$ may have $j$ axis poles if and only if, $Z(s)$ has them; it follows that all $j$ axis poles are simple and have positive real residues. Hence the minimum real value theorem (Theorem 2.5.2) may be used to show that $\operatorname{Re} Z_1(s)$ and $\operatorname{Re} Z_2(s)$ are also positive throughout the $r.h.s$ plane and, therefore, $Z_1(s)$ and $Z_2(s)$ are prf.

---

* Bott, R., and Duffin, R. J., "Impedance Synthesis Without Use of Transformers," *J. Appl. Phys.*, Vol. 20, p. 816, Aug., 1949.

† Hazony, D., "An Alternate Approach to the Bott Duffin Cycle," *IRE Trans. on Circuit Theory*, pgct Vol CT-9, Sept., 1961.

A similar development is also given in Tuttle, D. F., Jr., "Network Synthesis," John Wiley & Sons, New York, pp. 618–627, 1958.

## 5.4. AN ARBITRARY NETWORK FOR Z(s)

The problem of removing a pole or a zero at the origin or infinity is straightforward, since it is possible to tell whether such poles or zeros exist by inspection. Once these poles and zeros are removed, the degree of the denominator is the same as that of the numerator.

At this point note that $Z(k)$ is a ratio of positive numbers for all positive $k$. Also, observe that if the numerator and the denominator are of the same degree in $k$, $Z(k)$ is bounded ($0 < A < Z(k) < B < \infty$) for positive $k$. Now $Z(s)$ of Eq. 5.3.2 can be synthesized by removing a zero at infinity from $Z_1(s)$ and a zero at the origin from $Z_2(s)$:

$$Z(s) = k\,\frac{kZ(s) - sZ(k)}{k^2 - s^2} + s\,\frac{kZ(k) - sZ(s)}{k^2 - s^2} \qquad \begin{matrix} \textbf{5.3.2} \\ \textbf{5.4.1} \end{matrix}$$

where

$$Z(s) \equiv Z_1(s) + Z_2(s)$$

Because $Z(s)$ does not have a pole at infinity, $Z_1(s)$ approaches zero at infinity like $\dfrac{kZ(k)}{s}$. Removal of this zero permits rewriting $Z_1(s)$ as follows:

$$Z_1(s) = k\,\frac{kZ(s) - sZ(k)}{k^2 - s^2} = \frac{Z(k)}{\dfrac{kZ(k) - sZ(s)}{kZ(s) - sZ(k)} + \dfrac{s}{k}} \qquad \textbf{5.4.2}$$

At this point, let $\zeta$ denote

$$\zeta = \frac{kZ(s) - sZ(k)}{kZ(k) - sZ(s)} \qquad \textbf{5.4.3}$$

Note that $\zeta$ is prf, as it was generated by the removal of a zero at infinity, from a p.r. function. Similarly, removing the zero at the origin from $Z_2(s)$ of Eq. 5.4.1, we get

$$Z_2(s) = s\,\frac{kZ(k) - sZ(s)}{k^2 - s^2} = \frac{Z(k)}{\zeta + \dfrac{k}{s}} \qquad \textbf{5.4.4}$$

It follows that $Z(s)$ in Eq. 5.4.1 can be written in terms of $Z_1(s)$ and $Z_2(s)$ as given in Eqs. 5.4.2 and 5.4.4. Thus

$$Z(s) = \frac{Z(k)}{\dfrac{1}{\zeta} + \dfrac{s}{k}} + \frac{Z(k)}{\zeta + \dfrac{k}{s}} \qquad \textbf{5.4.5}$$

The fact that $\zeta$ as given in Eqs. 5.4.3, 5.4.4, and 5.4.5 is prf was pointed out by Richards* using a different approach. It follows from Eq. 5.4.5. that $Z(s)$ may be realized by the network in Fig. 5.4.

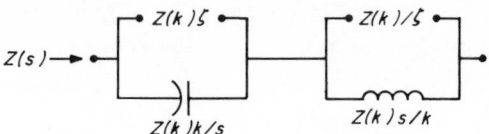

**Fig. 5.4. Realization of Z(s) in Eq. 5.4.5**

This network was pointed out by Bott and Duffin in 1949. They also demonstrated that since $k$ is arbitrary it can be utilized to some advantage in synthesis. This is discussed in the following section.

### THE BOTT-DUFFIN SYNTHESIS 5.5

In Example 5.2.2, it was shown that occasionally the "chop-chop" synthesis would lead to an impasse, namely, to a situation where the function is a minimum resistance but without a pole or a zero at the origin or at infinity. At this point, the Bott-Duffin synthesis may be utilized.

### Theorem 5.5.1 *The Bott-Duffin Theorem*

Given $Z(s)$ is prf, its numerator and denominator are of equal degree, and it is minimum resistive. Then, it is possible to select $k$ in Fig. 5.4 in such a manner that $\zeta = \dfrac{kZ(s) - sZ(k)}{kZ(k) - sZ(s)}$ has either a pole or a zero on the $j$ axis (and which is subsequently removable).

### *Proof*

If $Z(s)$ is minimum resistive, Ev $Z(j\omega_0) = 0$, and therefore $Z(j\omega_0)$ is an imaginary quantity. Then either $Z(j\omega_0)/j\omega_0$ or $j\omega_0Z(j\omega_0)$ is positive. Furthermore, since the degrees of the numerator and denominator are equal, $Z(k)$ is bounded and therefore $kZ(k)$ may assume any value from zero to infinity. It follows that if $j\omega_0Z(j\omega_0)$ is positive, a positive $k$ may be selected to make

$$k_0Z(k_0) - j\omega_0Z(j\omega_0) = 0 \qquad 5.5.1$$

This may be interpreted to mean that

$$k_0Z(k_0) - sZ(s) \qquad 5.5.2$$

---

* Richards, P. I., "A Special Class of Functions with Positive Real Part in a Half Plane," *Duke Math J.*, Vol. 14, pp. 777–786, 1947.

has a zero at $s = j\omega_0$. Similarly, if $Z(j\omega_0)/j\omega_0$ is positive, we make

$$k_0Z(s) - sZ(k_0) \qquad \qquad \textbf{5.5.3}$$

have a zero on the $j$ axis. Then $\zeta$ has either a pole or a zero on the $j$ axis. This completes the proof of the theorem.

### Example 5.5.1

Synthesize $Z(s) = (s^2 + s + 1)/(s^2 + s + 4)$ by the Bott-Duffin method.

### Solution

Eq. 5.2.11 reveals that Re $Z(j\omega_0) = 0$ for $\omega_0 = \sqrt{2}$. This yields

$$\frac{Z(j\omega_0)}{j\omega_0} = \frac{j \operatorname{Im} Z(j\omega_0)}{j\omega_0} = \frac{1}{2} \qquad \qquad \textbf{5.5.4}$$

and from Eq. 5.5.3 $k$ has to be chosen such that

$$\frac{Z(k)}{k} = \frac{1}{2} = \frac{1}{k}\frac{k^2 + k + 1}{k^2 + k + 4} \qquad \qquad \textbf{5.5.5}$$

Further algebraic manipulation gives

$$k^3 - k^2 + 2k - 2 = 0 \qquad \qquad \textbf{5.5.6}$$

This expression can be factored to give

$$(k^2 + 2)(k - 1) = 0 \qquad \qquad \textbf{5.5.7}$$

Therefore $k_0$ is unity and $Z(k_0)$ (with Eq. 5.5.5) equals 1/2. Now $\zeta$ may be evaluated for $k_0 = 1$ and $Z(k_0) = 1/2$, yielding

$$\zeta = \frac{k_0Z(s) - sZ(k_0)}{k_0Z(k_0) - sZ(s)} \qquad \qquad \textbf{5.4.3}$$

$$= \frac{Z(s) - s\,1/2}{1/2 - sZ(s)} \qquad \qquad \textbf{5.5.8}$$

Putting $Z(s) = (s^2 + s + 1)/(s^2 + s + 4)$ in Eq. 5.5.8 and cancelling $s - 1$ from both the numerator and the denominator we get

$$\zeta = \frac{s^2 + 2}{2s^2 + 3s + 4} \qquad \qquad \textbf{5.5.9}$$

Observe that $\zeta$ has a $j$ axis zero as predicted by the Bott-Duffin theorem. This zero now may be removed to give

$$\zeta = \frac{1}{2 + \dfrac{3s}{s^2 + 2}} \qquad \qquad \textbf{5.5.10}$$

which is realizable by means of a resistor, an inductor, and a capacitor. The final network is obtained by reconstructing Fig. 5.4 with $k = 1$, $Z(k) = \frac{1}{2}$, and $\zeta$ as given by Eq. 5.5.10.

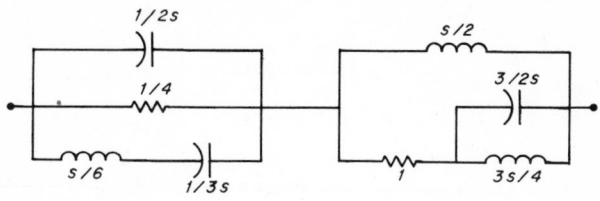

**Fig. 5.5. A network for** $Z(s) = \dfrac{s^2 + s + 1}{s^2 + s + 4}$

Essentially the Bott-Duffin synthesis (Fig. 5.5) is as follows. The method is applied to $Z(s)$ which is both minimum resistive and the degrees of both the numerator and the denominator are equal. For such functions $\zeta$ (as given by Eq. 5.5.8) is forced to have a $j$ axis pole or a zero [which is subsequently removed to yield a function lower in degree than $Z(s)$] by selecting a prescribed value of $k$. The method relies on the fact that $\zeta$ is realizable for any positive $k$ and that correspondingly $Z(s)$ (as represented in Fig. 5.4) is realizable for all positive $k$.

In conclusion of this section, observe that $(k^2 + 2)$ is a factor of Eq. 5.5.7. This is no accident, for

$$\frac{Z(k)}{k} - \frac{Z(j\omega_0)}{j\omega_0} = 0 \qquad\qquad \textbf{5.5.11}$$

when $k$ equals $j\omega_0$. Therefore, this expression must have the factor $(k^2 + \omega_0^2)$. This fact may be used as a computation aid. Similar argument would show that this factor is also present in

$$kZ(k) - j\omega_0 Z(\omega_0) \qquad\qquad \textbf{5.5.12}$$

as it is also zero when $k = j\omega_0$.

$$* \quad * \quad * \quad * \quad * \quad *$$

Thus any positive real impedance function can be realized in terms of series and parallel connections of $RLC$ elements and other networks whose impedance functions are reduced in degree. This was demonstrated in the course of the chapter by first using the "chop-chop" technique to reduce the degree of $Z(s)$ and then resorting to the Bott-Duffin synthesis when the "chop-chop" technique failed.

The over-all geometrical pattern of the synthesis was that of series and parallel combinations of elements. Another common pattern is that of tandem combinations, but this requires the application of some of the techniques used in conjunction with 2-port network synthesis (Chapter 6).

## PROBLEMS

5.1. Synthesize by the "chop-chop" technique

(a).
$$\frac{4s^2 + 2s + 1}{s(s^2 + s + 1)}$$

(b).
$$\frac{s^3 + 2s^2 + 3s + 2}{s^3 + s^2 + 2s + 1}$$

(c).
$$\frac{s^2 + s + 1}{s^3 + s^2 + 2s + 1}$$

(d).
$$\frac{s^3 + 4s^2 + 2s}{s^3 + s^2 + 2s + 1}$$

5.2. Realize the following impedance functions.

(a).
$$\frac{s^2 + s + 9}{s^2 + s + 4}$$

(b).
$$\frac{s^2 + 2s + 9}{s^2 + 2s + 1}$$

5.3. Use the Bott-Duffin synthesis on the following functions.

(a).
$$\frac{2s^3 + 2s^2 + 20s + 9}{s^3 + 4s^2 + 5s + 8}$$

(b).
$$\frac{s^3 + 3s^2 + s + 1}{s^3 + s^2 + 3s + 1}$$

5.4. Synthesize the function

$$\frac{m + \alpha n}{m + n}$$

where $m + n$ is a Hurwitz polynomial ($\alpha > 0$).

5.5. If $Z(s) = (m_1 + n_1)/(m_2 + n_2)$ is prf, show that $\zeta$ given by

$$\zeta = \frac{m_1 + \alpha n_2}{\alpha m_2 + n_2}$$

is also prf ($\alpha > 0$).

5.6. Find the minimum value of $\beta$ ($\beta > 0$) such that the impedance function

$$\gamma = \beta - \frac{s + 1}{s^2 + s + 1}$$

is a positive real function.

## FURTHER READING

Books

5.1. Balabanian, N., "Network Synthesis," Prentice Hall, Inc., Englewood Cliffs, N. J., 1958, Chapter 3.

5.2. Guillemin, E. A., "Synthesis of Passive Networks," John Wiley & Sons, New York, 1957, Chapter 10.

5.3. Storer, J. E., "Passive Network Synthesis," McGraw-Hill Book Co., Inc., New York, 1957, Chapter 9.

5.4. Tuttle, D. F., Jr. "Network Synthesis," John Wiley & Sons, New York, 1958, Chapter 10 (closely related).

5.5. Van Valkenburg, M. E., "Introduction to Modern Network Synthesis," John Wiley & Sons, New York, 1960, Chapter 7.

Related Papers

5.6. Fialkow, A. and Gerst, I., "Impedance Synthesis without Mutual Coupling," *Quarterly of Appl. Math.*, Vol. 12, pp. 420–422, Jan., 1955-

5.7. Pantell, R. H., "New Methods of Driving-point and Transfer Function Synthesis," *Proc. IRE*, Vol. 42, p. 861, 1954.

5.8. Reza, F. M., "A Supplement to the Brune Synthesis," *Communication and Electronics*, Am. Institute of Electrical Engineers, Vol. 75, pp. 85–90, March, 1955.

# CHAPTER 6

# *Some Properties of 2-Port Networks\**

## 6.1. INTRODUCTION

Four-terminal networks differ from two-terminal networks in their dependency on a two-loop system (Fig. 6.1).

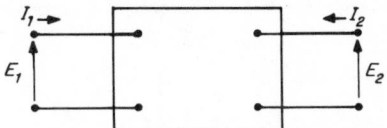

**Fig. 6.1. A 2-port network**

Let the 2-port network be made of linear lumped and passive elements. The network is subdivided into all possible loops so that no loops have parallel elements (Fig. 6.2).

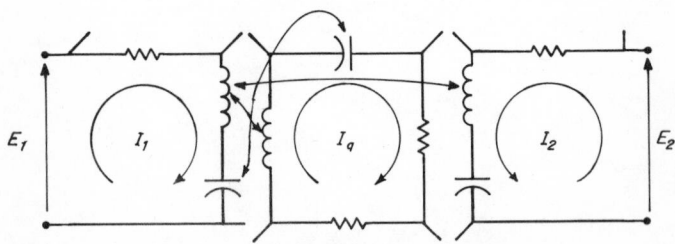

**Fig. 6.2. Loops in a 2-port network**

---

\* Commonly referred to also as four terminal or four pole networks.

Writing the loop equations in the Laplace transformation notation (assuming zero initial conditions), we get ($n$ = number of loops)

$$E_1(s) = \sum_{p=1}^{n} a_{1p} I_p(s)$$

$$E_2(s) = \sum_{p=1}^{n} a_{2p} I_p(s)$$

$$0 = \sum_{p=1}^{n} a_{3p} I_p(s)$$

$\cdot$

$\cdot$ **6.1.1**

$\cdot$

$$0 = \sum_{p=1}^{n} a_{qp} I_p(s)$$

$\cdot$

$\cdot$

$$0 = \sum_{p=1}^{n} a_{np} I_p(s)$$

Each loop contains no parallel elements; therefore $a_{qp}$ (the general loop impedance) will be of the form

$$a_{qp} = R_{qp} + sL_{qp} + \frac{1}{sC_{qp}} \qquad \textbf{6.1.2}$$

Equation 6.1.1 is a set of $n$ linear algebraic equations. Solving these equations (Cramer's rule may be used) for $I_1(s)$ and $I_2(s)$ in terms of $E_1(s)$ and $E_2(s)$, we obtain

$$I_1(s) = y_{11} E_1(s) + y_{12} E_2(s)$$
$$I_2(s) = y_{21} E_1(s) + y_{22} E_2(s)$$

**6.1.3**

Thus $y_{11}$, $y_{12}$, $y_{21}$, and $y_{22}$ are made up of sums and products of functions of the form of $a_{qp}$ (Eq. 6.1.2). All these terms are rational functions of $s$. Also, the results would come out in terms of polynomials. It follows that all these quantities are analytic, rational functions of $s$ throughout the complex plane except at their poles.

The same properties are ascribed to $z_{11}$, $z_{12}$, $z_{21}$, and $z_{22}$, respectively. These are obtained if Eqs. 6.1.3 are solved for $E_1(s)$ and $E_2(s)$ in terms of $I_1(s)$ and $I_2(s)$ as follows:

$$E_1(s) = z_{11}I_1(s) + z_{12}I_2(s)$$
$$E_2(s) = z_{21}I_1(s) + z_{22}I_2(s)$$

6.1.4

Suppose the 2-port network of Fig. 6.1 is converted into a 1-port one by loading the secondaries with $\zeta$, a driving point impedance function, as illustrated in Fig. 6.3.

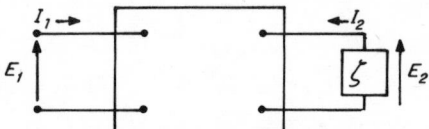

**Fig. 6.3. A terminated 2-port network—cascade network**

This termination imposes a constraint on Eqs. 6.1.4, namely

$$E_2(s) = -\zeta I_2(s)$$

6.1.5

which permits the elimination of $E_2(s)$ and $I_2(s)$ to give

$$\frac{E_1}{I_1} = Z_{in} = \frac{z_{11}\zeta + z_{11}z_{22} - z_{12}z_{21}}{\zeta + z_{22}}$$

6.1.6

This equation will be used frequently in the latter part of this chapter. Observe that $Z_{in}$ becomes $z_{11}$ if $\zeta$ is infinite. This means that $z_{11}$ must be prf (since now the network is essentially a 1-port one). Similar conclusions can be derived for $z_{22}$ as it is $Z_{in}$ as observed from the secondaries with the primaries open.

## 6.2. THE TRANSFORMER

The transformer is a 2-port device that occurs in nature in many forms. Two coils coupled magnetically form a transformer. Conceivably it is also possible that two capacitors may be somehow coupled electrically to produce a transformer. The equations for a lossless perfectly or unity coupled magnetic transformer (usually called a perfect transformer) are as follows:

$$E_1 = sL_1I_1 + s\sqrt{L_1L_2}\,I_2$$
$$E_2 = s\sqrt{L_1L_2}\,I_1 + sL_2I_2$$

6.2.1

These equations may be divided by each other to give a ratio $E_2/E_1$, which is independent of $I_1$ and $I_2$:

$$\frac{E_2}{E_1} = \sqrt{\frac{L_2}{L_1}} \qquad 6.2.2$$

(Since $\sqrt{L}$ of any coil is usually proportional to the number of turns, $\sqrt{L_1/L_2}$ is called the turn ratio.)

Equation 6.1.6 (the effect of $\zeta$ termination) is simplified for the unity coupled transformer because $z_{11}z_{22} - z_{12}z_{21}$ is zero. Thus

$$\frac{E_1}{I_1} = Z_{in} = \frac{sL_1\zeta}{\zeta + sL_2} \qquad 6.2.3$$

This equation is further reduced if $sL_2$ is much larger than $\zeta$, yielding

$$Z_{in} = \frac{L_1}{L_2}\zeta \qquad 6.2.4$$

In the limit when $sL_1 \to \infty$ and $sL_2 \to \infty$, the ratio $L_1/L_2$ is finite, and Eq. 6.2.4 is exact. In this case, the transformer is called an ideal transformer.

The currents cannot be found from Eq. 6.2.1, since the determinant is zero. However, conservation of power requires that

$$\text{Re }(E_1\bar{I}_1 + E_2\bar{I}_2) = 0 \qquad 6.2.5$$

Note that if $E_1$ is assumed real, $E_2$ (Eq. 6.2.2) is also real. Therefore

$$\frac{E_1}{E_2} = -\frac{\text{Re }I_2}{\text{Re }I_1} \qquad 6.2.6$$

The ratio of the currents also can be determined from the second equation of 6.2.1 by considering the load $\zeta$

$$s\sqrt{L_1L_2}\, I_1 + sL_2I_2 = -I_2\zeta \qquad 6.2.7$$

and therefore

$$\frac{I_1}{I_2} = -\frac{sL_2 + \zeta}{s\sqrt{L_1L_2}} \qquad 6.2.8$$

This ratio may assume any real value on the $j\omega$ axis if (depending on $\zeta$) $\zeta$ is capacitive. However, if $sL_2 \to \infty$ (the ideal transformer), $sL_2$ will predominate the numerator. Then Eq. 6.2.8 becomes

$$\frac{I_1}{I_2} = -\sqrt{\frac{L_2}{L_1}} = -\frac{E_2}{E_1}$$

Transformer properties also may be obtained through nonmagnetic couplings between elements. For example, a capacitive transformer with a unity coupling may be described by the following equations:

$$E_1 = \frac{1}{sC_1} I_1 + \frac{1}{s\sqrt{C_1 C_2}} I_2$$

$$E_2 = \frac{1}{s\sqrt{C_1 C_2}} I_1 + \frac{1}{sC_2} I_2$$

6.2.9

from which it follows that

$$\frac{E_2}{E_1} = \sqrt{\frac{C_1}{C_2}}$$

6.2.10

The capacitive transformer may be realized by means of two crystal transducers coupled mechanically (Fig. 6.4). Similar properties also may be obtained when two faces of a piezo-electric crystal (Fig. 6.5) are excited (the electric leads connected to these faces are the primaries) by means of an AC voltage. The corresponding crystal vibration cause voltages to appear on the other faces (the secondaries). The device also may be approximated by means of an ideal transformer terminated by a capacitor. Similarly a transformer which has resistive like couplings may be obtained by means of an ideal transformer terminated with a resistor, though there is no apparent physical reason against the existence of a resistive transformer in nature. The corresponding 2-port equations are given by

$$E_1 = r_{11}I_1 + \sqrt{r_{11}r_{22}}\, I_2$$

$$E_2 = \sqrt{r_{11}r_{22}}\, I_1 + r_{22}I_2$$

6.2.11

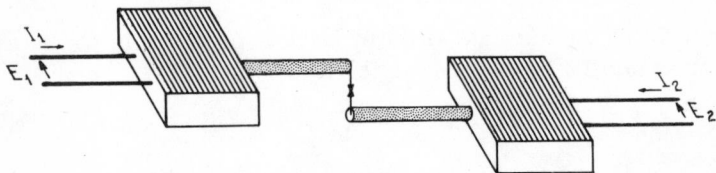

Fig. 6.4. Crystal transducers in cascade

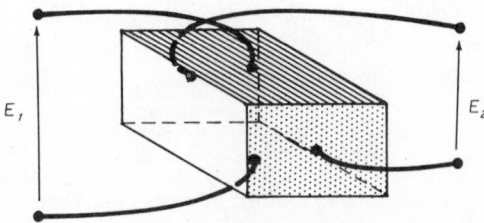

Fig. 6.5. A crystal transformer

## THE GYRATOR 6.3

The gyrator is a passive element which represents the idea of a pure coupling. It is described completely in terms of the impedance equations:

$$E_1 = z_{12}I_2$$
$$E_2 = -z_{12}I_1$$

6.3.1

Observe that only coupling terms are present as $z_{11} = z_{22} = 0$. This element was invented by Tellegen and was given the symbol shown in Fig. 6.6.

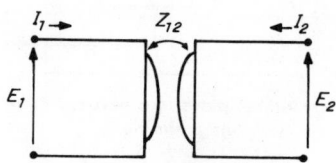

**Fig. 6.6. The gyrator symbol**

This element is very well approximated by the gyroscope shown in Fig. 6.7,

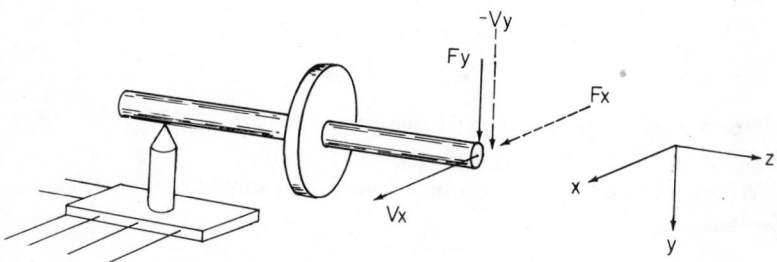

**Fig. 6.7. A gyroscope**

where the velocity in the $x$ direction $(V_x)$ is proportional to the vertical force $(F_y)$, whereas the force in the $x$ direction $(F_x$ broken line) produces a velocity $(-V_y)$ opposite in direction to the original vertical force $(F_y)$. Then

$$F_y = aV_x$$
$$F_x = -aV_y$$

6.3.2

where $a$ is a proportionality constant. These equations represent a true approximation for low-frequency application when acceleration forces can be ignored.

A crude approximation for the gyrator in a 2-port electrical-network sense is produced when a plate with strong Hall coefficient is placed in a perpendicular magnetic field (Fig. 6.8).

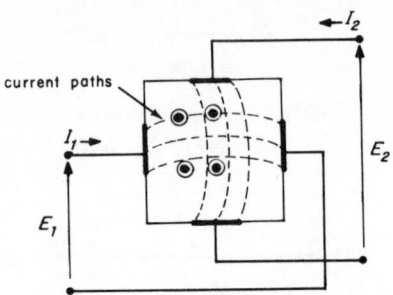

**Fig. 6.8.  A plate in a perpendicular magnetic field**

Owing to the Hall effect, a voltage $E_2$ will be generated which is proportional to $I_1$. This voltage results from the fact that the magnetic field displaces the path of $I_1$ in the upward direction. The same field would displace the path of $I_2$ towards the right, producing a negative voltage in the primary. The resulting equations are

$$E_1 = r_1 I_1 - a I_2$$
$$E_2 = a I_1 + r_2 I_2$$

6.3.3

where $r_1$ and $r_2$ are the ohmic resistances of the current's paths. For the gyrator to be ideal, $r_1$ and $r_2$ must be zero.

When the gyrator is terminated with the impedance $\zeta$, then by Eq. 6.3.1.

$$\frac{E_1}{I_1} = Z_{in} = \frac{z_{11}\zeta + z_{11}z_{22} - z_{12}z_{21}}{\zeta + z_{22}}$$

6.1.6
6.3.4

degenerates into

$$Z_{in} = \frac{z_{12}^2}{\zeta}$$

6.3.5

Thus the gyrator produces an input impedance which is proportional to $1/\zeta$, while the transformer produces an impedance which is proportional to $\zeta$. Observe that the gyrator would convert a capacitor into an inductor and vice versa (a "dualator").

The gyrator proves to be useful in network synthesis by permitting simple equivalent networks for complicated structures.

## Example 6.3.1

Find the input impedance of the network in Fig. 6.9.

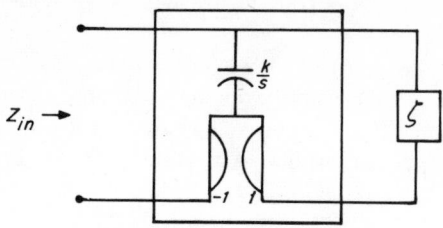

**Fig. 6.9. A gyrator network**

## Solution

$Z_{in}$ will be obtained from Eq. 6.3.4. In this equation

$$z_{22} = z_{11} = \frac{k}{s} + 0, \qquad \text{as } z_{11} = z_{22} = 0 \text{ for the gyrator}$$

$$z_{12} = \frac{k}{s} - 1, \qquad \text{where } -1 \text{ is } z_{12} \text{ for the gyrator}$$

and

$$z_{21} = \frac{k}{s} + 1 \qquad \text{where } +1 \text{ is } z_{21} \text{ for the gyrator}$$

It follows that Eq. 6.3.4 becomes

$$Z_{in} = \frac{\dfrac{k}{s}\,\zeta + \dfrac{k}{s} \times \dfrac{k}{s} - \left(\dfrac{k}{s} - 1\right)\left(\dfrac{k}{s} + 1\right)}{\zeta + \dfrac{k}{s}} = \frac{k\zeta + s}{k + s\zeta} \qquad \textbf{6.3.6}$$

But Eq. 6.3.6 can be expressed as

$$\frac{k\zeta + s}{k + s\zeta} = \frac{k\zeta}{k + s\zeta} + \frac{s}{k + s\zeta} \qquad \textbf{6.3.7}$$

yielding Fig. 6.10.

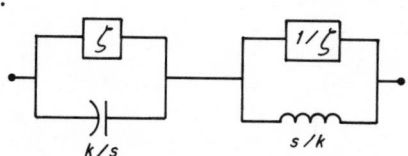

**Fig. 6.10. An equivalent network for Fig. 6.9**

This may be recognized as the Bott-Duffin network* for $Z_{in} = \dfrac{Z(s)}{Z(k)}$.

---

* Hazony, D. and Schott, F. W., "Cascade Representation of the Bott-Duffin Synthesis," *IRE Trans. on Circuit Theory*, Vol. CT-5, pp. 144–145, June, 1958.

## 6.4. CONSTRAINTS ON THE 2-PORT IMPEDANCE PARAMETERS

In future work, networks will be usually given in the gyrator form, and later on an equivalent structure will be provided without the gyrator.

From a synthesis point of view, 1-port networks are simpler than 2-port networks as there is only one impedance function to consider. But this impedance function must be prf. In a 2-port network there are four impedance functions. Are they prf? An investigation of Eqs. 6.1.4

$$E_1 = z_{11}I_1 + z_{12}I_2 \qquad \text{6.1.4}$$
$$E_2 = z_{21}I_1 + z_{22}I_2 \qquad \text{6.4.1}$$

reveals that two of them must be prf. These are $z_{11}$ and $z_{22}$. The first is obtained as $Z_{in}$ when the secondaries are open (infinite load), and since $Z_{in}$ is a two-terminal network impedance function, it must be prf. Similarly $z_{22}$ is prf as it is a driving point impedance function as viewed from the secondary when the primary is open.

Some constraints on the properties of $z_{12}$ and $z_{21}$ may be uncovered if power conservation rules are applied. Let us consider lossless networks. The principle of conservation of average power requires that on the $j$ axis

$$|E_1|\,|I_1|\cos\theta_1 + |E_2|\,|I_2|\cos\theta_2 = 0 \qquad \text{6.4.2}$$

where $\theta_1$ and $\theta_2$ are the respective phase angles. But these quantities can be expressed as

$$\text{Re } E_1\bar{I}_1 + \text{Re } E_2\bar{I}_2 = 0 \qquad \text{6.4.3}$$

Now Eqs. 6.4.1 may be used to compute Eq. 6.4.3. Thus

$$\text{Re } E_1\bar{I}_1 = \text{Re } z_{11}|I_1|^2 + \text{Re } z_{12}I_2\bar{I}_1$$

and

$$\text{Re } E_2\bar{I}_2 = \text{Re } z_{21}I_1\bar{I}_2 + \text{Re } z_{22}|I_2|^2 \qquad \text{6.4.4}$$

yielding

$$\text{Re } E_1\bar{I}_1 + \text{Re } E_2\bar{I}_2 = \text{Re } z_{11}|I_1|^2 + \text{Re }(z_{12}I_2\bar{I}_1 + z_{21}I_1\bar{I}_2) + \text{Re } z_{22}|I_2|^2 = 0 \qquad \text{6.4.5}$$

This equation is reduced to

$$\text{Re }(z_{12}I_2\bar{I}_1 + z_{21}I_1\bar{I}_2) = 0_{s=j\omega} \qquad \text{6.4.6}$$

since $\text{Re } z_{11} = \text{Re } z_{22} = 0$ in a lossless network on the $j$ axis. Eq. 6.4.6 has to be fulfilled for all values of the currents. Letting $I_1 = a_1 + jb_1$ and $I_2 = a_2 + jb_2$ in Eq. 6.4.6 and rearranging the terms, we obtain

$$(a_1a_2 + b_1b_2)\text{ Re }(z_{12} + z_{21}) + (a_2b_1 - b_2a_1)\text{ Im }(z_{12} - z_{21}) = 0 \qquad \text{6.4.7}$$

This equation can be true for all possible values of $a_1$, $a_2$, $b_1$, and $b_2$ if and only if

$$\text{Re } z_{12} = - \text{ Re } z_{21} \qquad \textbf{6.4.8}$$

$$\text{Im } z_{12} = \text{Im } z_{21} \qquad \textbf{6.4.9}$$

Equation 6.4.8 shows that a gyrator as defined in the last section (Eqs. 6.3.1) conserves power, whereas Eq. 6.4.9 shows that a transformer conserves power.

Digressing for a moment we note that Eq. 6.4.9 shows that $L_{pq} = L_{qp}$ in any two coupled coils. This insures that $T(s)$ is real in Eqs. 4.3.8 and 4.3.9.

Eqs. 6.4.8 and 6.4.9 can combine as

$$\bar{z}_{12} + z_{21} = 0 \qquad \textbf{6.4.10}$$

However, from the manner of its derivation Eq. 6.4.10 has been proven valid only on the $j$ axis.

To establish the corresponding constraint throughout the *r.h.s* plane, let the 2-port network be converted into a 1-port network by means of an ideal transformer as in Fig. 6.11.

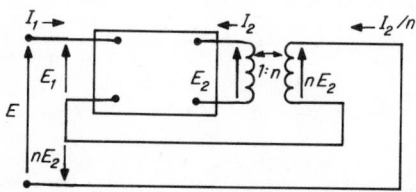

**Fig. 6.11. Conversion of a 2-port network into a 1-port network**

This permits treating the whole system as a driving point impedance function which may be computed as follows:

$$Z_{in} = \frac{E}{I_1} = \frac{E_1 - nE_2}{I_1} \qquad \textbf{6.4.11}$$

The ideal transformer has an arbitrary turn ratio designated by a letter $n$ which later will be permitted to vary. Observe that the transformer forces $I_2$ to be equal to $-nI_1$. Equation 6.4.11 now can be computed from Eq. 6.4.1 to give

$$E_1 = z_{11}I_1 - nI_1z_{12}$$

$$nE_2 = nz_{21}I_1 - n^2I_1z_{22}$$

These two equations may be subtracted to give

$$E_1 - nE_2 = [n^2z_{22} - n(z_{12} + z_{21}) + z_{11}]I_1 \qquad \textbf{6.4.12}$$

yielding

$$Z_{in} = \frac{E_1 - nE_2}{I_1} = n^2 z_{22} - n(z_{12} + z_{21}) + z_{11} \qquad \textbf{6.4.13}$$

which is prf since it represents a driving point impedance function. Thus

$$\text{Re } Z_{in} = \text{Re } n^2 z_{22} - \text{Re } n(z_{12} + z_{21}) + \text{Re } z_{11} \begin{array}{l} \geq 0 \quad \text{for Re } s = 0 \\ > 0 \quad \text{for Re } s > 0 \end{array} \qquad \textbf{6.4.14}$$

which may be grouped as follows:

$$\text{Re } z_{22}\left[\left(n - \frac{\text{Re }(z_{12} + z_{21})}{2\,\text{Re } z_{22}}\right)^2 + \frac{\text{Re } z_{11}}{\text{Re } z_{22}} - \frac{(\text{Re }(z_{12} + z_{21}))^2}{4(\text{Re } z_{22})^2}\right] \geq 0 \quad \textbf{6.4.15}$$

$$\text{for Re } s = 0$$

The only way that the inequality 6.4.15 may be maintained for all possible values of $n$ is

$$\text{Re } z_{22}\left[\frac{\text{Re } z_{11}}{\text{Re } z_{22}} - \frac{(\text{Re }(z_{12} + z_{21}))^2}{4(\text{Re } z_{22})^2}\right] \geq 0 \qquad \textbf{6.4.16}$$

Since both $\text{Re } z_{11}$ and $\text{Re } z_{22}$ are positive ($z_{11}$ and $z_{22}$ are prf), this can be expressed as

$$\text{Re } z_{11}\, \text{Re } z_{22} - \frac{(\text{Re }(z_{12} + z_{21}))^2}{4} \begin{array}{l} \geq 0 \quad \text{for Re } s = 0 \\ > 0 \quad \text{for Re } s > 0 \end{array} \qquad \textbf{6.4.17}$$

This equation is known as the *real part condition.*

Notice that if either $\text{Re } z_{11}$ or $\text{Re } z_{22}$ is zero, then

$$-\left(\text{Re }\left(\frac{z_{12} + z_{21}}{2}\right)\right)^2 \begin{array}{l} \geq 0 \quad \text{for Re } s = 0 \\ > * \quad \text{for Re } s > 0 \end{array} \qquad \textbf{6.4.18}$$

which can be true only with the equal sign. Then

$$\text{Re } z_{12} = -\text{Re } z_{21} \qquad \text{for Re } s \geq 0 \qquad \textbf{6.4.19}$$

This equation is stronger than the corresponding Eq. 6.4.8, since it is valid throughout the *r.h.s* plane. However, when the energy functions were used to derive the positive reality of an *RLC* network, no gyrator coupling was included. This was done in order to avoid complicating the derivation at that early stage. The introduction of gyrators changes only one of the energy functions, namely $F(s)$. Considerations similar to those introduced in Section 4.3 show that $F(s)$ remains positive for all $s$ even if gyrators are employed. Thus, even then, the application of the positive real requirement to Eq. 6.4.13 is justified.

---

* The equal sign may hold throughout the *r.h.s* plane if the function in question is identically zero.

## MORE CONSTRAINTS ON 2-PORT IMPEDANCE PARAMETERS* 6.5

If nonreciprocal elements are present, Eq. 6.4.17 does not tell the whole story. Additional constraints become evident if a gyrator is used to convert the corresponding 2-port network into a 1-port one (Fig. 6.12).

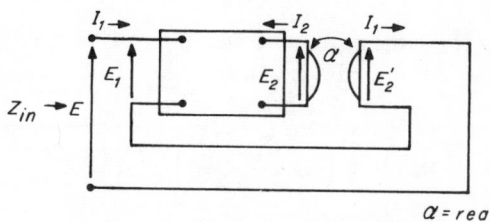

**Fig. 6.12.** Conversion of a 2-port network into a 1-port one using one gyrator

However $E'_2 = \alpha I_2$ and $E_2 = -\alpha I_1$ in a gyrator. These may be applied to Eqs. 6.4.1 to give

$$E_2 = z_{21}I_1 + z_{22}I_2$$

$$= -\alpha I_1 \qquad\qquad \text{6.5.1}$$

and therefore

$$\frac{I_2}{I_1} = -\frac{(z_{21} + \alpha)}{z_{22}} \qquad\qquad \text{6.5.2}$$

Furthermore (from the first of Eqs. 6.4.1)

$$E_1 = z_{11}I_1 + z_{12}I_2 \qquad\qquad \text{6.5.3}$$

Hence $Z_{in}$ becomes

$$Z_{in} = \frac{E_1 - E'_2}{I_1}$$

$$= \frac{E_1 - \alpha I_2}{I_1} \ (\text{as } E'_2 = -\alpha I_2) \qquad\qquad \text{6.5.4}$$

$$= z_{11} + (z_{12} - \alpha)\frac{I_2}{I_1} \qquad (\text{by } 6.5.3)$$

which reduce to

$$Z_{in} = z_{11} - \frac{(z_{12} - \alpha)(z_{21} + \alpha)}{z_{22}} \qquad (\text{by } 6.5.2) \qquad\qquad \text{6.5.5}$$

---

* Hazony, D., "Two Extensions of the Darlington Synthesis Procedure," *IRE Trans. on Circuit Theory*, Vol. CT-9, pp. 284–288, Sept., 1961.

Now this equation may be written in the form of Eq. 6.4.13 as follows:

$$Z_{in} = \frac{z_{11}z_{22} - z_{12}z_{21}}{z_{22}} - \alpha \left( \frac{z_{12}}{z_{22}} - \frac{z_{21}}{z_{22}} \right) + \frac{\alpha^2}{z_{22}}$$

$$= y_{11}^{-1} - \alpha \left( \frac{z_{12}}{z_{22}} - \frac{z_{21}}{z_{22}} \right) + \frac{\alpha^2}{z_{22}} \qquad \text{6.5.6}$$

By following the same arguments leading to Eqs. 6.4.16 and 6.4.17, we find that the only way Re $Z_{in}$ in Eq. 6.5.6 will be positive in the *r.h.s.* plane for all values of $\alpha$ is

$$\text{Re} \frac{1}{y_{11}} \times \text{Re} \frac{1}{z_{22}} - \left( \text{Re} \frac{z_{12} - z_{21}}{2z_{22}} \right)^2 \begin{array}{l} \geq 0 \text{ for Re } s = 0 \\ > 0 \text{ for Re } s > 0 \end{array} \qquad \text{6.5.7}$$

## 6.6. RESIDUE CONDITION

Equation 6.4.17 imposes a strong set of constraints on the impedance parameters of the 2-port network. This equation is written below for examination:

$$\text{Re } z_{11} \text{ Re } z_{22} - \frac{(\text{Re } (z_{12} + z_{21}))^2}{4} \begin{array}{ll} \geq 0 & \text{Re } s = 0 \qquad \text{6.4.17} \\ > 0 & \text{Re } s > 0 \qquad \text{6.6.1} \end{array}$$

Note, for example, if Re $z_{11}$ or Re $z_{22}$ is zero anywhere along the $j$ axis, then Re $(z_{12} + z_{21})$ must be zero there too. The argument may also be reversed to say that if Re $(z_{12} + z_{21})$ is not zero in the *r.h.s* plane and along the $j$ axis, then Re $z_{11}$ Re $z_{22}$ may not be zero there. It follows that if $(z_{12} + z_{21})$ has a pole on the $j$ axis, both $z_{11}$ and $z_{22}$ must have these poles. Let the respective residues be denoted by $k_{11}$, $k_{22}$, $k_{12}$, and $k_{21}$. The fact that $z_{11}$ and $z_{22}$ are prf suggests that near the pole they behave like

$$z_{11} \sim \frac{2k_{11}s}{s^2 + \omega_0^2}, \text{ and } z_{22} \sim \frac{2k_{22}s}{s^2 + \omega_0^2} \qquad \text{6.6.2}$$

where $k_{11}$ and $k_{22}$ are positive.

Furthermore, since $z_{12}$ and $z_{21}$ are real for $s = real$, it is assumed that their behavior near the pole is of the same form as that of $z_{11}$ and $z_{22}$; that is, it is supposed that in the neighborhood of a pole $z_{12}$ and $z_{21}$ will be given in the form

$$z_{12} \sim \frac{2k_{12}s}{s^2 + \omega_0^2}, \text{ and } z_{21} \sim \frac{2k_{21}s}{s^2 + \omega_0^2} \qquad \text{6.6.3}$$

Actually the residues need not necessarily be positive. To find out their exact value, let $s = j\omega_0 + \epsilon$. Then

$$\text{Re } z_{11} = \frac{2k_{11}}{\epsilon} \times \frac{\epsilon^2 + 2\omega_0^2}{\epsilon^2 + 4\omega_0^2}, \qquad \textbf{6.6.4a}$$

$$\text{Re } z_{22} = \frac{2k_{22}}{\epsilon} \times \frac{\epsilon^2 + 2\omega_0^2}{\epsilon^2 + 4\omega_0^2} \qquad \textbf{6.6.4b}$$

and

$$\frac{\text{Re } (z_{12} + z_{21})}{2} = \frac{(k_{12} + k_{21})}{\epsilon} \times \frac{\epsilon^2 + 2\omega_0^2}{\epsilon^2 + 4\omega_0^2} \qquad \textbf{6.6.4c}$$

Substituting these values in Eq. 6.6.1, we get

$$\left[\frac{2}{\epsilon} \times \frac{\epsilon^2 + 2\omega_0^2}{\epsilon^2 + 4\omega_0^2}\right]^2 \left(k_{11}k_{22} - \frac{(k_{12} + k_{21})^2}{4}\right) \geq 0 \qquad \textbf{6.6.5}$$

and consequently (as $\epsilon > 0$)

$$k_{11}k_{22} - \frac{(k_{12} + k_{21})^2}{4} \geq 0 \qquad \textbf{6.6.6}$$

Equation 6.6.6 was derived from the real part condition given by Eq. 6.6.1. This raises the question whether the additional constraint on the real part given by Eq. 6.5.7 effects the above inequality (Eq. 6.6.6). The answer is yes.

Application of the complete sequence of steps of Eqs. 6.6.2 to Eq. 6.5.7 would uncover some additional constraints. However, it turns out that the result would be the same if they are applied on $y_{11}^{-1}(s) = (z_{11}z_{22} - z_{12}z_{21})/z_{22}$, since it is also prf. This would yield

$$k_{11}k_{22} - k_{12}k_{21} \geq 0 \qquad \textbf{6.6.7}$$

This inequality is known as the *residue condition*. In case it is obeyed with the equal sign, the residues are said to be *compact*. Furthermore, to conform to the usual development, the term "residue condition" is used to refer to Eq. 6.6.7 when $k_{12} = k_{21}$ = real; in that case Eq. 6.6.7 becomes

$$k_{11}k_{22} - k'_{12}{}^2 \geq 0 \qquad \textbf{6.6.8}$$

where $k'_{12} = \text{Re } k_{12}$. This equation also may be obtained directly from Eq. 6.6.6. Equation 6.6.7 is called *the extended residue condition* when $k_{12}$ and $k_{21}$ are complex conjugates. The extended residue condition is sometimes written in the following form:

$$k_{11}k_{22} - k'_{12}{}^2 - \beta^2 \geq 0$$

$$\text{where } \beta = \text{Im } k_{12} \qquad \textbf{6.6.9}$$

This is useful when the 2-port networks impedance parameters are expanded in fractions of the form

$$z_{11} = \frac{2k_{11}s}{s^2 + \omega_0{}^2}, \qquad z_{12} = \frac{2(k'_{12}s + \beta\omega_0)}{s^2 + \omega_0{}^2}$$

$$z_{21} = \frac{2(k'_{12}s - \beta\omega_0)}{s^2 + \omega_0{}^2}, \qquad \text{and } z_{22} = \frac{2k_{22}s}{s^2 + \omega_0{}^2}$$

6.6.10

Then $2\beta$ is the coefficient of the $z_{12}$ term of the form $2\beta\omega_0/(s^2 + \omega_0{}^2)$. In general, if there is little chance of ambiguity, the prime over the $k_{12}$ in Eqs. 6.6.8 and 6.6.9 will be dropped.

## Example 6.6.1

Find the impedance parameters of the network in Fig. 6.13.

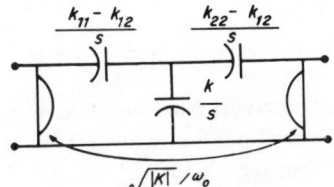

**Fig. 6.13. A gyrator and a T network connected in parallel**

*Solution*

One way to analyze this network is to add algebraically the $Y$ matrix of the gyrator to that of the $T$ network. Hence

$$[Y(s)] = [Y_T] + [Y_{\text{gyrator}}]$$

$$= \begin{bmatrix} \dfrac{sk_{22}}{|k|} & \dfrac{-sk_{12}}{|k|} + \dfrac{\omega_0}{\sqrt{|k|}} \\[3mm] \dfrac{-sk_{12}}{|k|} - \dfrac{\omega_0}{\sqrt{|k|}} & \dfrac{sk_{11}}{|k|} \end{bmatrix}$$

6.6.11

where $|k| = k_{11}k_{22} - k_{12}{}^2$

Converting Eq. 6.6.11 into the impedance matrix form, we get

$$[Z(s)] = \frac{1}{s^2 + \omega_0{}^2} \begin{bmatrix} k_{11}s & k_{12}s - \sqrt{|k|}\,\omega_0 \\[2mm] k_{12}s + \sqrt{|k|}\,\omega_0 & k_{22}s \end{bmatrix}$$

6.6.12

This is the required solution. Note that the extended residue condition (Eq. 6.6.9) is satisfied with the equal sign.

## PROBLEMS

**6.1.** Prove that both $z_{12}$ and $y_{12}$ are odd functions of $s$ for a lossless network.

**6.2.** Find the admittance matrix of the network of Fig. P 6.2.

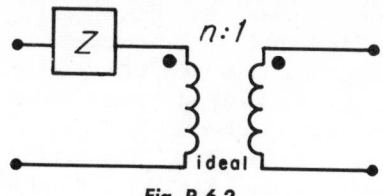

**Fig. P 6.2**

**6.3.** Write the equivalent impedance matrix of the two 2-port networks connected in series-series, in parallel-parallel, in tandem, in terms of the $Z$ parameters alone. Repeat for the admittance matrix.

**6.4.** Show that for a 2-port network terminated in $R$ ohms

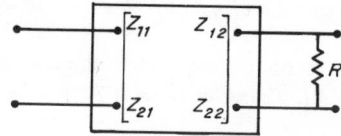

**Fig. P 6.4a**

$$z_{12} = \frac{Rz_{21}}{R + z_{22}}$$

and that (for $R = 1$)

$$T_{12} \equiv \left.\frac{E_2}{E_1}\right|_{I_2=0} = \frac{-y_{12}}{1 + y_{22}}$$

Also show that $y_{12} = Gy_{12}/(G + y_{22})$ in the following network:

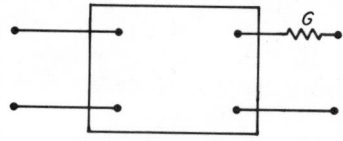

**Fig. P 6.4b**

**6.5.** Write the impedance matrix of the following network:

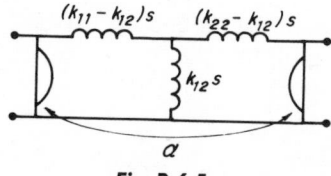

**Fig. P 6.5**

Also discuss the residue condition for this network.

## FURTHER READING

BOOKS

6.1. Balabanian, N., "Network Synthesis," Prentice Hall, Inc., Englewood Cliffs, N. J., 1958, Chapters 1 and 4.
6.2. Cauer, W., "Synthesis of Linear Communication Networks," McGraw-Hill Book Co., Inc., New York, 1958, Chapters 3 and 4.
6.3. Guillemin, E. A., "Synthesis of Passive Networks," John Wiley & Sons, New York, 1957, Chapter 6.
6.4. Kuh, E. S., and Pederson, D. O., "Principles of Circuit Synthesis," McGraw-Hill Book Co., Inc., New York, 1959, Chapters 4 and 5.
6.5. Van-Valkenburg, M. E., "Introduction to Modern Network Synthesis," John Wiley & Sons, New York, 1960, Chapter 2.

RELATED PAPERS

6.6. Bolinder, E. F., "Survey of Some Properties of Linear Networks," *IRE Trans on Circuit Theory*, Vol. CT-4, pp. 70–77, Sept., 1957 (excellent).
6.7. Bolinder, E. F., "Note on the Matrix Representation of Linear Two-Port Networks," *IRE Trans. on Circuit Theory*, Vol. CT-4, pp. 337–339, Dec., 1957.
6.8. Carlin, H. J., "Synthesis on non-reciprocal networks," *Proc. of Symp. on Modern Network Synthesis*, Polytech. Inst. of Brooklyn, Vol. 5, pp. 11–44, 1955.
6.9. Hogan, "The Elements of Nonreciprocal Microwave Devices," *Proc. IRE*, Vol. 44, pp. 1345–1368, Oct., 1956.
6.10. McMillan, E. M., "Violation of the Reciprocity Theorem in Linear Passive Electromechanical Systems," *J. Acoust. Soc. Amer.*, Vol. 18, pp. 344–347, Oct., 1946.
6.11. De Pian, L., "Passivity Conditions for Three Terminal Networks," *IRE Trans. on Circuit Theory*, Vol. CT-9, pp. 360–361, Sept., 1961.
6.12. Tellegen, B. D. H., "The Synthesis of Passive Resistanceless Four-Poles that May Violate the Reciprocity Relation," *Philips Res. Reports*, Vol. 3, pp. 321–337, Oct., 1946.
6.13. Tellegen, B. D. H., "The Synthesis of Passive Two-Poles by means of Networks containing Gyrators," *Philips Res. Reports*, Vol. 4, pp. 31–37, Feb., 1949.
6.14. Tellegen, B. D. H., and Klauss, E., "The Parameters of a Passive Four-Pole that May Violate the Reciprocity Relation," *Philips Res. Reports*, Vol. 5, pp. 81–86, April, 1950.

# Darlington's Synthesis | CHAPTER 7

In Chapter 5 a method was prescribed which makes it possible to synthesize any positive real function. According to this method, the function was first stripped of all its $j$ axis poles, zeros, and of its minimum resistance; then it was reduced further through the use of the Bott-Duffin synthesis procedure. This particular approach leads to a series-parallel geometrical configuration. At this point, the question might be raised concerning the possibility of cascade (tandem) synthesis.

Tandem 2-port synthesis implies the reduction of the impedance function by removal of a 2-port (denoted as a "buffer") network. Thus $Z(s)$ may be expressed in terms of a 2-port network terminated with an impedance function of lower degree. It will be shown in the following sections that any positive real function can be realized in this manner. All the elements involved in the synthesis are realizable, but transformers may have to be used. Also gyrators may be employed to effect a reduction in the number of elements involved.

The present chapter is essentially devoted to the Darlington synthesis and related subjects.

### RECIPROCAL DARLINGTON* SYNTHESIS 7.2

This procedure goes to the extreme of requiring that the final termination be 1 ohm. The word "extreme" is used to emphasize the fact that $Z(s)$ is expressed in terms of a 2-port network terminated by an impedance function which has the lowest possible degree,

---

\* Darlington S., "Synthesis of Reactance Four-Poles which Produce Prescribed Insertion Loss Characteristics," *J. Math. and Phys.*, Vol. 18, pp. 257–353, 1939.

namely zero. (A constant has a zero degree.) Furthermore, the associated 2-port network is lossless.

Darlington's procedure is perfectly general except for purely reactive networks. However, this particular case will not be considered here. The reason for the failure of the method (without adaptation) for realizing a reactance function is the fact that one would not expect to synthesize such a function in terms of a lossless network with a resistive termination.

Let the final termination be 1 ohm. Recalling the expression for an input impedance of a 2-port network terminated with $\zeta$ (Eq. 6.1.6), we get

$$Z_{in} = \frac{z_{11}\zeta + z_{11}z_{22} - z_{12}z_{21}}{\zeta + z_{22}} \qquad 7.2.1$$

which degenerates into

$$Z_{in} = z_{11} \frac{1 + (z_{11}z_{22} - z_{12}z_{21})/z_{11}}{1 + z_{22}} \qquad \begin{array}{l}1.4.5\\7.2.2\end{array}$$

if $\zeta$ is set to unity. This mathematical statement is to be compared with $Z(s)$ when expressed as

$$Z(s) = \frac{m_1 + n_1}{m_2 + n_2} \qquad 7.2.3$$

In an effort to cast $Z(s)$ in Eq. 7.2.3 into the form of Eq. 7.2.2 one might rewrite $Z(s)$ in two forms as follows:

| *Case A* | *Case B* |
|---|---|

$$Z(s) = \frac{m_1}{n_2} \times \frac{1 + \dfrac{n_1}{m_1}}{1 + \dfrac{m_2}{n_2}} \qquad\qquad Z(s) = \frac{n_1}{m_2} \times \frac{1 + \dfrac{m_1}{n_1}}{1 + \dfrac{n_2}{m_2}} \qquad 7.2.4$$

A comparison of Eqs. 7.2.4 and 7.2.2 yields two distinct possibilities:

| *Case A* | *Case B* | |
|---|---|---|

$$z_{11} = \frac{m_1}{n_2} \qquad\qquad\qquad z_{11} = \frac{n_1}{m_2} \qquad (a)$$

$$z_{22} = \frac{m_2}{n_2} \qquad\qquad\qquad z_{22} = \frac{n_2}{m_2} \qquad (b) \quad 7.2.5$$

$$\frac{z_{11}z_{22} - z_{12}z_{21}}{z_{11}} = \frac{n_1}{m_1} \qquad \frac{z_{11}z_{22} - z_{21}z_{12}}{z_{11}} = \frac{m_1}{n_1} \qquad (c)$$

The functions $z_{11}$ and $z_{22}$ as given above are realizable as lossless networks. This is true for $z_{22}$ as it is formed by taking the ratio of *even* over *odd* (or *odd* over *even*) parts of an Hurwitz polynomial

(Chapter 3). The same is also true for $z_{11}$, since the function obtained by interchanging the even part of the numerator and denominator of a positive real function is also prf (Theorem 2.6.1) and therefore $m_1 + n_2$ and $n_1 + m_2$ are also Hurwitz. Furthermore, the values of $z_{11}$ and $z_{22}$ as specified in Eqs. 7.2.5 (a) and (b) can be combined with (c) to give

$$
\begin{array}{cc}
\textit{Case A} & \textit{Case B} \\
z_{12}z_{21} = \dfrac{m_1m_2 - n_1n_2}{n_2{}^2} & z_{12}z_{21} = \dfrac{n_1n_2 - m_1m_2}{m_2{}^2} \quad \textbf{7.2.6}
\end{array}
$$

At this point $z_{12}$ and $z_{21}$ do not have to be equal. However, since historically they were made equal, let them be equal. Later this restriction will be removed to allow gyrators. Thus

$$
\begin{array}{cc}
\textit{Case A} & \textit{Case B} \\
z_{12} = \dfrac{\sqrt{m_1m_2 - n_1n_2}}{n_2} & z_{12} = \dfrac{\sqrt{n_1n_2 - m_1m_2}}{m_2} \quad \textbf{7.2.7}
\end{array}
$$

Recalling the fact that $m/n$ of a Hurwitz polynomial can be synthesized by expanding it first in a partial fraction (Chapter 3), one might try to do the same for $z_{12}$ in Eqs. 7.2.7, since the corresponding poles are the same as those for $z_{11}$ and $z_{22}$ and therefore the residue condition of the previous chapter (Section 6.6) *might* be satisfied.

## Example 7.2.1

Synthesize $Z(s) = (s^2 + s + 1)/(4s^2 + s + 1)$ by means of the Darlington procedure.

### Solution

$$
\begin{array}{cc}
\textit{Case A} & \textit{Case B} \\[4pt]
z_{11} = \dfrac{m_1}{n_2} = \dfrac{s^2 + 1}{s} & z_{11} = \dfrac{n_1}{m_2} = \dfrac{s}{4s^2 + 1} \quad \text{(a)} \\[10pt]
z_{22} = \dfrac{m_2}{n_2} = \dfrac{4s^2 + 1}{s} & z_{22} = \dfrac{n_2}{m_2} = \dfrac{s}{4s^2 + 1} \quad \text{(b)} \\[10pt]
z_{12} = \dfrac{\sqrt{m_1m_2 - n_1n_2}}{n_2} = \dfrac{2s^2 + 1}{s} & z_{12} = \sqrt{-1}\,\dfrac{\sqrt{m_1m_2 - n_1n_2}}{m_2} \\[10pt]
& = j\,\dfrac{2s^2 + 1}{4s^2 + 1} \quad \text{(c)}
\end{array}
$$

**7.2.8**

*Case A* seems to be satisfactory as far as $z_{12}$ is concerned, whereas in *Case B* $z_{12}$ has an imaginary coefficient. Conceivably in the future some physical significance may be ascribed to a 2-port network whose $z_{12}$ has imaginary coefficients. Presently, however, such networks are ruled out. Consequently only *Case A* may be used for this particular example. (In no case are both *Case A* and *Case B* applicable since one of them will yield an imaginary $z_{12}$.) Thus we find for *Case A* the conditions

$$
\begin{aligned}
z_{11} &= \begin{bmatrix} s \\ 2s \\ 4s \end{bmatrix} + \begin{bmatrix} 1/s \\ 1/s \\ 1/s \end{bmatrix} \\
z_{12} &= \\
z_{22} &=
\end{aligned}
\qquad \textbf{7.2.9}
$$

A check of the residue condition, $(k_{11}k_{22} - k_{12}{}^2) \geq 0$, shows that it is satisfied with the equal sign for both the pole at infinity and at zero. The network in Fig. 7.1 is a physical realization of Eqs. 7.2.9.

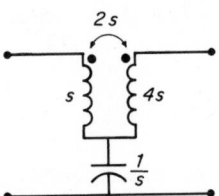

**Fig. 7.1. A realization of Eqs. 7.2.9**

Thus the realization of $Z(s) = (s^2 + s + 1)/(4s + s + 1)$ will be completed by terminating the 2-port network with a 1-ohm resistor. Observe that the transformer is represented by the first column on the right of Eq. 7.2.9, whereas the capacitor is represented by the second.

But what happens if $z_{12}$ comes out irrational? Similarly, the student might wonder if the residue condition is satisfied generally. In preparing to answer these questions, assume that $z_{12}$ is rational. Thus it can be expanded in a partial fraction, and it is now possible to show that here the residue condition is satisfied. This may be done as follows.

Let $j\omega_0$ be a zero of $n_2$. Then (for *Case A*)

$$
k_{11} = \left. \frac{m_1}{\dfrac{d}{ds} n_2} \right|_{s=j\omega_0} , \qquad
k_{22} = \left. \frac{m_2}{\dfrac{d}{ds} n_2} \right|_{s=j\omega_0}
\qquad \textbf{7.2.10}
$$

and

$$
k_{12} = \left. \frac{\sqrt{m_1 m_2 - n_1 n_2}}{\dfrac{d}{ds} n_2} \right|_{s=j\omega_0} = \left. \frac{\sqrt{m_1 m_2}}{\dfrac{d}{ds} n_2} \right|_{s=j\omega_0}
$$

as $n_2(j\omega_0) = 0$. Thus $k_{11}k_{22} - k_{12}^2$ may be evaluated from Eqs. 7.2.10, yielding

$$k_{11}k_{22} - k_{12}^2 = \frac{m_1 m_2}{\left(\dfrac{d}{ds} n_2\right)^2} - \frac{\sqrt{(m_1 m_2)^2}}{\left(\dfrac{d}{ds} n_2\right)^2}\Bigg|_{s=j\omega_0} = 0 \qquad \textbf{7.2.11}$$

It is therefore *satisfied with the equal sign*.

If $z_{12}$ is not rational, it can be made rational by selective multiplication of both the numerator and the denominator by surplus factors. A specific example will illustrate the procedure.

### Example 7.2.2

Synthesize $Z(s) = \dfrac{s+1}{s+4}$ by means of the Darlington procedure.

### Solution

Proceeding in the manner discussed above, we obtain

| *Case A* | *Case B* | |
|---|---|---|
| $z_{11} = \dfrac{1}{s}$ | $z_{11} = \dfrac{s}{4}$ | |
| $z_{22} = \dfrac{4}{s}$ | $z_{22} = \dfrac{s}{4}$ | **7.2.12** |
| $z_{12} = \dfrac{\sqrt{4-s^2}}{s}$ | $z_{12} = \dfrac{\sqrt{s^2-4}}{4}$ | |

Both *Case A* and *Case B* fail since $z_{12}$ is not rational. However, if both the numerator and denominator are first multiplied by $s+2$, $z_{12}$ comes out rational for *Case A*.

Thus we now consider

$$Z(s) = \frac{s+1}{s+4} = \frac{(s+1)(s+2)}{(s+4)(s+2)} = \frac{s^2+3s+2}{s^2+6s+8} \qquad \textbf{7.2.13}$$

and consequently (applying Eqs. 7.2.5 and 7.2.7) we get

$$z_{11} = \frac{s^2+2}{6s}, \qquad z_{22} = \frac{s^2+8}{6s}$$

and

$$z_{12} = \frac{\sqrt{m_1 m_2 - n_1 n_2}}{6s} = \frac{\sqrt{(s^2+2)(s^2+8) - 18s^2}}{6s} = \frac{s^2-4}{6s} \qquad \textbf{7.2.14}$$

The final network may be realized as in Fig. 7.2.

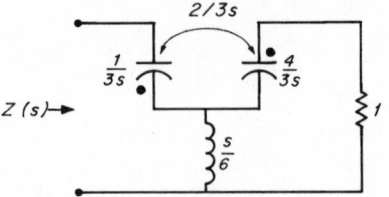

**Fig. 7.2. A Darlington realization of Z(s)**
$$= \frac{s+1}{s+4}$$

The perfect capacitive transformer may be replaced by an ideal transformer (of turn ratio of 2) loaded by $1/3s$ on its low turns side facing $Z(s)$ in Fig. 7.2. The same effect also will be obtained by loading the high turn side with $4/3s$. Corresponding equivalent networks are given in Fig. 7.3.

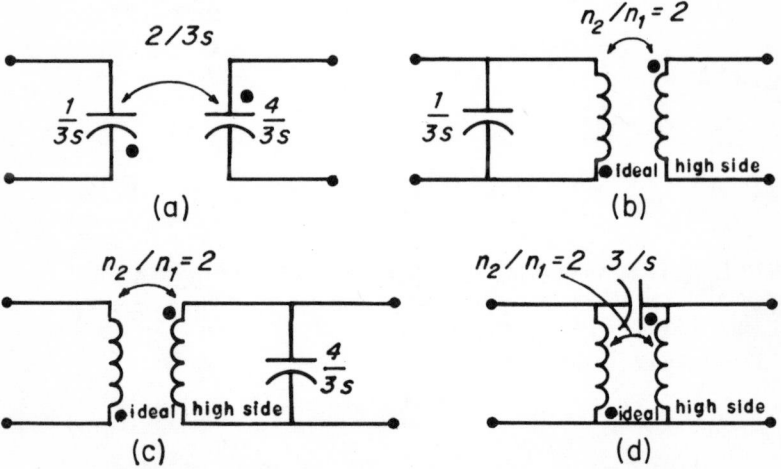

**Fig. 7.3. Equivalent circuits for the capacitive transformer of Fig. 7.2**

It was shown by means of Example 7.2.2 that, if a straightforward application of the Darlington procedure leads to a 2-port network with irrational $z_{12}$, it is still possible to find a suitable network if both the numerator and the denominator are multiplied by a predetermined auxiliary polynomial. The general method for obtaining this polynomial may be derived by examining closely the value of $z_{12}$.

$$\text{Case A} \qquad\qquad\qquad \text{Case B}$$

$$z_{12} = \frac{\sqrt{m_1 m_2 - n_1 n_2}}{n_2} \qquad\qquad z_{12} = \frac{\sqrt{n_1 n_2 - m_1 m_2}}{m_2} \qquad \begin{array}{l} 7.2.7 \\ 7.2.15 \end{array}$$

In this equation $z_{12}$ is dependent on the numerator of the even part of $Z(s)$ since

$$\text{Ev } Z(s) = \frac{m_1 m_2 - n_1 n_2}{m_2{}^2 - n_2{}^2} \qquad\qquad 7.2.16$$

Thus $z_{12}$ is rational only if the numerator of Ev $Z(s)$ [num. Ev $Z(s)$] is a perfect square. If this is not the case naturally, it can be induced artificially if both the numerator and the denominator of Ev $Z(s)$ are multiplied by a polynomial $m_0{}^2 - n_0{}^2$ which equals $m_1 m_2 - n_1 n_2$. Thus

$$\begin{aligned} \text{Ev } Z(s) &= \frac{m_1 m_2 - n_1 n_2}{m_2{}^2 - n_2{}^2} \times \frac{m_0{}^2 - n_0{}^2}{m_0{}^2 - n_0{}^2} \\ &= \frac{(m_1 m_2 - n_1 n_2)^2}{(m_2{}^2 - n_2{}^2)(m_0{}^2 - n_0{}^2)} \end{aligned} \qquad 7.2.17$$

On the other hand, this same result would be achieved if both the numerator and the denominator of $Z(s)$ were multiplied at the outset by $m_0 + n_0$, and if the even part of the resulting $Z(s)$ were computed in the usual manner. This is done as follows:

$$\begin{aligned} Z(s) &= \frac{m_1 + n_1}{m_2 + n_2} \times \frac{m_0 + n_0}{m_0 + n_0} \\ &= \frac{(m_1 m_0 + n_1 n_0) + (n_1 m_0 + m_1 n_0)}{(m_2 m_0 + n_2 n_0) + (n_2 m_0 + m_2 n_0)} \end{aligned} \qquad 7.2.18$$

and the corresponding even part is

$$\begin{aligned} \text{Ev } Z(s) &= \frac{(m_1 m_0 + n_1 n_0)(m_2 m_0 + n_2 n_0) - (n_1 m_0 + m_1 n_0)(n_2 m_0 + m_2 n_0)}{(m_2 m_0 + n_2 n_0)^2 - (n_2 m_0 + m_2 n_0)^2} \\ &= \frac{(m_1 m_2 - n_1 n_2)(m_0{}^2 - n_0{}^2)}{(m_2 + n_2)(m_0 + n_0)(m_2 - n_2)(m_0 - n_0)} \qquad\qquad 7.2.19 \\ &= \frac{(m_1 m_2 - n_1 n_2)(m_0{}^2 - n_0{}^2)}{(m_2{}^2 - n_2{}^2)(m_0{}^2 - n_0{}^2)} \end{aligned}$$

Therefore, to obtain a Darlington's realization for $Z(s)$, the equivalent expression of $Z(s)$ as given in Eq. 7.2.18 should be utilized. However, it still remains to evaluate $m_0 + n_0$ from the equation

$$m_0{}^2 - n_0{}^2 = m_1 m_2 - n_1 n_2 \qquad\qquad 7.2.20$$

bearing in mind that $m_0 + n_0$ must be a Hurwitz polynomial. Theoretically, the problem is straightforward. The polynomial $m_1m_2 - n_1n_2$ is positive on the $j$ axis [$Z(s)$ is prf]. This puts a restriction on the distribution of zeros in the complex plane. More precisely:

### Theorem 7.2.1

If $Z(s)$ is prf, the zeros of the numerator of its even part, $(m_1m_2 - n_1n_2)$ lie symmetrically about both the real and the imaginary axis, and all the $j$ axis zeros are of even multiplicity. (This property of the zeros is called quadrantal symmetry, Fig. 7.4.)

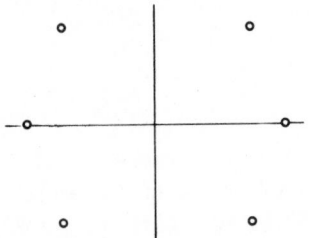

**Fig. 7.4. Quadrantal symmetry**

### Proof

Factoring $m_1m_2 - n_1n_2$ in the following manner, we get

$$m_1m_2 - n_1n_2 = (-s^2 + a_0^2)\prod_p[(s^2 + a_p^2)^2 - b_p^2s^2)] \geq 0 \text{ for } s = j\omega$$

where all the coefficients $a_p{}^2$ and $b_p{}^2$ are real and positive, since otherwise one of these factors will be negative for some $s = j\omega_p$. But this factorization already proves the theorem, since each of its factors possesses the required quadrantal symmetry. Now if $b_p = 0$, the factor $(s^2 + a_p^2)^2$ is of even multiplicity. That is, $j$ axis zeros are of even multiplicity as required. The special case where the factor $[(s^2 + a_p^2)^2 + b_p{}^2s^2]^2$ is present also leads to even multiplicity $j$ axis zeros. This completes the proof of the theorem.

Thus $m_0 + n_0$ may be obtained by selecting all the $l.h.s$ plane zeros (excluding all $j$ axis zeros) of $m_1m_2 - n_1n_2$. In practice, however, $m_0 + n_0$ is assumed with arbitrary coefficients which are determined later by performing the identity of Eq. 7.2.20.

**Example 7.2.3**

Determine $m_0 + n_0$ such that $m_0{}^2 - n_0{}^2 = s^4 + 2s^2 + 9$.

*Solution*

Suppose that $m_0 + n_0$ be written as

$$m_0 + n_0 = s^2 + as + b \qquad \textbf{7.2.21}$$

Then

$$
\begin{aligned}
m_0{}^2 - n_0{}^2 &= (s^2 + b)^2 - a^2 s^2 \\
&= s^4 + (2b - a^2)s^2 + b^2
\end{aligned}
\qquad \textbf{7.2.22}
$$

$a$ and $b$ are obtained from the identity

$$s^4 + (2b - a^2)s^2 + b^2 = s^4 + 2s^2 + 9 \qquad \textbf{7.2.23}$$

yielding $b^2 = 9$ or $b = 3$. Therefore $2b - a^2 = 2 = 6 - a^2$ or $a = 2$, and finally

$$m_0 + n_0 = s^2 + 2s + 3 \qquad \textbf{7.2.24}$$

The positive roots of $b^2 = 9$ and $a^2 = 4$ are chosen so that $m_0 + n_0$ must be Hurwitz.

**Example 7.2.4**

Find the Darlington network for $Z(s)$ given by

$$Z(s) = \frac{s^2 + 4s + 9}{s^2 + 2s + 1} \qquad \textbf{7.2.25}$$

*Solution*

First evaluate Ev $Z(s)$ to ascertain whether or not its numerator is a perfect square. This yields

$$
\begin{aligned}
\text{Ev } Z(s) &= \frac{(s^2 + 9)(s^2 + 1) - 8s^2}{(s^2 + 1)^2 - 4s^2} \\
&= \frac{s^4 + 2s^2 + 9}{s^4 - 2s^2 + 1}
\end{aligned}
\qquad \textbf{7.2.26}
$$

The numerator is not a perfect square, and an auxilliary polynomial $m_0 + n_0$ must be found. However the numerator here is the same as the polynomial of Eq. 7.2.23, and we therefore choose $m_0 + n_0 = s^2 + 2s + 3$ as was shown in Eq. 7.2.24. Then $Z(s)$ becomes

$$
\begin{aligned}
Z(s) &= \frac{(s^2 + 4s + 9)(s^2 + 2s + 3)}{(s^2 + 2s + 1)(s^2 + 2s + 3)} \\
&= \frac{s^4 + 6s^3 + 20s^2 + 30s + 27}{s^4 + 4s^3 + 8s^2 + 8s + 3}
\end{aligned}
\qquad \textbf{7.2.27}
$$

Now the required lossless 2-port network may be determined as follows: The appropriate functions are

$$z_{11} = \frac{m_1}{n_2} = \frac{s^4 + 20s^2 + 27}{4s(s^2 + 2)} = \left[\frac{s}{4}\right] + \left[\frac{27}{8s}\right] + \left[\frac{9s}{8(s^2 + 2)}\right]$$

$$z_{12} = \frac{\sqrt{m_1 m_2 - n_1 n_2}}{n_2} = \frac{s^4 + 2s^2 + 9}{4s(s^2 + 2)} = \left[\frac{s}{4}\right] + \left[\frac{9}{8s}\right] + \left[\frac{-9s}{8(s^2 + 2)}\right] \quad \textbf{7.2.28}$$

$$z_{22} = \frac{m_2}{n_2} = \frac{s^4 + 8s^2 + 3}{4s(s^2 + 2)} = \left[\frac{s}{4}\right] + \left[\frac{3}{8s}\right] + \left[\frac{9s}{8(s^2 + 2)}\right]$$

The realization of these yields the network shown in Fig. 7.5.

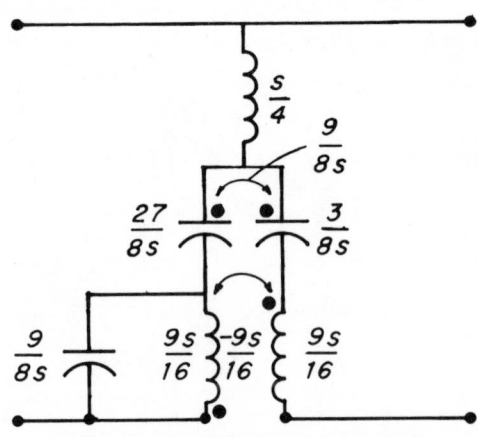

**Fig. 7.5. A realization of Eqs. 7.2.28**

The final network for $Z(s)$ of Eq. 7.2.25 is obtained by terminating the network in Fig. 7.5 with a 1-ohm resistance.

At this point it is worthwhile to note several possible ways (Fig. 7.6) of realizing the following four-terminal network impedance matrix:

$$[Z(s)] = \frac{s}{s^2 + \omega_0^2} \begin{bmatrix} \alpha & \sqrt{\alpha\beta} \\ \sqrt{\alpha\beta} & \beta \end{bmatrix} \quad \textbf{7.2.29}$$

The network of Fig. 7.6a was used in Fig. 7.5, whereas the network (c) will be used to get the standard Darlington $D$ section in Chapter 8, Section 8.6, Fig. 8.8.

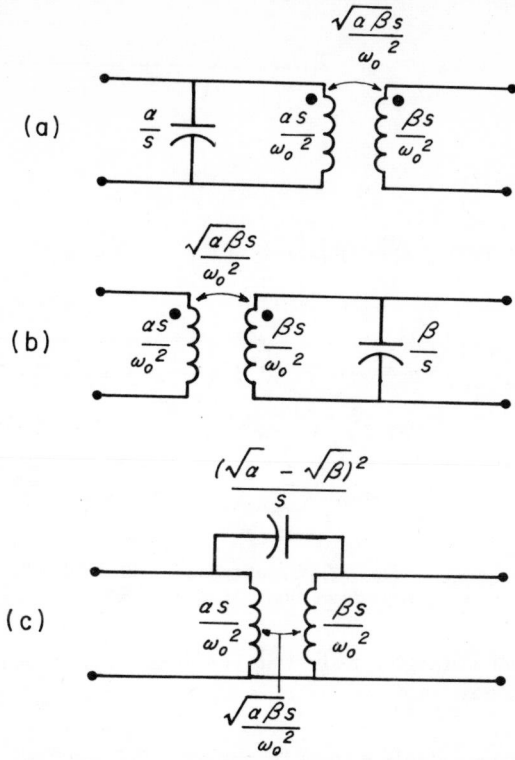

**Fig. 7.6.** *Equivalent realizations of $Z(s)$ in Eq. 7.2.29*

## EQUIVALENT DARLINGTON NETWORKS 7.3

The ability to multiply both the numerator and the denominator by an auxilliary polynomial to obtain a rational $z_{12}$ in the Darlington procedure may be used also to produce equivalent networks. This may be done by first obtaining the appropriate polynomial for a rational $z_{12}$ and then multiplying by still another polynomial which is already a perfect square. An example illustrates the procedure.

### Example 7.3.1

Obtain the Darlington network for $Z(s) = 1$.

### Solution

$Z(s)$ can be expressed in the following form:

$$Z(s) = \frac{1}{1} = \frac{1}{1} \times \frac{(s+k)^2}{(s+k)^2} = \frac{s^2 + 2sk + k^2}{s^2 + 2sk + k^2}$$

**7.3.1**

The factor $m_1 m_2 - n_1 n_2 = (s^2 + k^2)^2 - 4 s^2 k^2 = (s^2 - k^2)^2$. Thus

$$z_{11} = z_{22} = \frac{s^2 + k^2}{2ks} \qquad \textbf{7.3.2a}$$

and

$$z_{12} = \pm \frac{s^2 - k^2}{2ks} \qquad \textbf{7.3.2b}$$

But these are the impedance functions of the lattice in Fig. 7.7.

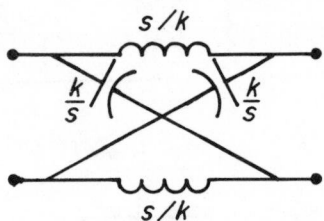

**Fig. 7.7. A realization for the impedance functions of Eq. 7.3.2**

Again the final Darlington realization is obtained by terminating Fig. 7.7 with a 1-ohm resistance.

Ordinarily one would refrain from excessive use of surplus factors, as they introduce an increase in the total number of elements. For this reason it is advisable to factor $m_1 m_2 - n_1 n_2$ first and remove all the square terms. Then the surplus factor $m_0 + n_0$ will be equated with the remainder. However, economy in the number of elements is not necessarily the sole factor in synthesis. For example, in the synthesis of 2-port networks, one realization of a particular $z_{11}$ may not accommodate the required $z_{12}$.

## 7.4. SCALING CONSTANTS

Darlington's procedure is not only sensitive to the presence of surplus factors but also to the impedance level. A proper manipulation of a constant multiplier could change the turn ratio of all the transformers. This fact may be utilized to produce a particular transformer with a 1:1 turn ratio. Consequently this transformer might be removed from the network without otherwise altering its configuration.

## Example 7.4.1

Find a Darlington network for $Z(s)$ given by

$$Z(s) = \frac{2s + 1}{s + 2} \qquad \textbf{7.4.1}$$

### Solution

Evaluate Ev $Z(s)$ to find

$$\text{Ev } Z(s) = \frac{2(1 - s^2)}{4 - s^2} \qquad \textbf{7.4.2}$$

The necessary surplus factor is $s + 1$. Multiplying numerator and denominator by this factor we get

$$\alpha Z(s) = \frac{\alpha(2s + 1)}{(s + 2)} \frac{(s + 1)}{(s + 1)} = \frac{\alpha(2s^2 + 3s + 1)}{s^2 + 3s + 2} \qquad \textbf{7.4.3}$$

Also both sides of Eq. 7.4.3 were multiplied by the constant $\alpha$ for the purpose of scaling.

Direct application of the Darlington synthesis procedure yields

$$z_{11} = \frac{m_1}{n_2} = \frac{\alpha(2s^2 + 1)}{3s} \qquad \textbf{7.4.4a}$$

$$z_{12} = \frac{\sqrt{m_1 m_2 - n_1 n_2}}{3s} = \frac{\sqrt{\alpha}\sqrt{(2s^2 + 1)(s^2 + 2) - 9s^2}}{3s} \qquad \textbf{7.4.4b}$$

$$= \sqrt{2\alpha}\frac{1 - s^2}{3s}$$

and

$$z_{22} = \frac{m_2}{n_2} = \frac{s^2 + 2}{3s} \qquad \textbf{7.4.4c}$$

These can be rewritten as

$$
\begin{aligned}
z_{11} &= \left[ \frac{\alpha}{3s} \right] + \left[ \frac{2\alpha}{3} s \right] \\
z_{12} &= \left[ \frac{\sqrt{2\alpha}}{3s} \right] + \left[ \frac{-\sqrt{2\alpha}}{3} s \right] \\
z_{22} &= \left[ \frac{2}{3s} \right] + \left[ \frac{1}{3} s \right]
\end{aligned}
\qquad \textbf{7.4.5}
$$

Observe that the transformer associated with the first column can become ineffective if $\alpha = 2$ (the turn ratio becomes 1:1). Choosing $\alpha = 2$, we get the possible realization in Fig. 7.8.

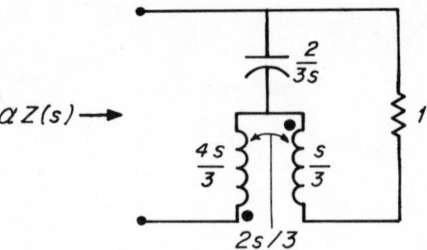

**Fig. 7.8. A Darlington realization of Eq. 7.4.3**

To obtain a realization for $Z(s)$ of Eq. 7.4.1 all the impedances must be scaled down by the factor $\alpha$ (Fig. 7.9).

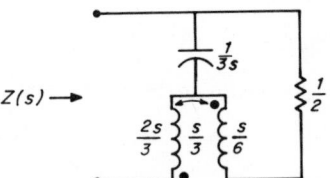

**Fig. 7.9. A Darlington realization
of Eq. 7.4.1**

Observe that one final effect of scaling the function is that the terminal impedance is no longer 1 ohm.

## 7.5. NONRECIPROCAL DARLINGTON SYNTHESIS*†

One of the characteristics of the Darlington synthesis is the use of surplus factors in order to make $z_{12}$ a rational function of $s$. The use of surplus factors may be avoided if gyrators are used, namely if the associated lossless 2-port network contains nonreciprocal elements. To construct the impedance matrix of the required 2-port network, remember that $m_1 m_2 - n_1 n_2$ can be written in terms of the polynomial $m_0{}^2 - n_0{}^2$ (Section 7.2), where $m_0 + n_0$ is the surplus factor in the standard Darlington synthesis. Equations 7.2.5 and 7.2.6 can now be written as follows:

---

* Hazony, D., "Two extensions of the Darlington synthesis procedure." *IRE Trans. on Circuit Theory*, Vol. CT-9, pp. 284–288, Sept., 1961.
† By nonreciprocity we mean that $z_{ij} \neq z_{ji}$.

$$\textit{Case A}$$

$$z_{11} = \frac{m_1}{n_2}$$

$$z_{22} = \frac{m_2}{n_2}$$

$$z_{12}z_{21} = \frac{m_1 m_2 - n_1 n_2}{n_2{}^2}$$

$$= \frac{m_0{}^2 - n_0{}^2}{n_2{}^2}$$

$$= \frac{(m_0 + n_0)(m_0 - n_0)}{n_2 \qquad n_2}$$

$$\textit{Case B}$$

$$z_{11} = \frac{n_1}{m_2} \qquad \text{(a)}$$

$$z_{22} = \frac{n_2}{m_2} \qquad \text{(b)}$$

$$z_{12}z_{21} = \frac{n_1 n_2 - m_1 m_2}{m_2{}^2}$$

$$= \frac{n_0{}^2 - m_0{}^2}{m_2{}^2}$$

$$= \frac{(n_0 + m_0)(n_0 - m_0)}{m_2 \qquad m_2}$$

**7.2.5**
**7.5.1**

**7.2.6**
**7.5.2**

which permit the choice

$$\textit{Case A}$$

$$z_{12} = \frac{m_0 + n_0}{n_2}$$

$$z_{21} = \frac{m_0 - n_0}{n_2}$$

$$\textit{Case B}$$

$$z_{12} = \frac{n_0 + m_0}{m_2}$$

$$z_{21} = \frac{n_0 - m_0}{m_2}$$

**7.5.3a**

**7.5.3b**

## Example 7.5.1

Synthesize $Z(s) = \dfrac{s + a}{s + b}$ by the nonreciprocal Darlington procedure.

## Solution

Equations 7.5.1 and 7.5.3 give

$$\textit{Case A} \qquad\qquad\qquad \textit{Case B}$$

$$z_{11} =$$

$$z_{22} =$$

$$z_{12} = \frac{s + \sqrt{ab}}{s}$$

$$z_{21} = \frac{-s + \sqrt{ab}}{s}$$

Case A:

$$
\begin{bmatrix} \dfrac{a}{s} \\[2mm] \dfrac{b}{s} \\[2mm] \dfrac{\sqrt{ab}}{s} \\[2mm] \dfrac{\sqrt{ab}}{s} \end{bmatrix}
+
\begin{bmatrix} \\ \\ 1 \\ -1 \end{bmatrix}
$$

Case B:

$$z_{12} = \frac{s + \sqrt{ab}}{b} = \begin{bmatrix} \dfrac{s}{b} \\[2mm] \dfrac{s}{b} \\[2mm] \dfrac{s}{b} \\[2mm] \dfrac{s}{b} \end{bmatrix} + \begin{bmatrix} \\ \\ \sqrt{\dfrac{a}{b}} \\ -\sqrt{\dfrac{a}{b}} \end{bmatrix}$$

$$z_{21} = \frac{s - \sqrt{ab}}{b}$$

**7.5.4**

The first column of *Case A* is realizable in terms of a capacitive transformer. The second column of *Case A* can be realized in terms of a series gyrator. The corresponding network is shown in Fig. 7.10a.

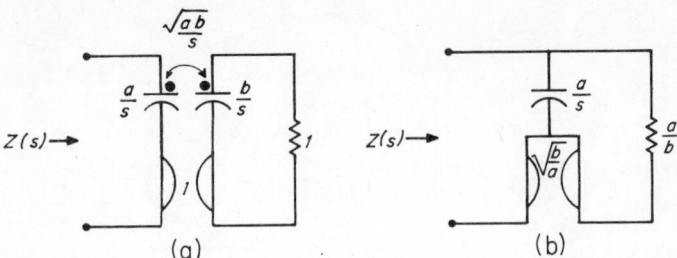

**Fig. 7.10.** Realizations of $Z(s) = \dfrac{s + a}{s + b}$ by means of nonreciprocal Darlington synthesis

In Fig. 7.10b the capacitive transformer is eliminated by first scaling $Z(s)$ by the constant $\dfrac{b}{a}$ (Section 7.4). Thus, choosing

$$\frac{bZ(s)}{a} = \frac{\dfrac{sb}{a} + b}{s + b} \qquad\qquad \textbf{7.5.5}$$

and applying Eqs. 7.5.1 and 7.5.3, we get a network which requires no transformers. The original function, $Z(s)$, (Fig. 7.10b) is obtained by multiplying each impedance by $a/b$.

The first column of *Case B* in Eqs. 7.5.4 turns out to be simple to identify as an inductor, whereas the second is again a gyrator. The final network is given in Fig. 7.11.

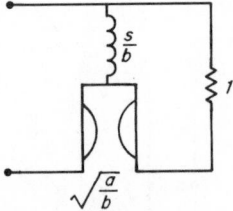

**Fig. 7.11.** An equivalent network to Fig. 7.10

Observe that if $a = b$, the networks of Figs. 7.10 and 7.11 represent constant resistant networks.

### Example 7.5.2

Synthesize $Z(s) = (1 + as + bs^2)/(1 + cs + ds^2)$ by the nonreciprocal Darlington procedure.

*Solution*

Applying Eqs. 7.5.1 and 7.5.3, we get

$$
\begin{array}{cc}
\textit{Case A} & \textit{Case B}
\end{array}
$$

$$
z_{11} = \left[\dfrac{1}{cs}\right] + \left[\dfrac{bs}{c}\right]
$$

$$
z_{22} = \left[\dfrac{1}{cs}\right] \quad \left[\dfrac{ds}{c}\right]
$$

$$
z_{12} = \left[\dfrac{1}{cs}\right] \quad \left[\dfrac{\sqrt{bd}}{c}s\right] + \left[\dfrac{e}{c}\right]
$$

$$
z_{21} = \left[\dfrac{1}{cs}\right] \quad \left[\dfrac{\sqrt{bd}}{c}s\right] + \left[-\dfrac{e}{c}\right]
$$

$$
z_{11}:\ \left[\dfrac{as}{1+ds^2}\right]
$$

$$
z_{22}:\ \left[\dfrac{cs}{1+ds^2}\right]
$$

$$
z_{12}:\ \left[\dfrac{es}{1+ds^2} + \dfrac{1-\sqrt{\dfrac{b}{d}}}{1+ds^2}\right] + \left[\sqrt{\dfrac{b}{d}}\right]
$$

$$
z_{21}:\ \left[\dfrac{es}{1+ds^2} - \dfrac{1-\sqrt{\dfrac{b}{d}}}{1+ds^2}\right] + \left[-\sqrt{\dfrac{b}{d}}\right]
$$

$$
7.5.6
$$

where $e^2 = ac - (\sqrt{b} - \sqrt{d})^2$, and it is positive by the requirements of realizability.

The first two columns of *Case A* in Eqs. 7.5.6 satisfy the residue condition and, therefore, may be realized by reciprocal networks. The third column represents a gyrator. The final network is given in Fig. 7.12.

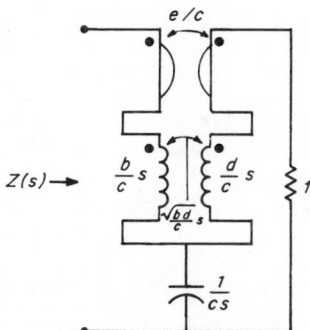

**Fig. 7.12. A nonreciprocal Darlington realization of**
$$
Z(s) = \frac{1 + as + bs^2}{1 + cs + ds^2}
$$

The first column of *Case B* satisfies the extended residue condition (Eq. 6.6.9), and therefore it can be realized by means of a gyrator and three capacitors as was shown in Example 6.6.1. The final network is shown in Fig. 7.13, where $\delta^2$ is an arbitrary positive constant due to prior scaling. Note that if $\delta$ is chosen as either $c/e$ or $e/a$, one of the series capacitors becomes a short circuit, whereas if it is made equal to $\sqrt{c/a}$, the two capacitors become equal.

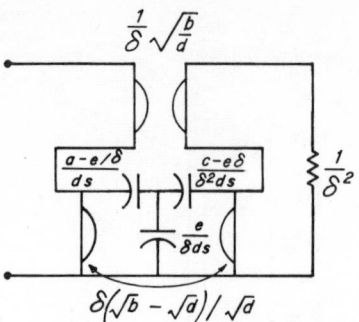

**Fig. 7.13. An equivalent network
to Fig. 7.12**

If $e$ is chosen negative (realizability only requires that $e^2 > 0$), or if $\delta$ is chosen so that one of the series capacitors is negative (that is, $\delta > c/e$ or $\delta < e/a$), the $T$ network will have to be replaced by the equivalent capacitive transformer.

*Case B* demonstrates the difficulties encountered in the general nonreciprocal Darlington synthesis. Note that in the neighborhood of a $j$ axis pole, the 2-port impedance function will be of the form

$$z_{11} = \frac{k_{11}}{s + j\omega_0}, \quad z_{22} = \frac{k_{22}}{s + j\omega_0} \qquad \text{7.5.7a}$$

and

$$z_{12} = \frac{k_{12}}{s + j\omega_0}, \quad z_{21} = \frac{k_{21}}{s + j\omega_0} \qquad \text{7.5.7b}$$

where the $k$'s are given by (note that these correspond to *Case B* in Eqs. 7.5.1 to 7.5.3)

$$k_{11} = \left.\frac{n_1}{\dfrac{d}{ds}\, m_2}\right|_{s+j\omega_0=0}$$

$$k_{22} = \left.\frac{n_2}{\dfrac{d}{ds}\, m_2}\right|_{s+j\omega_0=0} \qquad \text{7.5.8}$$

$$\operatorname{Re} k_{12} = \left.\frac{n_0}{\dfrac{d}{ds}\, m_2}\right|_{s+j\omega_0=0} = \operatorname{Re} k_{21}$$

$$j \operatorname{Im} k_{12} = \left.\frac{m_0}{\dfrac{d}{ds}\, m_2}\right|_{s+j\omega_0=0} = -j \operatorname{Im} k_{21}$$

Furthermore, since $j\omega_0$ is a zero of $m_2$, it is clear from Eq. 7.2.20 that

$$m_1(j\omega_0)[m_2(j\omega_0) = 0] - n_1(j\omega)n_2(j\omega_0) = m_0^2(j\omega_0) - n_0^2(j\omega_0) \qquad \textbf{7.5.9}$$

from which follows

$$k_{11}k_{22} - k_{12}k_{21} = 0 \qquad \textbf{7.5.10}$$

Thus this procedure obeys the extended residue condition (Eq. 6.6.7) with the equal sign. Therefore, corresponding to each pole, a 2-port network (of the form of Fig. 6.13) is added in series-series connection. One such network is the lower part of the lossless network of Fig. 7.13. The gyrator on top of that figure is due to a constant nonreciprocal term in $z_{12}$ and $z_{21}$.

## AN EVEN-PART SPLIT TO AVOID SURPLUS FACTORS 7.6

It has been shown that it is possible to devise a Darlington type of synthesis without recourse to surplus factors if gyrators are employed. Furthermore, this synthesis is capable of utilizing both *Case A* and *Case B* networks. It is also possible to avoid using surplus factors if the requirement of cascade synthesis is relaxed. Thus, recognition of the fact that $m_1m_2 - n_1n_2 = m_0^2 - n_0^2$ is the numerator of Ev $Z(s)$, permits splitting the even part as follows:

$$\text{Ev } Z(s) = \frac{m_0^2}{m_2^2 - n_2^2} + \frac{-n_0^2}{m_2^2 - n_2^2} \qquad \textbf{7.6.1}$$

$$= \text{Ev } Z_1(s) + \text{Ev } Z_2(s)$$

Each of the terms on the right of Eq. 7.6.1 has a perfect square numerator which means that the corresponding $z_{12}$ for each is rational. Furthermore, $z_{22}$ is easily computed for each term, since only $m_2$ and $n_2$ are necessary. Thus for the first term [Ev $Z_1(s)$], $z_{22} = m_2/n_2$ and $z_{12} = m_0/n_2$, and since the residue condition is satisfied with the equal sign, $z_{11}$ may be constructed from $z_{12}$ and $z_{22}$. Similarly, for the second term [Ev $Z_2(s)$], $z_{22} = n_2/m_2$, $z_{12} = n_0/m_2$, and $z_{11}$ again is reconstructed from $z_{22}$ and $z_{12}$.

Applying these techniques to example 7.5.2, we get

$$\text{Ev } Z(s) = \frac{(1 + \sqrt{bd}\, s^2)^2}{(1 + ds^2)^2 - c^2s^2} + \frac{e^2}{c^2}\frac{-(cs)^2}{(1 + ds^2)^2 - c^2s^2} \qquad \textbf{7.6.2}$$

Thus for the first term on the right side of Eq. 7.6.2

$$z_{22} = \frac{1 + ds^2}{cs} \qquad \textbf{7.6.3a}$$

$$z_{12} = \frac{1 + \sqrt{bd}\, s^2}{cs} \qquad \textbf{7.6.3b}$$

and therefore (by the residue condition)

$$z_{11} = \frac{1 + bs^2}{cs} \qquad \text{7.6.3c}$$

Similarly, for the second term (scaled by $e^2/c^2$)

$$z_{22} = \frac{cs}{1 + ds^2} = z_{12} = z_{22} \qquad \text{7.6.4}$$

The network in Fig. 7.14 results. Note that in addition to the loss of the cascade nature of the synthesis, two resistors are required instead of one. On the other hand, two transformers would have been required for the standard Darlington synthesis.

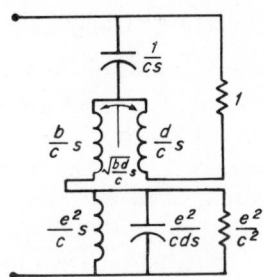

**Fig. 7.14. An equivalent network to Fig. 7.12**

## PROBLEMS

7.1. Realize by the Darlington synthesis

(a). $\dfrac{s^2 + s + 9}{s^2 + s + 4}$

(b). $\dfrac{s^2 + 2s + 9}{s^2 + 2s + 1}$

(c). $\dfrac{2s^3 + 2s^2 + 20s + 9}{s^3 + 4s^2 + 5s + 8}$

(d). $\dfrac{s^3 + 3s^2 + s + 1}{s^3 + s^2 + 3s + 1}$

7.2. Use a reciprocal Darlington to realize the following:

$$\frac{s^2 + s + 2}{s^2 + s + 1}, \qquad \frac{s^2 + 2s + 3}{s^2 + 2s + 1}$$

7.3. Solve the problems of (2) by splitting the even part (Section 7.6).

7.4. Solve the problems of (2) by a nonreciprocal Darlington synthesis.

## FURTHER READING

7.1. Balabanian, N., "Network Synthesis," Prentice Hall, Inc., Englewood Cliffs, N. J., 1958, Chapter 6.

7.2. Guillemin, E. A., "Synthesis of Passive Networks," John Wiley & Sons, New York, 1957, Chapter 9.

7.3. Storer, J. E., "Passive Network Synthesis," McGraw-Hill Book Co., Inc., New York, 1957, Chapter 8.

7.4. Tuttle, D. F., Jr., "Network Synthesis," John Wiley & Sons, New York, 1958, Chapter 9.

7.5. Van Valkenburg, M. E., "Introduction to Modern Network Synthesis,' John Wiley & Sons, New York, 1960, Chapter 14.

# CHAPTER 8 | *Cascade 1-Port Synthesis**

## 8.1. INTRODUCTION

The Darlington procedure makes it possible to reduce the degree of an impedance function to zero. The Bott-Duffin synthesis does not reduce the degree at all, except that $Z(s)$ is tailored and $k$ chosen so that the final impedance has a zero or a pole on the $j$ axis. This chapter will discuss the problem of degree reduction in general. The starting point will be the Bott-Duffin synthesis. The cascade form of the synthesis (Example 6.3.1) will be utilized for its geometrical simplicity. Accordingly, the Bott-Duffin network may be expressed in the form of Fig. 8.1.

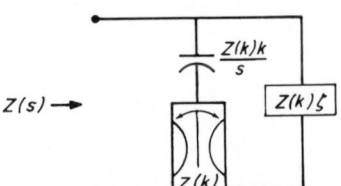

**Fig. 8.1. An equivalent for the Bott-Duffin network**

In this network the termination $\zeta$ is given by

$$\zeta = \frac{kZ(s) - sZ(k)}{kZ(k) - sZ(s)} \qquad \text{8.1.1}$$

The fact that $\zeta$ is prf if $Z(s)$ is prf was shown by Richards. Henceforth the statement of Eq. 8.1.1 will be called Richards' theorem. Note that both the numerator and the denominator reduce to zero at the real axis point $s = k$. This means that both the numerator

---

* Hazony, D., "Zero Cancellation Synthesis Using Impedance Operators," *IRE Trans. on Circuit Theory*, Vol. CT–8, pp. 114–120, June, 1961.

and the denominator share the factor $s - k$. If there is another common factor at $s = k_0$ (which means that the effective degree is smaller by 1), then again both the numerator and the denominator are zero at this point. Therefore

$$kZ(k_0) - k_0 Z(k) = 0$$

and

$$kZ(k) - k_0 Z(k_0) = 0$$

8.1.2

These equations are solved for $k_0$ and $Z(k_0)$ in terms of $k$ and $Z(k)$ yielding

$$k_0 = \pm k$$

$$Z(k_0) = \pm Z(k)$$

8.1.3

These results may be interpreted to say that the only way $\zeta$ can have a numerator and denominator common factor, in addition to $s - k$, is that $k_0 = -k$ and $Z(k_0) = -Z(k)$. This is possible if $k$ is chosen such that

$$k = -k_0$$

and

$$Z(k_0) + Z(-k_0) = 2 \operatorname{Ev} Z(k_0) = 0$$

8.1.4

Thus Richards' theorem (Eq. 8.1.1) could be used to reduce $Z(s)$ if Ev $Z(k)$ is zero for some $k = -k_0 > 0$. This fact was also shown by Richards.

## Example 8.1.1

Synthesize $Z(s) = \dfrac{s^3 + 2s^2 + s + 1}{s^3 + s^2 + 2s + 1}$ in terms of $\zeta$ of reduced degree.

## Solution

Computing Ev $Z(s)$, we get

$$\operatorname{Ev} Z(s) = \frac{(2s^2 + 1)(s^2 + 1) - s^2(s^2 + 1)(s^2 + 2)}{(s^2 + 1)^2 - s^2(s^2 + 2)^2}$$

$$= \frac{(1 + s^2)^2(1 - s^2)}{(s^2 + 1)^2 - s^2(s^2 + 2)^2}$$

8.1.5a

Consequently

$$\operatorname{Ev} Z(k) = \operatorname{Ev} Z(1) = 0$$

8.1.5b

showing that it is possible to select $k = 1$. This will make $Z(k)$ also unity, and $\zeta$ becomes

$$\zeta = \frac{Z(s) - s}{1 - sZ(s)} = \frac{(s^2 + 1)(1 - s^2)}{(s^2 + s + 1)(1 - s^2)}$$

8.1.6

The final network is given in Fig. 8.2.

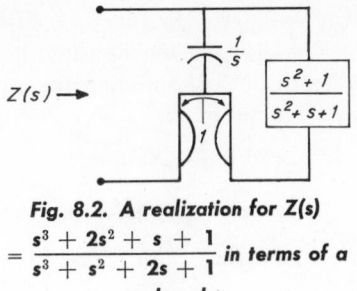

**Fig. 8.2.** A realization for Z(s)

$$= \frac{s^3 + 2s^2 + s + 1}{s^3 + s^2 + 2s + 1} \text{ in terms of a}$$

**reduced** $\zeta$

At this point some other questions may arise. Is this sort of reduction always possible? What happens if $k_0$ cannot be real? Fortunately, it is always possible to reduce $Z(s)$ in this manner. However, Richards' theorem has to be modified to handle two arbitrary constants which may be complex conjugates.

## 8.2. EXTENSION OF RICHARDS' THEOREM

In an attempt to extend Richards' theorem, one may apply the theorem twice as follows.

The first application yields $Z_1(s)$ given by

$$Z_1(s) = \frac{aZ(s) - sZ(a)}{aZ(a) - sZ(s)} \qquad \textbf{8.2.1}$$

Whereas an additional application of Richards' theorem on $Z_1(s)$ yields $\zeta(s)$ defined as

$$\zeta(s) = Z(a)Z_1(b) \cdot \frac{bZ_1(s) - sZ_1(b)}{bZ_1(b) - sZ_1(s)} \qquad \textbf{8.2.2}$$

$\zeta(s)$ can be expressed in terms of $Z(s)$ if $Z_1(s)$ of Eq. 8.2.1 is substituted in Eq. 8.2.2. Thus

$$\zeta(s) = \frac{\left[1 + s^2 \dfrac{aZ(b) - bZ(a)}{ab(aZ(a) - bZ(b))}\right] Z(s) - s \left[\dfrac{Z(a)Z(b)}{ab} \dfrac{a^2 - b^2}{aZ(a) - bZ(b)}\right]}{\left[1 + s^2 \dfrac{aZ(a) - bZ(b)}{ab(aZ(b) - bZ(a))}\right] - sZ(s)\left[\dfrac{a^2 - b^2}{aZ(b) - bZ(a)}\right]\dfrac{1}{ab}}$$

**8.2.3**

This is the desired extension. $\zeta(s)$ is a function of two arbitrary constants, $a$ and $b$, which can be utilized to reduce the degree of $\zeta(s)$ by 2 by forcing the numerator and the denominator to have the common factor $[s^2 + (a + b)s + ab]$. This will be done by selecting $a$ and $b$ as roots of Ev $Z(s) = 0$ (Eq. 8.1.4). At this point, however, two tasks present themselves: (I). to ascertain that $Z(s)$ can be physically realized in terms of $\zeta(s)$, and (II). to show that $\zeta(s)$ is prf. The first assignment (I) will be attained by extending the nonreciprocal Darlington procedure to include arbitrary terminations, which is accomplished in the following section. On the other hand, in Section 8.4, assignment (II) is discussed.

## A DARLINGTON PROCEDURE WITH ARBITRARY TERMINATIONS 8.3

Let $\zeta$ of Eq. 8.2.3 be expressed as

$$\zeta = \frac{m_2 Z(s) - n_1}{m_1 - n_2 Z(s)} \qquad \text{8.3.1}$$

where

$$m_1 = 1 + s^2 \frac{aZ(a) - bZ(b)}{ab[aZ(b) - bZ(a)]}$$

$$m_2 = 1 + s^2 \frac{aZ(b) - bZ(a)}{ab[aZ(a) - bZ(b)]}$$

$$n_1 = s \frac{(a^2 - b^2)Z(a)Z(b)}{ab[aZ(a) - bZ(b)]} \qquad \text{8.3.2}$$

$$n_2 = s \frac{a^2 - b^2}{ab[aZ(b) - bZ(a)]}$$

$a$ and $b$ are positive or complex conjugates with a positive real part (Re $a \neq 0$). This presentation permits solving Eq. 8.3.1 for $Z(s)$ to give

$$Z(s) = \frac{m_1 \zeta + n_1}{m_2 + n_2 \zeta} \qquad \text{8.3.3}$$

This form of $Z(s)$ can now be identified with the input impedance of a four-terminal network with $\zeta$ termination:

$$Z_{in}(s) = \frac{z_{11} \zeta + z_{11} z_{22} - z_{12} z_{21}}{\zeta + z_{22}} \qquad \begin{matrix} \text{6.1.6} \\ \text{8.3.4} \end{matrix}$$

Proceeding along the lines of the general derivation of the Darlington synthesis, one may select (for *Case A*)

$$z_{11} = \frac{m_1}{n_2} \qquad \text{8.3.5a}$$

$$z_{22} = \frac{m_2}{n_2} \qquad \text{8.3.5b}$$

$$z_{12} z_{21} = \frac{m_1 m_2 - n_1 n_2}{n_2{}^2} \qquad \text{8.3.5c}$$

and, therefore, (like in Eqs. 7.5.3 $m_0^2 - n_0^2 = m_1 m_2 - n_1 n_2$)

$$z_{12} = \frac{m_0 + n_0}{n_2} \text{ and } z_{21} = \frac{m_0 - n_0}{n_2} \qquad \textbf{8.3.5d}$$

Continuing now by substituting $m_1$, $m_2$, $n_1$, and $n_2$ with their respective values as given in Eqs. 8.3.2 and finding $m_0$ and $n_0$ (this involves a great deal of algebra), we get

$$
\begin{aligned}
z_{11} &= \left[ \frac{ab[bZ(a) - aZ(b)]}{s(b^2 - a^2)} \right] + \left[ s\frac{bZ(b) - aZ(a)}{b^2 - a^2} \right. \\
z_{12} &= \left[ \frac{ab[bZ(a) - aZ(b)]}{s(b^2 - a^2)} \right] + \left[ s\frac{bZ(a) - aZ(b)}{b^2 - a^2} \right. \quad + \left[ \frac{bZ(a) - aZ(b)}{b - a} \right. \\
z_{21} &= \left[ \frac{ab[bZ(a) - aZ(b)]}{s(b^2 - a^2)} \right] + \left[ s\frac{bZ(a) - aZ(b)}{b^2 - a^2} \right. \quad - \left[ \frac{bZ(a) - aZ(b)}{b - a} \right. \\
z_{22} &= \left[ \frac{ab[bZ(a) - aZ(b)]}{s(b^2 - a^2)} \right] + \left[ s\frac{[bZ(a) - aZ(b)]^2}{(b^2 - a^2)[bZ(b) - aZ(a)]} \right]
\end{aligned}
$$

**8.3.6**

The first column on the right represents a capacitor, the second may be realized by means of a perfect transformer, whereas the last column may be represented by means of a gyrator. The final network may be as shown in Fig. 8.3.

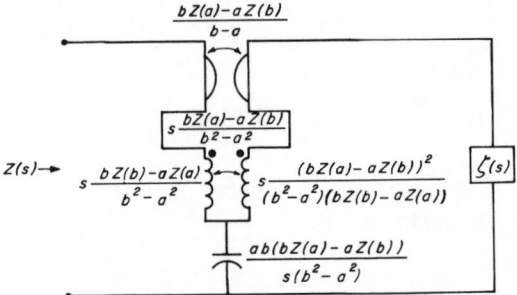

**Fig. 8.3. A realization of Z(s) in terms of $\zeta$ of Eq. 8.3.1**

## Example 8.3.1

Synthesize $Z(s) = \dfrac{s^3 + 12s^2 + 6s + 2}{s^3 + s^2 + 5s + 2}$ by means of the network of Fig. 8.3 for the special case $a = \bar{b} = 1 + j$. [These are roots of Ev $Z(s) = 0$].

## Solution

To obtain values for each of the circuit elements requires evaluation of terms of the type $Z(a)$, $aZ(a) - bZ(b)$, etc. These are as follows (for $a = \bar{b} = 1 + j$):

$$Z(a) = \frac{6 + 32j}{5 + 9j}, \quad Z(b) = \frac{6 - 32j}{5 - 9j}, \quad Z(a)Z(b) = 10$$

$$bZ(b) - aZ(a) = -8j$$

$$bZ(a) - aZ(b) = -4j$$

From Eqs. 8.3.1 and 8.3.2

$$\zeta = \frac{\left(1 + \dfrac{s^2}{4}\right) Z(s) - \dfrac{5s}{2}}{(1 + s^2) - \dfrac{sZ(s)}{2}} = \frac{s + 2}{4s + 2} \qquad \textbf{8.3.7}$$

Substituting these values in Fig. 8.3, we get Fig. 8.4.

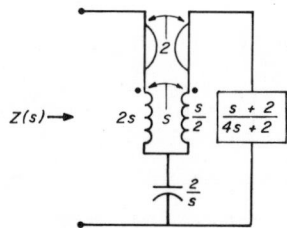

**Fig. 8.4. A realization for Z(s)**
$$= \frac{s^3 + 12s^2 + 6s + 2}{s^3 + s^2 + 5s + 2}$$

Observe that $\zeta$ in Eq. 8.3.7 is reduced in degree. This is no accident as $a$ and $b$ are roots of Ev $Z(s) = 0$. This fact may be predicted from the arguments leading to Eq. 8.1.4. This also will be discussed in Section 8.4 (Note 1).

### POSITIVE REALNESS OF $V$ AND $\zeta^*$   8.4

In this section we shall show that all the members of Fig. 8.3 are realizable.

---

* Case Project Staff, Scientific Rep. #23 AF 19(604)-3887, prepared for the USAF Cambridge Research Center, Bedford, Massachusetts, 1 Jan, 1961, to March, 1961.

**Theorem 8.4.1**

If $Z(s)$ is an $RLC$ driving point impedance function (prf), then $\zeta(s)$ and $V(s)$ as defined below are prf:

$$\zeta(s) = \frac{m_2 Z(s) - n_1}{m_1 - n_2 Z(s)} \qquad \text{8.4.1a}$$

$$V(s) = \frac{m_1 + n_1}{m_2 + n_2} \qquad \text{8.4.1b}$$

where

$$m_1 = 1 + s^2 \frac{aZ(a) - bZ(b)}{ab\big(aZ(b) - bZ(a)\big)}$$

$$m_2 = 1 + s^2 \frac{aZ(b) - bZ(a)}{ab\big(aZ(a) - bZ(b)\big)}$$

$$n_1 = s \frac{(a^2 - b^2)Z(a)Z(b)}{ab\big(aZ(a) - bZ(b)\big)}$$

$$n_2 = s \frac{a^2 - b^2}{ab\big(aZ(b) - bZ(a)\big)}$$

and where $a$ and $b$ are constants which are either positive or complex conjugates with positive real parts. $V(s)$ is constructed in such a manner as to insure that both the numerator and denominator of $\zeta(s)$ in Eq. 8.4.1 have the factors $(s - a)(s - b)$. The special case $\text{Re } Z(a) = \text{Re } Z(b) = 0 = \text{Re } a = \text{Re } b$ is taken up in section 8.5.

*Proof*

Define an auxiliary function $F(s)$ as follows:*

$$F(s) = s \frac{ab A + s^2 B - sZ(s)}{s^4 - s^2(a^2 + b^2) + a^2 b^2} \qquad \text{8.4.2}$$

$$A = \frac{aZ(b) - bZ(a)}{a^2 - b^2} \text{ and } B = \frac{aZ(a) - bZ(b)}{a^2 - b^2}$$

$F(s)$ is constructed specifically so that its only *r.h.s* plane poles are cancelled by some of the zeros of the numerator. Hence it is analytic in the *r.h.s* plane. Now we shall prove that $F(s)$ is also prf for the following reasons:

(1). The constants $A$ and $B$ are real if $a$ and $b$ are real. They are also real if $a = \bar{b}$ as can be shown by setting $a = x + jy$ and $Z(s) = U + jV$. Hence on the $j$ axis, $\text{Re } F(s)$ is given by

$$\text{Re } F(j\omega) = \frac{\omega^2 \text{ Re } Z(j\omega)}{\omega^4 + \omega^2(a^2 + b^2) + a^2 b^2}$$

---

* It will be shown in Chapter 9 (Problem 9.7) that $F(s)$ has a physical interpretation.

Thus Re $F(j\omega)$ is positive, since Re $Z(j\omega)$ is positive.

(2). $F(s)$ may have $j$ axis poles only if $Z(s)$ has them. Consequently, possible $j$ axis poles are simple with positive residues.

These two conditions together with the fact that $F(s)$ is analytic in the r.h.s plane are sufficient, according to the minimum real value theorem, to assure also that Re $F(s) > 0$ in the r.h.s plane, and therefore $F(s)$ is prf.

To obtain $\zeta$, note that the inverse of $F(s)$ has a pole at the origin and another at infinity. Removal of these poles yields (after some algebra)

$$F'(s)^{-1} \equiv F(s)^{-1} - \frac{1}{s}\frac{ab}{A} - s\,\frac{1}{B} \equiv \frac{B}{A}\,\zeta \qquad 8.4.3$$

This equation shows that $\dfrac{ab}{A}$ is a residue of a pole at the origin. Similarly, $1/B$ is the residue of a pole at infinity. Because $F(s)^{-1}$ is prf, these residues must be positive. Then $B/A$ is also positive. It follows that since $\dfrac{B}{A}\,\zeta$ is formed by removing the poles at the origin and at infinity of a positive real function, it is prf, and thus $\zeta$ is also prf. Note that the capacitor in Fig. 8.3 is given in terms of $abA/s$. It is prf, since $A$ is positive. Similarly, the first inductor on the left is prf, since it is given in terms of $sB$ and since $B$ is positive. It follows that the rest of the elements are realizable. To show that $V$ is prf, express $Z(s)$ of Eq. 8.4.1 in terms of $\zeta$. This gives

$$Z(s) = \frac{m_1\zeta + n_1}{m_2 + n_2\zeta} \qquad \begin{matrix} 8.3.3 \\ 8.4.4 \end{matrix}$$

It is seen that $V$ may be obtained from this expression if $\zeta$ is set to unity. Hence if $\zeta$ is set to unity in Fig. 8.3, the network would yield $V$. Since the network is realizable, $V$ is prf.

Thus we have shown that both $V$ and $\zeta$ are prf.

*Proof completed*

## Note 1

$(s + a)(s + b)$ is a factor in the numerator and denominator of $\zeta$ if and only if Ev $Z(a) =$ Ev $Z(b) = 0$. Hence if Ev $Z(a) =$ Ev $Z(b) = 0$, $\zeta^*$ is 2 less in degree than $Z(s)$. The proof may be obtained by utilizing the fact that both the numerator and the denominator of $\zeta$ in Eq. 8.4.1 vanish for $s = -a$ and $s = -b$, if and only if Ev $Z(a) = 0$ and Ev $Z(b) = 0$ respectively.

---

\* Observe that the factors $(s-a)$ and $(s-b)$ are built into the numerator and the denominator. Therefore, $\zeta$ is of the same degree as $Z(s)$ if Ev $Z(a) \neq 0 \neq$ Ev $Z(b)$.

This fact was utilized in Example 8.3.1 to synthesize $Z(s) = (s^3 + 12s^2 + 6s + 2)/(s^3 + s^2 + 5s + 2)$ in terms of $\zeta$ two less in degree than $Z(s)$. One can verify that the values of $a$ and $b$ suggested there ($a = \bar{b} = 1 + j$) are roots of Ev $Z(s) = 0$. In general, the numerator of Ev $Z(s)$ can be written in the form $(m_0 - n_0)(m_0 + n_0)$, where $m_0 + n_0$ is Hurwitz (Theorem 7.2.1). Thus any two real or complex roots of $m_0 - n_0$ will satisfy the requirement of Ev $Z(a) =$ Ev $Z(b) = 0$. Then, if $Z(s)$ is prf (and of degree not less than 2), it can always be realized in terms of Fig. 8.3 with $\zeta$ two less in degree than $Z(s)$. An exception to the rule is a function with even part zeros at infinity only. For example, let Ev $Z(s)$ be

$$\text{Ev } Z(s) = \frac{1}{m_2{}^2 - n_2{}^2}$$

In this case it is difficult to choose the proper $a$ and $b$. However, this function has a $j$ axis zero that can be removed. This function will be treated later in the chapter on even-part synthesis (Section 9.3).

**Note 2**

The numerator of Ev $V$ equals $(s^2 - a^2)(s^2 - b^2)$, and if Ev $Z(a) =$ Ev $Z(b) = 0$, then num. Ev $Z(s) =$ num. Ev $V \times$ Ev $\zeta$. The first statement can be verified by direct manipulation. To prove the second statement, Ev $Z(s)$ may be computed from

$$Z(s) = \frac{m_1\zeta + n_1}{m_2 + n_2\zeta} \qquad \text{8.4.4a}$$

$$= \frac{m_1(\text{Ev } \zeta + \text{Od } \zeta) + n_1}{m_2 + n_2(\text{Ev } \zeta + \text{Od } \zeta)} \qquad \text{8.4.4b}$$

to yield

$$\text{Ev } Z(s) = \frac{(m_1 m_2 - n_1 n_2) \text{ Ev } \zeta}{(m_2 + n_2 \text{ Od } \zeta)^2 - n_2{}^2(\text{Ev } \zeta)^2}$$
$$= \frac{(\text{num. Ev } V) \text{ Ev } \zeta}{(m_2 + n_2 \text{ Od } \zeta)^2 - n_2{}^2(\text{Ev } \zeta)^2} \qquad \text{8.4.5}$$

Observe that $\zeta$ is reduced in degree by 2 since Ev $Z(a) =$ Ev $Z(b) = 0$. (See Note 1.) Therefore, the numerator of its even part is 4 less in degree than num. Ev $Z(s)$. Also from the first statement of Note 2 the degree of numerator of Ev $V$ is 4. Thus the degree of the numerators on both sides of Eq. 8.4.5 are equal, and the numerators are equal. This completes the proof of the note. However Eq. 8.4.5 is true even if Ev $Z(a) \neq 0 \neq$ Ev $Z(b)$ (that is, $\zeta$ is not reduced). In this case the numerator and the denominator contain common factors, since then both are of higher degrees than the corresponding ones of Ev $Z(s)$.

It is sometimes convenient to say that if the degree of $\zeta$ is reduced by 2, the two-port network associated with Fig. 8.3 "pulls out" 4 even-part zeros. These zeros are $(s^2 - a^2)(s^2 - b^2)$.

Observe that the two-port network associated with Fig. 8.3 can be synthesized by applying the nonreciprocal Darlington synthesis on $V$ and removing the 1-ohm termination. This is the reason for calling $V$ an impedance operator.

In conclusion, this section has shown that extending Richards' theorem to include two arbitrary constants instead of one makes it possible to devise a synthesis procedure which is as follows:

(1). Form the even part of $Z(s)$ and determine either any two positive roots or any two complex conjugate roots with a positive real part. Let these roots be $a$ and $b$.

(2). Evaluate $\zeta$ by means of Eq. 8.4.1a for the values of $a$ and $b$ as determined above.

(3). Construct the network of Fig. 8.3.

The procedure is repeated until the final impedance (which is another $\zeta$) is of degree 1 or less.

The special case where Ev $Z(s)$ is zero on the $j$ axis, say at $s = j\omega_0$, and if $a$ and $b$ are chosen, $a = -b = j\omega_0$ leads to the Brune network which is discussed in the following section. For this case, the gyrator vanishes. The gyrator may also vanish if the extended Richards' theorem is applied twice with the same constants $a$ and $b$. Then the combined network (i.e., two networks of the type of Fig. 8.3 connected in tandem) has an equivalent reciprocal configuration. This subject is discussed in the last section of this chapter. In the following chapter it will be shown that the extension of Richards' theorem also may be utilized to give other synthesis procedures which do not require transformers or gyrators but in which the cascade nature of the synthesis may be lost.

### THE BRUNE SYNTHESIS 8.5

The gyrator term of Fig. 8.3

$$\frac{bZ(a) - aZ(b)}{b - a} \qquad \qquad 8.5.1$$

vanishes if $Z(s)$ is minimum resistive at $j\omega_0$ and if $a = -b = j\omega_0$. The corresponding network is shown in Fig. 8.5.*

---

\* In Fig. 8.5 and Eq. 8.5.2 $Z'$ means $\dfrac{dZ}{ds}$.

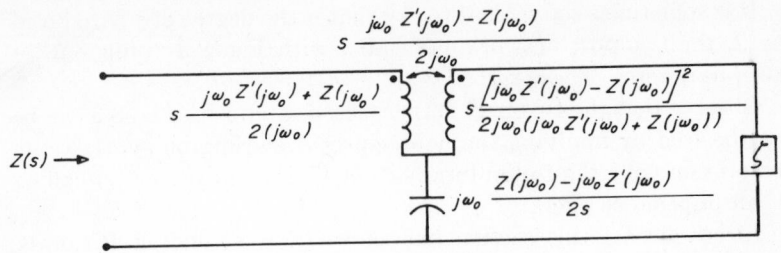

*Fig. 8.5. The Brune network*

This network was discovered by Brune and was the first that could handle minimum resistance driving point impedance functions ($\omega_0 \neq 0$). For this reason it is still often used to demonstrate the realizability of positive real impedance functions. For this network $\zeta$ degenerates into

$$\zeta = \frac{\left[1 + s^2 \dfrac{Z(j\omega_0) - j\omega_0 Z'(j\omega_0)}{-\omega_0^2(Z(j\omega_0) + j\omega_0 Z'(j\omega_0))}\right] Z(s) - s \dfrac{2(Z(j\omega_0))^2}{j\omega_0(Z(j\omega_0) + j\omega_0 Z'(j\omega_0))}}{1 + s^2 \dfrac{Z(j\omega_0) + j\omega_0 Z'(j\omega_0)}{-\omega_0^2(Z(j\omega_0) - j\omega_0 Z'(j\omega_0))} - s \dfrac{2Z(s)}{j\omega_0(Z(j\omega_0) - j\omega_0 Z'(j\omega_0))}}$$

$$\text{8.5.2}$$

We pause to ascertain that $\zeta$ is prf. Following the arguments of the proof of Theorem 8.4.1, one sees that $\zeta$ is defined and hence is prf if $A$ and $B$ are finite and nonzero. Letting $a = \bar{b} = j\omega_0 + \epsilon$ ($\epsilon \to 0^+$) yields

$$2A = \frac{1}{\epsilon}\left\{\text{Ev } Z(j\omega_0) + \epsilon\left(\text{Ev } Z'(j\omega_0) - \frac{\text{Od } Z(j\omega_0)}{j\omega_0}\right)\right\}$$

$$= \text{Ev } Z'(j\omega_0) - \frac{\text{Od } Z(j\omega_0)}{j\omega_0} = \frac{d}{d\omega_0}\text{Im } Z(j\omega_0) - \frac{\text{Im } Z(j\omega_0)}{\omega_0} \quad \text{8.5.3}$$

$$= Z'(j\omega_0) - \frac{Z(j\omega_0)}{j\omega_0}$$

where higher order terms in $\epsilon$ are neglected. In analyzing Eq. 8.5.3, note that Ev $Z(s)$ may have only zeros of even multiplicity on the $j$ axis. Then if Ev $Z(j\omega_0) = 0$, $Z'(j\omega_0) = 0$. Similarly $2B$ becomes

$$2B = Z'(j\omega_0) + \frac{Z(j\omega_0)}{j\omega_0} = \frac{d}{d\omega_0}\text{Im } Z(j\omega_0) + \frac{\text{Im } Z(j\omega_0)}{\omega_0} \quad \text{8.5.4}$$

Thus $A$ and $B$ are finite. It is yet to be shown that they are nonzero. We shall state the problem precisely:

**Theorem 8.5.1**

If $Z(s)$ is prf and if

(I). it has no $j$ axis poles or zeros

(II). Re $Z(j\omega_0) = 0$    $\omega_0 \neq 0, \infty$

then the quantities $A$ and $B$ defined in Eqs. 8.5.3 and 8.5.4 are positive and nonzero. Precisely it is required to show that

$$\frac{d}{d\omega_0} \operatorname{Im} Z(j\omega_0) \pm \frac{\operatorname{Im} Z(j\omega_0)}{\omega_0} > 0 \qquad \text{strict inequality} \quad \textbf{8.5.5}$$

**Proof** *

Consider the integral

$$\frac{1}{2\pi j} \oint_C W(s)\ ds \equiv \frac{1}{2\pi j} \int_C \frac{Z(s) - Z(s_0)}{s - s_0}\ ds \qquad \textbf{8.5.6}$$

where the integration contour is given in Fig. 8.6. Here $s_0$ is on the $j$ axis. Note that $s - s_0$ is a factor of $Z(s) - Z(s_0)$.

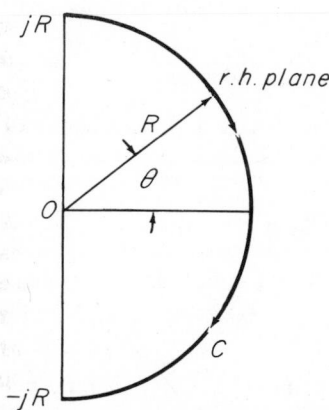

**Fig. 8.6. Integration contour for 8.5.6**

Because $Z(s)$ has no singularities in the $r.h.$plane and along the $j$ axis, the same is true for $W$. Thus the value of the integral is zero. Splitting the integral in two gives (let $s - s_0 \sim Re^{j\theta}$ along the arc)

$$\lim_{R\to\infty} \frac{1}{2\pi j} \int_{-jR}^{jR} \frac{Z(s) - Z(s_0)}{s - s_0}\ ds$$

$$= \lim_{R\to\infty} \frac{1}{2\pi j} \int_{-\pi/2}^{+\pi/2} \frac{(Z(Re^{j\theta} + s_0) - Z(s_0))jR\ d\theta}{R} \qquad \textbf{8.5.7}$$

$$= \frac{1}{2}\left(Z(\infty) - Z(s_0)\right)$$

---

* The crucial part of the proof is along the lines given in Tuttle, D. F., Jr., "Network Synthesis," John Wiley & Sons, New York, 1958, p. 517.

Next, the change of variable $s = j\omega$ is introduced. Then

$$Z(j\omega_0) - Z(\infty) = \frac{j}{\pi} \int_{-\infty}^{\infty} \frac{(Z(j\omega) - Z(j\omega_0))\,d\omega}{\omega - \omega_0} \qquad \text{8.5.8}$$

The point $s = \infty$ is on the real axis; hence, $Z(\infty)$ is real. Thus if we take the imaginary parts of both sides of 8.5.8, we have

$$\operatorname{Im} Z(j\omega_0) = \frac{1}{\pi} \int_{-\infty}^{\infty} \frac{(\operatorname{Re} Z(j\omega) - \operatorname{Re} Z(j\omega_0))\,d\omega}{\omega - \omega_0} \qquad \text{8.5.9}$$

Now we shall make use of the fact that on the $j$ axis $\operatorname{Re} Z(s) = \operatorname{Ev} Z(s) = \operatorname{Ev} Z(-s)$. This makes it possible to put 8.5.9 into the form

$$\operatorname{Im} Z(j\omega_0) = \frac{2\omega_0}{\pi} \int_{0}^{\infty} \frac{\operatorname{Re} Z(j\omega) - \operatorname{Re} Z(j\omega_0)}{\omega^2 - \omega_0^2}\,d\omega \qquad \text{8.5.10}$$

At this stage, we can demonstrate that $A$ and $B$ are nonzero in 8.5.3 and 8.5.4. Differentiation of both sides of 8.5.10 yields

$$\frac{d}{d\omega_0} \operatorname{Im} Z(j\omega_0) = \frac{2}{\pi} \int_{0}^{\infty} \frac{\operatorname{Re} Z(j\omega) - \operatorname{Re} Z(j\omega_0)}{\omega^2 - \omega_0^2}\,d\omega +$$

$$\frac{2\omega_0}{\pi} \int_{0}^{\infty} \frac{(\omega_0^2 - \omega^2)\dfrac{d}{d\omega_0} \operatorname{Re} Z(j\omega_0) + 2(\operatorname{Re} Z(j\omega) - \operatorname{Re} Z(j\omega_0))\omega_0}{(\omega^2 - \omega_0^2)^2}\,d\omega \qquad \text{8.5.11}$$

Setting $\operatorname{Re} Z(j\omega_0) = 0 = \dfrac{d}{d\omega_0} \operatorname{Re} Z(j\omega_0)$ and noting that the first term on the right of 8.5.11 equals $\operatorname{Im} Z(j\omega_0)/\omega_0$, we get

$$\frac{d}{d\omega_0} \operatorname{Im} Z(j\omega_0) - \frac{\operatorname{Im} Z(j\omega_0)}{\omega_0} = \frac{4\omega_0^2}{\pi} \int_{0}^{\infty} \frac{\operatorname{Re} Z(j\omega)\,d\omega}{(\omega^2 - \omega_0^2)^2} \qquad \text{8.5.12}$$

Recall that it was assumed that $Z(s)$ has no poles or zeros on the $j$ axis. This means that $Z(s)$ is not a reactance function and $\operatorname{Re} Z(j\omega) \not\equiv 0$. Thus the integral on the right of 8.5.12 is positive, since the integrand is never negative. Note that 8.5.12 applies to an admittance function as well. However

$$\operatorname{Im} Y(j\omega_0) = -\frac{1}{\operatorname{Im} Z(j\omega_0)},$$

and

$$\frac{d}{d\omega_0} \operatorname{Im} Y(j\omega_0) = \left(\frac{d}{d\omega_0} \operatorname{Im} Z(j\omega_0)\right) \Big/ (\operatorname{Im} Z(j\omega_0))^2.$$

Hence

$$\frac{d}{d\omega_0} \operatorname{Im} Y(j\omega_0) - \frac{\operatorname{Im} Y(j\omega_0)}{\omega_0} > 0 \qquad \text{by 8.5.12}$$

$$= \frac{1}{(\operatorname{Im} Z(j\omega_0))^2} \times \left(\frac{d}{d\omega_0} \operatorname{Im} Z(j\omega_0) + \frac{\operatorname{Im} Z(j\omega_0)}{\omega_0}\right) \qquad \text{8.5.13}$$

Thus

$$\frac{d}{d\omega_0} \text{Im } Z(j\omega_0) \pm \frac{\text{Im } Z(j\omega_0)}{\omega_0} > 0 \qquad \textbf{8.5.5}$$

Then both $A$ and $B$ in 8.5.3 and 8.5.4 are positive and nonzero. This completes the proof of the theorem.

Observe that this theorem assures that the coefficient of each member of the lossless section of Figure 8.5 is finite, nonzero, and positive. Hence the section is prf. Furthermore note that $F(s)$ as defined in Eq. 8.4.2.

$$F(s) = s \frac{ab\,A + s^2B - s\,Z(s)}{s^4 - s^2(a^2 + b^2) + a^2b^2} \qquad \begin{matrix} \textbf{8.4.2} \\ \textbf{8.5.14} \end{matrix}$$

is finite if $A$ and $B$ are finite. Hence following the line of development in Section 8.4 it is prf. Since $\zeta$ also may be obtained from Eq. 8.4.3,

$$F(s)^{-1} - \frac{1}{s}\frac{ab}{A} - s\frac{1}{B} \equiv \frac{B}{A}\,\zeta \qquad \begin{matrix} \textbf{8.4.3} \\ \textbf{8.5.15} \end{matrix}$$

$\zeta$ is prf.

Historically, the Brune network was not derived by the method shown above. It was discovered by an extension of the "chop-chop" technique to permit removal of transformers. Brune* observed that if the reactive part is removed from a minimum resistive (at $j\omega_0$) function (let this part be called $L_1s$), such that the remainder is zero at $j\omega_0$, then this permits the removal of a $j\omega_0$ zero. The rest of the function is not prf. However, it becomes prf if another inductance, $L_3$, is removed (Fig. 8.7.) such that all of the three inductors form the equivalent of a perfectly coupled transformer. One of the series inductors is necessarily negative.

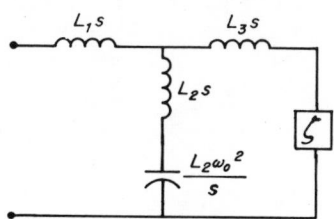

**Fig. 8.7. An equivalent network
to Fig. 8.5**

---

* Brune, O., "Synthesis of a Finite Two-Terminal Network Whose Driving Point Impedance is a Prescribed Function of Frequency," *J. Math. Phys*, Vol. 10, pp. 191–236, 1931.

The proof by Brune of the realizability of the network is different from that given here. Attention is called to the fact that the network associated with the synthesis "pulls out" four $j$ axis zeros of Ev $Z(s)$.

## 8.6. THE DARLINGTON D SECTION

The Brune network is restricted to minimum resistive impedance functions. This restriction is avoided by the removal of the so-called Darlington $D$ section which is illustrated in Fig. 8.8.

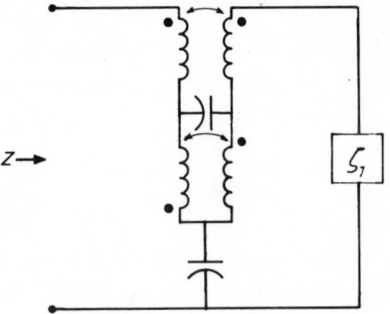

**Fig. 8.8. Removal of a Darlington D section**

This network can be arrived at by combining two sections of Fig. 8.3 in tandem* (Fig. 8.9), with each having the same constants

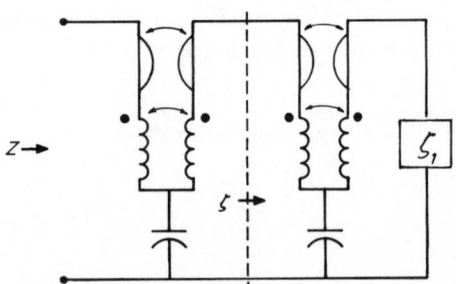

**Fig. 8.9. Forming the Darlington D section**

---

*Murdoch, J. B., "Driving Point Impedance Synthesis using Impedance Operators," Ph.D. Dissertation pp. 92–97, (Case Institute of Technology Engineering Division), Aug. 1961. Also appeared in Scientific Report No. 27 AF 19(604)-3887 for the USAF Cambridge Research Center, Bedford, Massachusetts.

$a$ and $b$, that is, the final term which is another $\zeta$, say $\zeta_1$, is obtained by applying Eq. 8.3.1 twice. Specifically it is noted that

$$\zeta = \frac{m_2 Z(s) - n_1}{m_1 - n_2 Z(s)} \qquad \begin{matrix} 8.3.1 \\ 8.6.1 \end{matrix}$$

and $\zeta_1$ is given by

$$\zeta_1 = \frac{m_2^1 \zeta - n_1^1}{m_1^1 - n_2^1 \zeta} \qquad 8.6.2$$

Combining these two equations to eliminate $\zeta$ and solving for $Z(s)$, we·get

$$Z(s) = \frac{(m_1 m_1^1 + n_1 n_2^1)\zeta_1 + n_1 m_2^1 + m_1 n_1^1}{m_2 m_2^1 + n_2 n_1^1 + (n_2 m_1^1 + m_2 n_2^1)\zeta_1} \qquad 8.6.3$$

Associated with Eqs. 8.6.1 and 8.6.2 are the operators $V$ and $V_1$, respectively. The operator associated with Eq. 8.6.3 may be obtained by setting $\zeta_1$ to unity. This operator will be called the combined operator and will be denoted by $V_2$. When we follow the same arguments previously advanced (Note 2, Section 8.4), the numerator of Ev $V_2 = (m_1 m_2 - n_1 n_2)(m_1^1 m_2^1 - n_1^1 n_2^1) = $ (num. Ev $V \times$ num. Ev $V_1$). Observe, therefore, that if both utilize the same constants $a$ and $b$, num. Ev $V_2 = (1 - s^2(a^2 + b^2)/a^2 b^2 + s^4/a^2 b^2)^2$. Thus $z_{12}$ of the final two-port network is

$$z_{12} = \frac{\left(1 - s^2 \dfrac{a^2 + b^2}{a^2 b^2} + \dfrac{s^4}{a^2 b^2}\right)}{n_2 m_1^1 + m_2 n_2^1} \qquad 8.6.4$$

It is rational, but one of its terms in a partial fraction expansion will have a negative coefficient (since the numerator is not Hurwitz). This accounts for the negative polarity of one of the transformers of Fig. 8.8.* If the constants $a$ and $b$ are selected to give Ev $Z(a) = $ Ev $Z(b) = 0$, both $\zeta$ and $\zeta_1$ will be 2 less in degree than $Z(s)$ (Note 1, Section 8.4).

## Example 8.6.1

Synthesize $Z(s) = (s^3 + 12s^2 + 6s + 2)/(s^3 + s^2 + 5s + 2)$ by removing a Darlington type $D$ section.

### Solution

This impedance was synthesized by removing the gyrator, transformer, and capacitor section (Example 8.3.1). Its even part numerator has the factor

---

* Setting $a$ or $b$ to zero would result in the elimination of the top transformer of Fig. 8.8. Also, the capacitor loading of the second transformer will vanish. The network, then, is called the Darlington $C$ section.

$1 + s^4/4$, that is, $a = \bar{b} = 1 + j$. Hence selecting the same constants for a new operator, $V_1$, (operating on $\zeta$) will yield a new termination, $\zeta_1$. The numerator of Ev $V_1$ is also $(1 + s^4/4)$; therefore, the numerator of Ev $V_2$, the resulting combined operator, will be $(1 + s^4/4)^2$. Proceeding along these same lines starting with $\zeta = (s + 2)/(4s + 2)$ (Eqs. 8.3.1 and 8.3.2) and interchanging $Z(s)$ with $\zeta$ and $\zeta$ with $\zeta_1$ we obtain

$$\zeta(a) = \frac{3 + j}{6 + 4j}, \ \zeta(b) = \frac{3 - j}{6 - 4j}, \ a\zeta(a) - b\zeta(b) = \frac{8j}{13}$$

$$a\zeta(b) - b\zeta(a) = \frac{14j}{13}$$

8.6.5

Thus

$$\zeta_1 = \frac{\left(1 + \frac{7}{8} s^2\right)\zeta - \frac{5}{8} s}{\left(1 + \frac{2}{7} s^2\right) - \frac{13}{7} s\zeta} = \frac{1 + \frac{7}{8} s}{1 + \frac{8}{7} s}$$

8.6.6

Equation 8.6.6 may be solved for $\zeta$ to find

$$\zeta = \frac{\left(1 + \frac{2}{7} s^2\right)\zeta_1 + \frac{5}{8} s}{\left(1 + \frac{7}{8} s^2\right) + \frac{13}{7} s\zeta_1}$$

8.6.7

and similarly Eq. 8.3.7 may be solved for the original $Z(s)$:

$$Z(s) = \frac{(1 + s^2)\zeta + \frac{5}{2} s}{\left(1 + \frac{s^2}{4}\right) + \frac{1}{2} s\zeta}$$

8.6.8

Eliminating $\zeta$ from Eqs. 8.6.7 and 8.6.8 we get

$$Z(s) = \frac{\left(1 + \frac{83}{14} s^2 + \frac{2}{7} s^4\right)\zeta_1 + \frac{5}{16} s (10 + 9 s^2)}{\left(1 + \frac{23}{16} s^2 + \frac{7}{32} s^4\right) + \frac{1}{28} s\zeta_1(66 + 17 s^2)}$$

8.6.9

from which $V_2$, the combined impedance operator, may be obtained by setting $\zeta_1$ to unity. Synthesis of $V_2$ for its associated two-port network yields

$$z_{11} = \left[\frac{8s}{17}\right] + \left[\frac{71656}{561} \frac{s}{17s^2 + 66}\right] + \left[\frac{28}{66s}\right]$$

$$z_{22} = \left[\frac{49s}{136}\right] + \left[\frac{5194}{561} \frac{s}{17s^2 + 66}\right] + \left[\frac{28}{66s}\right]$$

$$z_{12} = \left[\frac{7s}{17}\right] + \left[\frac{19292}{561} \frac{s}{17s^2 + 66}\right] + \left[\frac{28}{66s}\right]$$

8.6.10

From these the final representation of $Z(s)$ is given in Fig. 8.10.

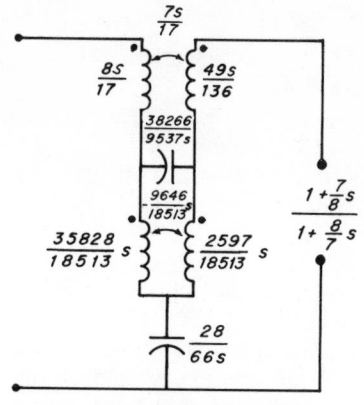

**Fig. 8.10. Realization of Z(s)**
$$= \frac{s^3 + 12s^2 + 6s + 2}{s^3 + s^2 + 5s + 2} \text{ by removal}$$
**of a Darlington D section**

Observe that if $\zeta_1$ is 2 less in degree than $Z(s)$, then the Darlington $D$ section also "pulls out" four zeros of Ev $Z(s)$.

## PROBLEMS

8.1. Realize by reducing the degree of $\zeta$ through the use of Richards' theorem.

(a).
$$Z(s) = \frac{s^3 + 3s^2 + s + 1}{s^3 + s^2 + 3s + 1}$$

(b).
$$Z(s) = \frac{s^3 + 4s^2 + s + 1}{s^3 + s^2 + 4s + 1}$$

8.2. Realize by reducing the degree of $\zeta$ by 2, using nonreciprocal networks.

(a).
$$Z(s) = \frac{s^3 + 7s^2 + 9s + 8}{s^3 + 2s^2 + 3s + 1}$$

(b).
$$Z(s) = \frac{s^3 + 12s^2 + 9s + 8}{s^3 + s^2 + 2s + 1/2}$$

(c).
$$Z(s) = \frac{s^3 + 3s^2 + s + 1}{s^3 + s^2 + 3s + 1}$$

8.3. Synthesize by removing a Darlington $D$ section so that $\zeta$ is 2 less in degree than $Z(s)$:

$$Z(s) = \frac{s^3 + 7s^2 + 9s + 8}{s^3 + 2s^2 + 3s + 1}$$

## FURTHER READING

Books

8.1. Balabanian, N., "Network Synthesis," Prentice-Hall, Inc., Englewood Cliffs, N. J., 1958, Chapter 6.
8.2. Guillemin, E. A., "Synthesis of Passive Networks," John Wiley & Sons, New York, 1957, Chapter 9.
8.3. Tuttle, D. F., Jr., "Network Synthesis," John Wiley & Sons, New York, 1958, Chapter 9.

Related Papers

8.4. Fialkow, A., and Gerst, I., "Impedance Synthesis Without Minimization," J. Math. and Physics, Vol. 34, pp. 160–168, October, 1955.
8.5. Murdoch, J. B., "Driving Point Impedance Synthesis using Impedance Operators," Ph.D. Dissertation, Case Institute of Technology, Aug., 1961.
   Also see Scientific Report No. 27 AF 19(604) 3887 prepared for the USAF Cambridge Research Center, Bedford, Massachusetts.
   A part of this material appears in Murdoch, J. B., and Hazony, D., "Cascade Driving Point Synthesis by Removal of Sections Containing Arbitrary Constants," IRE Trans on Circuit Theory, March, 1962.
8.6. Youla, D. C., "A New Theory of Cascade Synthesis," IRE Trans. on Circuit Theory, Vol. CT-9, pp. 244–260, September, 1961.

# *Even-Part Synthesis* | CHAPTER 9

In the previous chapter, devoted to cascade synthesis, frequent use was made of the numerator of Ev $Z(s)$. For example, it was necessary to obtain two roots of the numerator of Ev $Z(s)$ in order to reduce the degree of the terminating $\zeta$. In this chapter, the even part of $Z(s)$ will be investigated more extensively. We will show that Ev $Z(s)$ can be utilized for other synthesis purposes, such as the reduction and elimination of transformers. Moreover, in our consideration of the 2-port problem, the even part of $z_{11}$ will be employed to realize $z_{11}$ when the zeros of $z_{12}$ are specified.

For the sake of uniqueness, it is assumed throughout this chapter that all $j$ axis poles have been removed from $Z(s)$. Then $Z(s)$ is said to be *minimum reactive*.

### TRANSFORMERLESS DARLINGTON SYNTHESIS 9.1

In Chapter 7 it was demonstrated that the evaluation of $z_{12}$ in the Darlington lossless 2-port network is related to Ev $Z(s)$. Recall that for *Case A*, $z_{11} = m_1/n_2$, $z_{22} = m_2/n_2$, and $z_{12} = \sqrt{m_1 m_2 - n_1 n_2}/n_2$. Thus if Ev $Z(s)$ is known, both $z_{22}$ and $z_{12}$ can be determined ($z_{22}$ from the denominator and $z_{12}$ from the numerator). Furthermore, as the residue condition is satisfied with the equal sign, $z_{11}$ can be determined from $z_{12}$ and $z_{22}$ [provided $Z(s)$ is a minimum reactance]. Thus the synthesis may be accomplished from Ev $Z(s)$ alone. But the numerator of Ev $Z(s)$ must be a perfect square if $z_{12}$ ($= z_{21}$) is to be rational. Remember that in order to make $z_{12}$ rational it is necessary to multiply both the numerator or the denominator by $m_0 + n_0$ such that $m_0^2 - n_0^2 = m_1 m_2 - n_1 n_2$ ($=$ num. Ev $Z(s)$). Alternatively, it was shown that it is possible to split the even part into two parts

$$\text{Ev } Z(s) = \frac{m_0^2}{m_2^2 - n_2^2} + \frac{-n_0^2}{m_2^2 - n_2^2}$$

7.6.1<br>9.1.1

and then realize each part separately (Section 7.6).

At this point, the question of whether or not it is possible to split the even part in other ways, and for other purposes, might be raised.

**Example 9.1.1**

Synthesize $Z(s) = (s^2 + 3s + 3)/(s^2 + 2s + 1)$ by splitting the even part so that no transformers are essential.

*Solution*

Evaluation of Ev $Z(s)$ gives

$$\text{Ev } Z(s) = \frac{(s^2 + 3)(s^2 + 1) - 6s^2}{(s^2 + 1)^2 - 4s^2}$$

$$= \frac{s^4 - 2s^2 + 3}{(s^2 + 1)^2 - 4s^2}$$

9.1.2

This expression can be split into three parts each of which gives positive values along the $j$ axis:

$$\text{Ev } Z(s) = \underbrace{\frac{s^4}{(s^2 + 1)^2 - 4s^2}}_{= \text{ Ev } Z_1} + \frac{1}{2}\underbrace{\frac{-4s^2}{(s^2 + 1)^2 - 4s^2}}_{+ \frac{1}{2}\text{ Ev } Z_2} + 3\underbrace{\frac{1}{(s^2 + 1)^2 - 4s^2}}_{+ 3 \text{ Ev } Z_3} \quad 9.1.3$$

$Z_2$ is scaled by 2 in order to eliminate a transformer; $Z_3$ is scaled by $\frac{1}{3}$ for the same purpose. Note that $Z_1$, $Z_2$, and $Z_3$ have positive real parts along the $j$ axis. Furthermore, their denominator is necessarily the same as that of $Z(s)$; hence, they are analytic in the *r.h.s* plane. Thus, according to the minimum real-part theorem (2.5.2), the corresponding impedances are prf. However, it is also possible to show that they are prf by direct synthesis. Synthesizing $Z_1$, we first get

$$z_{22} = \frac{m_2}{n_2} = \frac{s^2 + 1}{2s} = \frac{s}{2} + \frac{1}{2s}$$

9.1.4a

$$z_{12} = \frac{\sqrt{\text{num. Ev } Z_1}}{n_2} = \frac{s^2}{2s} = \frac{s}{2}$$

9.1.4b

and recalling that the residue condition is satisfied with the equal sign, we obtain $z_{11} = s/2$. The final network for $Z_1$ is given by Fig. 9.1.

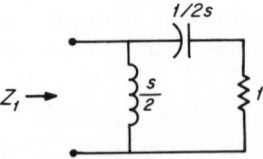

**Fig. 9.1. Realization of $Z_1$ in Eq. 9.1.3**

A similar approach to Ev $Z_2$ yields (here *Case B* of Darlington's synthesis is used)

$$z_{22} = \frac{n_2}{m_2} = \frac{2s}{s^2 + 1} \qquad \textbf{9.1.5a}$$

and

$$z_{12} = \frac{\sqrt{-\text{num. Ev } Z_2}}{m_2} = \frac{2s}{s^2 + 1} \qquad \textbf{9.1.5b}$$

Again, since the residue condition is satisfied with the equal sign, $z_{11}$ equals $2s/(s^2 + 1)$ also (Fig. 9.2).

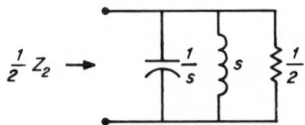

**Fig. 9.2. Realization of $\frac{1}{2}Z_2$ in Eq. 9.1.3**

Note that the terminal resistance is $\frac{1}{2}$ ohm owing to the scaling constant, 2.

Applying the same method to Ev $Z_3$ of Eq. 9.1.2, we get

$$z_{22} = \frac{m_2}{n_2} = \frac{s^2 + 1}{2s} = \frac{s}{2} + \frac{1}{2s} \qquad \textbf{9.1.6a}$$

and

$$z_{12} = \frac{\sqrt{\text{num. Ev } z_3}}{n_2} = \frac{1}{2s} \qquad \textbf{9.1.6b}$$

Therefore $z_{11} = z_{12} = \frac{1}{2s}$. The final network for $3Z_3$ is given in Fig. 9.3.

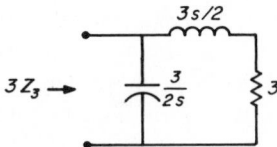

**Fig. 9.3. Realization of $3Z_3$ in Eq. 9.1.3**

It is noted that Ev $Z(s)$ of Eq. 9.1.2 also can be split in another manner (which requires no transformers), namely

$$\text{Ev } Z(s) = \frac{s^4 - 2s^2 + 3}{(s^2 + 1)^2 - 4s^2} = \frac{(s^2 + 1)^2}{(s^2 + 1)^2 - 4s^2}$$

$$- \frac{4s^2}{(s^2 + 1) - 4s^2} + 2\frac{1}{(s^2 + 1)^2 - 4s^2} \qquad \textbf{9.1.7}$$

This example is used to illustrate the flexibility in performing the even-part split for synthesis purposes. However, the problem of even-part synthesis (for the sake of transformer elimination) becomes more and more difficult as the degree of the impedance is increased. For example, a straightforward application of the Darlington synthesis to functions of the type

$$\text{Ev } Z(s) = \frac{1}{m^2 - n^2} \qquad \textbf{9.1.8}$$

(A function mentioned in Section 8.4) will lead to the use of many transformers if $m + n$ is of degree 3 or higher. The same is true for functions of the type

$$\text{Ev } Z(s) = \frac{(-s^2)^p}{m^2 - n^2} \qquad \textbf{9.1.9}$$

$$(p = \text{positive integer})$$

However, no transformer will be necessary if only one double zero at a time is removed from the even part at zero or infinity. [Note that Ev $Z(s)$ in Eq. 9.1.8 has all its zeros at infinity, whereas in Eq. 9.1.9 they are at either zero or infinity or both.]

## 9.2. MIYATA SYNTHESIS

This method applies to driving point impedance functions which can be put in the form of

$$\text{Ev } Z(s) = \sum_{p=0}^{q} \frac{a_p(-s^2)^p}{m^2 - n^2} \qquad \textbf{9.2.1}$$

$$a_p > 0$$

An application of the straightforward Darlington synthesis to each member of Eq. 9.2.1 may lead to networks with transformers. However, observe that each member has all its even-part zeros either at zero or at infinity or both. This may be interpreted to mean that suitable lossless 2-port networks might be found which are capable of removing these even-part zeros in much the same manner that the zero cancellation network (Fig. 8.3 or the Darlington $D$ section) was able to remove other zeros of the even part.

### Example 9.2.1

In Example 9.1.1, the Darlington procedure was used to synthesize the function $Z_1$ from its even part given by

$$\text{Ev } Z_1 = \frac{s^4}{(s^2 + 1)^2 - (2s)^2} \qquad \textbf{9.2.2}$$

Investigate the effect of removing the zero at the origin through the removal of a parallel inductor.

*Solution*

The fact that Ev $Z_1$ has a zero at the origin dictates that $Z_1$ is zero there (since otherwise $Z_1(s) \neq$ real for $s = 0$). This means that $Z_1$ can be written as

$$Z_1 = \frac{m_1 + n_1}{m_2 + n_2} = \frac{s(m'_1 + n'_1)}{m_2 + n_2} \qquad 9.2.3$$

and therefore

$$\text{Ev } Y_1 = \frac{m_1 m_2 - n_1 n_2}{-s^2(m'^2_1 - n'^2_1)} = \frac{-s^2}{m'^2_1 - n'^2_1} \qquad 9.2.4$$

(since $m_1 m_2 - n_1 n_2 = s^4$ in Eq. 9.2.2). The removal of an inductor in parallel reduces the degree of $Y_1$ (and therefore of $Z_1$), but it does not change the even part of $Y_1$. Thus by writing

$$Y'_1 = Y_1 - \frac{1}{Ls} \qquad 9.2.5$$

it also follows that

$$\text{Ev } Y'_1 = \text{Ev } Y_1 = \frac{-s^2}{m'^2_1 - n'^2_1} \qquad 9.2.6$$

Now $Y'_1$ is reduced in degree [from $Z(s)$], and its even-part numerator is num. $\frac{\text{Ev } Z(s)}{-s^2}$. To compute the value of $Y'_1$, the polynomial $m_1 + n_1$ must be evaluated. This amounts to evaluating $Z(s)$ from Ev $Z(s)$. Accordingly, assume that $Z$ may be written in the form

$$Z = \frac{as^2 + bs}{s^2 + 2s + 1} \qquad 9.2.7$$

and therefore

$$\text{Ev } Z(s) = \frac{as^4 + (a - 2b)s^2}{(s^2 + 1)^2 - (2s)^2} \qquad 9.2.8$$

indicating that $a = 1$, $b = \frac{1}{2}$. Hence (by Eq. 9.2.6) Ev $Y'_1 = (-s^2)/(\frac{1}{4} - s^2)$.

The results of Eq. 9.2.6 can be generalized to say that if num. Ev $Z(s)$ contains the factor $(-s^2)$, a shunting inductor may be removed from the total network, thereby effecting the reduction of num. Ev $Z(s)$ by $(-s^2)$. Similarly, if Ev $Z(s)$ has a zero at infinity, a shunting capacitor may be removed. (The proof of this statement also may be obtained by changing the zero at infinity into one at the origin through the transformation of $s = 1/s_1$. This will permit the removal of a shunting inductor which later is retransformed into a capacitor through the reverse transformation $s_1 = 1/s$.) If the analysis is continued along the same line, Ev $Y'_1$ now may be reduced further by the removal of a series capacitor. This will remove another double zero at the origin, yielding

$$\text{Ev } Z'_2 = \frac{m_1 m_2 - n_1 n_2}{s^4 (m'^2_2 - n'^2_2)} \qquad 9.2.9$$

If, at any time, the zeros at the origin are exhausted, a switch is made towards the removal of the zeros at infinity. In this manner each member of Ev $Z(s)$ in Eq. 9.2.1 is realized without transformers. However, since each realization is a degeneracy of the Darlington synthesis, the final termination is resistive (i.e., when the degree is finally reduced to zero the impedance is a resistance).

Note that in the example above $Z_1$ had to be computed from Ev $Z_1$ prior to the evaluation of Ev $Y'_1$. Actually, this information was not necessary for the proving of Eq. 9.2.6. In Chapter 11 (Section 11.3) it will be shown that each member of Eq. 9.2.1 may be realized directly by means of a suitable continued fraction expansion of $m_2/n_2$. However, on the basis of historical development, the Miyata synthesis requires that each member of Eq. 9.2.1 be converted into its complete form.

## 9.3. MIYATA SYNTHESIS—EVALUATION FROM THE EVEN PART

In the previous section it was shown that impedance functions having an even part of the type

$$\text{Ev } Z_p = \frac{(-s^2)^p}{m^2 - n^2} \qquad 9.3.1$$

can be realized by a repeated removal of a zero at the origin (and) or at infinity. However, the method calls for a prior evaluation of $Z_p$ from Ev $Z_p$. It turns out that once $Z_0$ is evaluated from $1/(m^2 - n^2)$, the other terms can be computed from it. This is done in the following manner:

(1). Multiply $Z_0$ by $(-s^2)^p$. The even part of $(-s^2)^p Z_0$ is, therefore, $(-s^2)^p/(m^2 - n^2)$ [since $(-s^2)^p$ is even and does not change the value of Ev $Z_0$].

(2). Divide the numerator of $(-s^2)^p$ Ev $Z_0$ by the denominator in long division until the remainder, $Z_p$, has a numerator which does not exceed the degree of the denominator. $Z_p$ is the required impedance.

To prove this statement, define $F(s)$ as follows:

$$F(s) = (-s^2)^p Z_0 \qquad 9.3.2$$

Hence Ev $F(s) = (-s^2)^p/(m^2 - n^2)$, since Ev $Z_0 = 1/(m^2 - n^2)$. Now use long division to write $F(s)$ in terms of $Z_p$ with a numerator which does not exceed the degree of the denominator. Thus

$$F(s) = M + N + Z_p \qquad \qquad \textbf{9.3.3}$$

Where $M + N$ is a polynomial in $s$ ($M$ even, $N$ odd). Note that since $Z(s)$ is assumed to be minimum reactive (no $j$ axis poles) then $F(s)$ approaches a zero or a constant as $s$ approaches infinity. Then $M$ must be zero or a constant. Let that constant be lumped with $Z_p$. It follows that Ev $F(s) = $ Ev $Z_p = (-s^2)^p/(m^2 - n^2)$ and it is positive along the $j$ axis. Then, by the minimum real-part theorem, $Z_p$ is prf (note that the poles of $Z_p$ are the same as those of $Z_0$). The factor $N$ does not enter into the calculation, since its even part is zero.

**Example 9.3.1**

Realize $Z(s)$ from Ev $Z(s)$ given by

$$\text{Ev } Z(s) = \frac{-s^6 + s^4 - s^2 + 1}{(s^2 + 1)^2 - s^2(s^2 + 2)^2} \qquad \qquad \textbf{9.3.4}$$

*Solution*

Let $Z_0$ be given by

$$Z_0 = \frac{as^2 + bs + c}{s^3 + s^2 + 2s + 1} \qquad \qquad \textbf{9.3.5}$$

But num. Ev $Z_0 = 1 = (a - b)s^4 + (a - 2b + c)s^2 + c$; therefore, $a = b = c = 1$. Hence

$$Z_0 = \frac{s^2 + s + 1}{s^3 + s^2 + 2s + 1} \qquad \qquad \textbf{9.3.6}$$

It follows that

$$F_1 = -s^2 Z_0$$

$$= \frac{-s^4 - s^3 - s^2}{s^3 + s^2 + 2s + 1}$$

$$= -s + \underbrace{\frac{s^2 + s}{s^3 + s^2 + 2s + 1}}_{Z_1} \qquad \qquad \textbf{9.3.7}$$

The function $F_2$ becomes

$$F_2 = \frac{s^6 + s^5 + s^4}{s^3 + s^2 + 2s + 1}$$

$$= s^3 - s + \underbrace{\frac{2s^2 + s}{s^3 + s^2 + 2s + 1}}_{Z_2} \qquad \qquad \textbf{9.3.8}$$

$F_3$ is obtained by multiplying $Z_0$ by $(-s^2)^3$:

$$F_3 = \frac{-s^8 - s^7 - s^6}{s^3 + s^2 + 2s + 1}$$

$$= -s^5 + s^3 - 2s + \underbrace{\frac{s^3 + 4s^2 + 2s}{s^3 + s^2 + 2s + 1}}_{Z_3} \qquad 9.3.9$$

The final network is obtained by repeated inversions of the $Z_p$'s and is given in Fig. 9.4.

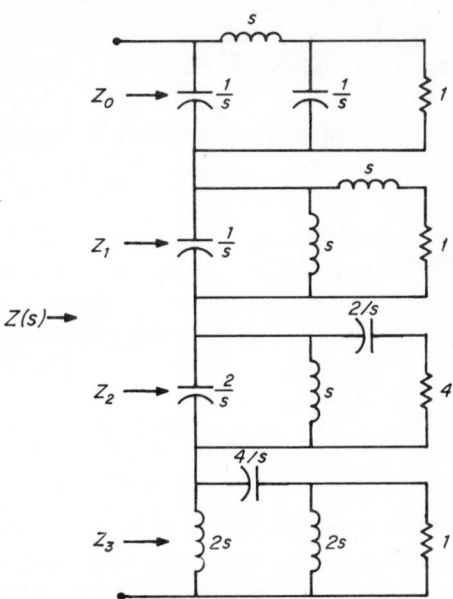

**Fig. 9.4. Miyata network for Ev $Z(s)$**
$$= \frac{-s^6 + s^4 - s^2 + 1}{(s^2 + 1)^2 - s^2(s^2 + 2)^2}$$

## 9.4. EXTENSION OF MIYATA SYNTHESIS

The Miyata synthesis is useful if num. Ev $Z(s)$, defined as $P$, can be expressed as

$$P = \text{num. Ev } Z(s) = \sum_p a_p(-s^2)^p = a_0 + a_1z + \cdots + a_nz^n \qquad 9.4.1$$

where $a_p \geq 0$ and $z = -s^2$. This section will be devoted to showing that if num. Ev $Z(s)$ does not have factors of the form $(s^2 + \omega_0^2)^2$, that is, $(-z + \omega_0^2)^2$, then it could be improved into the form of Eq. 9.4.1 by use of surplus factors.

## Example 9.4.1

Use surplus factors to put num. Ev $Z(s)$ of the following function (Eq. 9.4.2) in the form of Eq. 9.4.1:

$$\text{Ev } Z(s) = \frac{s^4 + s^2 + 1}{(s^2 + 1)^2 - s^2} \qquad \textbf{9.4.2}$$

One method for determining a suitable surplus factor will be given later. Here we shall try the factor $(1 - s^2)$.

### Solution

Multiplication of the numerator and denominator by the factor $(1 - s^2)$ gives

$$\text{Ev } Z(s) = \frac{-s^6 + 1}{(2s^2 + 1)^2 - s^2(s^2 + 2)^2} \qquad \textbf{9.4.3}$$

which is in the required form.

In search of a surplus factor [which will put num. Ev $Z(s)$ into the form of Eq. 9.4.1], note that a product of two polynomials with positive coefficients yields another polynomial with positive coefficients. Thus, suppose the numerator of Ev $Z(s)$ is *not* in the form of Eq. 9.4.1 owing to the presence of one factor of the form

$$f(z) = (z_1{}^2 - 2Az_1 + B^2)$$
$$A > 0 < B^2 \qquad \textbf{9.4.4}$$

where the requirements of realizability specify that $f(z)$ be positive for positive $z$. Hence either the zeros of $f(z)$ are real and equal or they are complex conjugates. In the first case, $f$ will always have a zero on the real axis of $z$ irrespective of the surplus factors. This means that some of the coefficients always will be negative. This problem will be treated in the following section. In the second case (zeros are complex), let $f(z)$ be normalized as follows:

$$f(z) = z^2 - 2z \cos \theta + 1 \qquad \textbf{9.4.5}$$

where $z = z_1/B$ and $\cos \theta = A/B$. It follows that a surplus factor which will make $f(z)$ have positive coefficients also will make num. Ev $Z(s)$ have the form of Eq. 9.4.1. One surplus factor (from Poincaré) is the following:

$$z^{n-1} + \frac{\sin 2\theta}{\sin \theta} z^{n-2} + \cdots + \frac{\sin (n - 1)\theta}{\sin \theta} z + \frac{\sin n\theta}{\sin \theta} \qquad \textbf{9.4.6}$$

which, upon multiplication with $f(z)$ (Eq. 9.4.5)), yields

$$z^{n+1} - \frac{\sin (n + 1)\theta}{\sin \theta} z + \frac{\sin n\theta}{\sin \theta} \qquad \textbf{9.4.7}$$

where $n$ is the largest integer for which $\sin n\theta \geq 0$ [note that $\sin (n + 1)\theta < 0$].

Return now to Example 9.4.1; there, $f(z)$ is given by

$$f = z^2 - z + 1 = z^2 - 2z \cos \frac{\pi}{3} + 1 \qquad \textbf{9.4.8}$$

Hence $n = 3$ and Eq. 9.4.6 becomes $z(z + 1)$. This is essentially the same factor as was used in the example $(- s^2 + 1)$, except for the additional factor $z$ which may be dropped since (even if kept) it will be cancelled in computing the improved even part.

The method loses its usefulness when $\cos \theta \to 1$, since then $n$ (Eq. 9.4.6) approaches infinity. This means that Ev $Z(s)$ has the factor $(s^2 + \omega_0^2)^2$. Here we have to abandon the present approach and use a Darlington-like synthesis. This subject will be developed in the following sections.

## 9.5. J AXIS EVEN PART ZEROS

In this section we develop a transformerless synthesis when Ev $Z(s)$ has the factor $(s^2 + \omega_0^2)^2$. This case cannot be attacked by Miyata synthesis, since the numerator cannot be put into the form

$$P = \sum_p^n a_p(-s^2)^p \qquad \begin{matrix} \textbf{9.4.1} \\ \textbf{9.5.1} \end{matrix}$$

$$a_p \geq 0$$

Instead this problem will be treated by the Darlington synthesis. The even part will be multiplied by surplus factors and split. However, the emphasis will be on eliminating transformers.

**Example 9.5.1**

Realize $Z(s) = (s^2 + s + 1)/(s^2 + s + 4)$ without transformers.

*Solution*

Obtaining Ev $Z(s)$, we get

$$\text{Ev } Z(s) = \frac{(s^2 + 2)^2}{(s^2 + 4)^2 - s^2} \qquad \textbf{9.5.2}$$

This expression is multiplied by the auxilliary polynomial $(k^2 - s^2)/(k^2 - s^2)$ to give

$$\text{Ev } Z(s) = \frac{(s^2 + 2)^2(k^2 - s^2)}{\underbrace{((k + 1)s^2 + 4k)^2}_{m^2} - \underbrace{s^2(s^2 + (k + 4))^2}_{n^2}}$$

$$= \underbrace{\frac{k^2(s^2 + 2)^2}{m^2 - n^2}}_{\text{Ev } Z_1} + \underbrace{\frac{-s^2(s^2 + 2)^2}{m^2 - n^2}}_{\text{Ev } Z_2} \qquad \textbf{9.5.3}$$

The Darlington synthesis will be applied to Ev $Z_1$ and Ev $Z_2$. The constant $k$ will be chosen so that no transformers will result. Hence, for $Z_1$,

$$z_{22} = \frac{m}{n} = \frac{(k+1)s^2 + 4k}{s(s^2 + (k+4))} \qquad 9.5.4$$

and

$$z_{12} = \frac{\sqrt{\text{num. Ev } z_1}}{n} = \frac{k(s^2 + 2)}{s(s^2 + k + 4)} \qquad 9.5.5$$

Since for the Darlington synthesis the residue condition must be satisfied with the equal sign, $z_{11}$ will be computed from $z_{12}$ and $z_{22}$.

Note that there are two distinct cases which will lead to no transformers: Case A, $z_{22}$ has the same zeros and poles as $z_{12}$; Case B, the zero of $z_{12}$ will cancel its pole. These cases are interpreted to say that

Case A, $$\frac{4k}{k+1} = 2$$

and $\qquad\qquad\qquad\qquad\qquad\qquad\qquad\qquad\qquad$ 9.5.6

Case B, $$k + 4 = 2$$

Solving these for $k$, we get $k = 1$ or $k = -2$, respectively. Hence $k = 1$ (Case A) is acceptable.

A similar approach in solving for $Z_2$ gives

$$z_{22} = \frac{n}{m} = \frac{s(s^2 + k + 4)}{(k+1)s^2 + 4k} \qquad 9.5.7$$

and

$$z_{12} = \frac{\sqrt{-\text{num. Ev } z_2}}{m} = \frac{s(s^2 + 2)}{(k+1)s^2 + 4k} \qquad 9.5.8$$

The situation here is similar to that above. No transformers will result if $z_{22}$ and $z_{12}$ have the same poles and zeros or if $z_{12}$ will degenerate into $s/(k+1)$, owing to the fact that the zero of $z_{12}$ cancels with its pole. The first case leads to Case B in Eq. 9.5.6, whereas the second leads to Case A in Eq. 9.5.6. Hence setting $k = 1$ will satisfy the requirement of no transformers for both Ev $Z_1$ and Ev $Z_2$ in Eq. 9.5.3. Rewriting Eq. 9.5.3 accordingly, we get

$$\text{Ev } Z(s) = \frac{(s^2 + 2)^2}{4(s^2 + 2)^2 - s^2(s^2 + 5)^2} + \frac{-s^2(s^2 + 2)^2}{4(s^2 + 2)^2 - s^2(s^2 + 5)^2}$$

$$\qquad\qquad\qquad\qquad\qquad 9.5.9$$

$$= \frac{1}{4} \text{Ev } Z_1 + \text{Ev } Z_2$$

Here Ev $Z_1$ is scaled by 4 to eliminate a transformer. Computing the parameters of the respective Darlington lossless networks, we get

(1). For $Z_1$, $z_{22} = z_{12} = 2(s^2 + 2)/s(s^2 + 5)$, and therefore the residue condition dictates that $z_{11} = z_{12} = z_{22}$.

(2). For $Z_2$, $z_{22} = s(s^2 + 5)/2(s^2 + 2) = s/2 + 3s/2(s^2 + 2)$, and $z_{12} = s(s^2 + 2)/2(s^2 + 2) = s/2$. Hence $z_{11} = s/2$.

As was expected, in no case is a transformer necessary. The final network is given in Fig. 9.5. Note that this is the same network that was obtained by the Bott-Duffin synthesis of the same problem (Section 5.5)

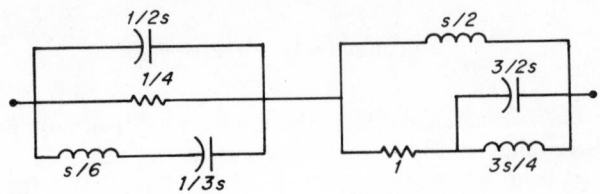

**Fig. 9.5. A network for** $Z(s) = \dfrac{s^2 + s + 1}{s^2 + s + 4}$

Now we shall apply this method to a general minimum resistive $(0 < \omega_0 < \infty)$ impedance function of degree 2. Here the even part assumes the form

$$\text{Ev } Z(s) = \frac{(s^2 + \omega_0^2)^2}{(s^2 + d)^2 - c^2 s^2} \qquad 9.5.10$$

which now is multiplied by $(k^2 - s^2)/(k^2 - s^2)$ and yields:

$$\text{Ev } Z(s) = \frac{k^2(s^2 + \omega_0^2)^2}{((c + k)s^2 + dk)^2 - s^2(s^2 + d + ck)^2}$$
$$+ \frac{- s^2(s^2 + \omega_0^2)^2}{((c + k)s^2 + dk)^2 - s^2(s^2 + d + ck)^2} \qquad 9.5.11$$

Each of these terms can be realized by the Darlington synthesis without transformers if either of the following is satisfied:

Case A: $\qquad \dfrac{dk}{c + k} = \omega_0^2 \qquad$ that is $k = \dfrac{c\omega_0^2}{d - \omega_0^2}$

$\qquad\qquad\qquad\qquad\qquad\qquad\qquad\qquad\qquad\qquad 9.5.12$

Case B: $\qquad d + ck = \omega_0^2 \qquad$ that is $k = \dfrac{\omega_0^2 - d}{c}$

These correspond to Cases A and B of Eq. 9.5.6. Note that necessarily one of them gives a positive $k$. Hence a solution is assured.

In the next two sections it will be shown that this procedure can be generalized for impedance functions of higher degree. Operator synthesis will be utilized.

## 9.6. IMPEDANCE OPERATOR SYNTHESIS

In the previous chapter (Section 8.4), it was demonstrated that the form of $Z(s)$ in Eq. 8.3.3 lends itself to network synthesis. (This form is usually obtained by using Richards' theorem or its extensions.) Use is thus made of the expression for $Z(s)$ in the form

$$Z(s) = \frac{m_1 \zeta + n_2}{m_2 + n_2 \zeta}$$ 
 
8.3.3
9.6.1

and also the impedance operator $V(s)$, as defined by

$$V(s) = \frac{m_1 + n_1}{m_2 + n_2}$$ 

8.4.1b
9.6.2

To understand the approach of this section, observe that $V(s)$ can be obtained from $Z(s)$, in Eq. 9.6.1, by replacing $\zeta$ with 1 ohm. Conversely, it is possible to synthesize $V(s)$ in a manner such that, when the resistive element—or elements— is, or are, interchanged with $\zeta$, $Z(s)$ is obtained.

$V(s)$ can be made a minimum resistance by removing a constant value $\alpha$. Then

$$V(s) = \alpha + \frac{(m_1 - \alpha m_2) + n_1 - \alpha n_2}{m_2 + n_2}$$ 

9.6.3

Now $\zeta$ can be inserted to give

$$Z(s) = \alpha \frac{m_2 \zeta + n_2}{m_2 + n_2 \zeta} + \frac{(m_1 - \alpha m_2)\zeta + n_1 - \alpha n_2}{m_2 + n_2 \zeta}$$ 

9.6.4a

$$= \alpha \frac{m_2 \zeta + n_2}{m_2 + n_2 \zeta} + \beta \frac{(1 + As^2)\zeta + Bs}{1 + Ds^2 + Cs\zeta}$$ 

9.6.4b

$$= \alpha Z_1 + \beta Z_2$$ 

9.6.4c

$\alpha$, $\beta$, $A$, $B$, $C$, and $D$ are positive constants. The first term on the right of Eq. 9.6.4 can be represented as shown in Fig. 9.6.

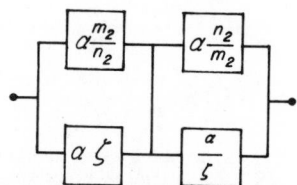

**Fig. 9.6. A realization of the first term on the right of Eq. 9.6.4**

The second term on the right of Eq. 9.6.4 has minimum resistance operator, $V(s)$, associated with it. Thus num. Ev $V$ has the perfect square factor $(1 + s^2\sqrt{AD})^2$, and $V(s)$ can be synthesized by the Darlington method. The resistive termination is replaced with $\zeta$ to represent the second term on the right of Eq. 9.6.4, as shown in Fig. 9.7.

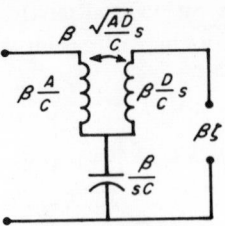

**Fig. 9.7. A realization of the second term on the right of Eq. 9.6.4**

Thus following the rules suggested by Eqs. 9.6.3 and 9.6.4 it is possible to synthesize $Z(s)$ through its operator $V(s)$. However, the rules are considerable more relaxed if $V(s)$ is synthesized from its even part. Then it is even possible to select the numerator in such a way as to eliminate transformers.

## 9.7. IMPEDANCE OPERATOR EVEN PART SYNTHESIS

One reason that makes it possible to synthesize an impedance function from its operators is that the distributive law of algebra is maintained if two operators have the same denominator. Thus $Z_1 = (m_1\zeta + n_1)/(m_2 + n_2\zeta)$, $Z_2 = (m_1{}^*\zeta + n_1{}^*)/(m_2 + n_2\zeta)$, and therefore $Z(s) = Z_1 + Z_2 = ((m_1 + m_1{}^*)\zeta + (n_1 + n_1{}^*))/(m_2 + n_2\zeta)$. However the reverse operation must be exercised with care as was shown in the previous section. Also, common factors should not be cancelled; otherwise, for example, terms like

$$Z(s) = \frac{m\zeta + n}{m + n\zeta}$$

where

$$V(s) = \frac{m + n}{m + n}$$

9.7.1

reduce to insignificance if $V(s)$ is set to 1. These considerations, however, are taken care of automatically if $V(s)$ is synthesized from its even part.

**Example 9.7.1**

Let $Z(s)$ be given by

$$Z(s) = \frac{m_1\zeta + n_1}{m_2 + n_2\zeta} \equiv V\zeta$$

9.7.2

(meaning $V$ operating on $\zeta$)

where $V = (s^2 + 3s + 3)/(s^2 + 2s + 1)$. Synthesize this function without transformers.

## Solution

Construct Ev $V(s)$ which gives

$$\text{Ev } V(s) = \frac{s^4 - 2s^2 + 3}{(s^2 + 1)^2 - 4s^2}$$

$$= \frac{s^4}{(s^2 + 1)^2 - 4s^2} + \frac{-2s^2}{(s^2 + 1)^2 - 4s^2} + \frac{3}{(s^2 + 1)^2 - 4s^2}$$

9.7.3

Each one of these can be synthesized by the Darlington procedure. No transformer will result. (See Fig. 9.8 and Example 9.1.1).

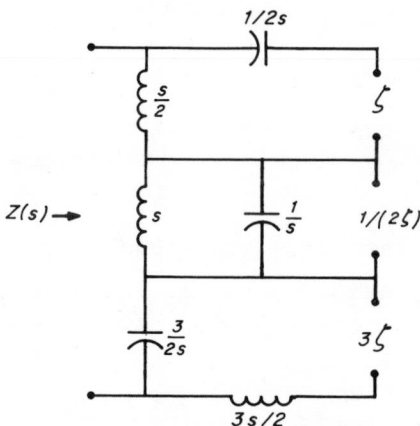

**Fig. 9.8. A realization of Z(s)**
$$= \frac{(s^2 + 3)\, \zeta + 2s}{s^2 + 1 + 2s\, \zeta}$$

Note the inversion of $\zeta$ in the center network. This is due to the fact that the middle term of Eq. 9.7.3 is realized by Darlington synthesis, *Case B*.

Perhaps the predominant reason for the fact that the even-part synthesis is useful for operator synthesis is that the denominator is undisturbed by the split. In addition, recall that (Section 8.4)

$$\text{Ev } Z(s) = \frac{\text{num. Ev } V(s) \text{ Ev } \zeta}{(m_2 + n_2 \text{ Od } \zeta)^2 - n_2^2 (\text{Ev } \zeta)^2}$$

8.4.5
9.7.4

Hence if num. Ev $V$ is split, the sum of the splits will reconstruct the desired Ev $Z(s)$.

The even part $V(s)$ split can also be used when the numerator of

Ev $V(s)$ has a $j$ axis zero. Equation 9.7.4 shows that then Ev $Z(s)$ has that zero as well. Hence this situation arises when $Z(s)$ is minimum resistive and the problem also appears when the minimum resistance is removed from the operator (see Eq. 9.6.3).

### Example 9.7.2

Realize $Z(s)$ when Ev $V(s)$ is given by

$$\text{Ev } V(s) = \frac{(1 + s^2/\omega_0^2)^2}{(1 + Ds^2)^2 - C^2s^2} \qquad \textbf{9.7.5}$$

$$D > 0 < C$$

This case corresponds to the second term on the right of Eq. 9.6.4, that is

$$Z_2 = \frac{(1 + As^2)\zeta + Bs}{1 + Ds^2 + Cs\zeta} \qquad \begin{matrix}\textbf{9.6.4b}\\\textbf{9.7.6}\end{matrix}$$

### Solution

The attack on this problem is similar to that used in Example 9.5.1, namely it is necessary to use surplus factors. But $V(s)$ is an operator, and the choice of surplus factors effects the termination. One way of obtaining the desired factor is to use Richards' theorem. Hence let $\zeta$ be given by $\zeta = \zeta(k)(k\zeta_1 + s)/(k + s\zeta_1)$. This will modify Eqs. 9.7.5 and 9.7.6 as follows:

$$\frac{Z_2}{\zeta(k)} = \frac{\big((1 + As^2)k + Bs^2/\zeta(k)\big)\zeta_1 + s\big(1 + As^2 + Bk/\zeta(k)\big)}{k + Ds^2k + Cs^2\zeta(k) + s\zeta_1\big(1 + Ds^2 + Ck\zeta(k)\big)} \qquad \textbf{9.7.7}$$

and therefore

$$\text{Ev } V_1 = \frac{(1 + s^2/\omega_0^2)^2(1 - s^2/k^2)}{\big(1 + s^2(D + C\zeta(k)/k)\big)^2 - s^2\big(1/k + C\zeta(k) + Ds^2/k\big)^2}$$

which may be split as follows:

$$\text{Ev } V_1 = \frac{(1 + s^2/\omega_0^2)^2}{\big(1 + s^2(D + C\zeta(k)/k)\big)^2 - s^2\big(1/k + C\zeta(k) + Ds^2/k\big)^2}$$
$$+ \frac{1}{\omega_0^4 D^2} \frac{-(\omega_0^2 Ds/k)^2(1 + s^2/\omega_0^2)^2}{\big(1 + s^2(D + C\zeta(k)/k)\big)^2 - s^2\big(1/k + C\zeta(k) + Ds^2/k\big)^2} \qquad \textbf{9.7.8}$$

where $(\omega_0^2 D/k)^2$ is a scaling constant. Each of the two expressions on the right of Eq. 9.7.8 can be synthesized by the Darlington synthesis. Furthermore, no transformers will be necessary if either

$$\zeta(k)/k = (1 - D\omega_0^2)/C\omega_0^2 \qquad \textbf{9.7.9a}$$

or

$$\zeta(k)k = -(1 - D\omega_0^2)/C \qquad \textbf{9.7.9b}$$

Hence one of these always may be satisfied for some $k > 0$ if $\zeta(s)$ has neither a zero nor a pole at either the origin or at infinity. However these restrictions are minor, since if $\zeta$ has a $j$ axis zero or a pole, its even-part numerator has it too and therefore $Z(s)$ must have it (see Eq. 9.7.4). Then it could have been removed a priori.

For further illustration, assume that Eq. 9.7.9a is satisfied. This allows Eq. 9.7.8 to be simplified as follows:

$$\text{Ev } V_1 = \frac{(1 + s^2/\omega_0^2)^2}{(1 + s^2/\omega_0^2)^2 - s^2\left(\dfrac{1}{k} + C\zeta(k) + Ds^2/k\right)^2}$$

$$+ \frac{1}{\omega_0^4 D^2} \frac{-\left(\dfrac{\omega_0^2 Ds}{k}\right)^2 (1 + s^2/\omega_0^2)^2}{(1 + s^2/\omega_0^2)^2 - s^2\left(\dfrac{1}{k} + C\zeta(k) + Ds^2/k\right)^2} \qquad \textbf{9.7.10}$$

$$\equiv \text{Ev } V_2 + \frac{1}{\omega_0^4 D^2} \text{Ev } V_3$$

Now apply a Darlington process to Ev $V_2$ and Ev $V_3$ and multiply the network of $V_3$ by $1/\omega_0^4 D^2$. This example which is similar to Example 9.5.1 leads to Fig. 9.9.

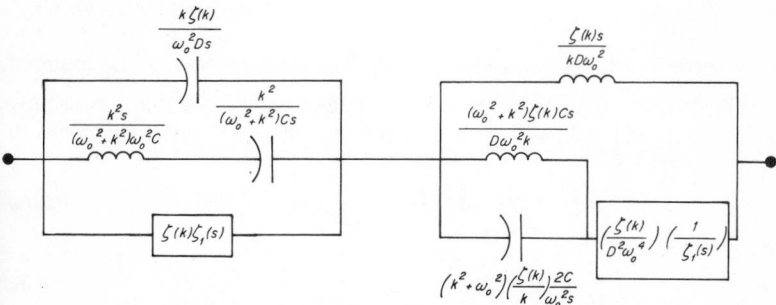

**Fig. 9.9. A network corresponding to Eq. 9.7.10**

## SYNTHESIS OF $Z_{11}$ WHEN THE ZEROS OF $Z_{12}$ ARE PRESCRIBED  9.8

So far the even part of $Z(s)$ was utilized in a synthesis procedure in which no transformers were desired. At this point the abundance of solutions offered by the even-part synthesis will be utilized to satisfy some transfer impedance requirements. $Z(s)$, the driving point impedance function, will now become $z_{11}$ of a two-port network. It will be completely specified in terms of a positive, real, impedance function. In addition, the zeros of $z_{12}$ will also be given, with the proviso that the real part condition (Eq. 6.4.17) is satisfied:

$$\text{Re } z_{11} \text{ Re } z_{22} - (\text{Re } z_{12})^2 \geqq 0 \text{ for Re } s = 0 \qquad \textbf{6.4.17}$$
$$> 0 \text{ for Re } s > 0 \qquad \textbf{9.8.1}$$

The problem will be attacked by splitting Ev $z_{11}$. One of the members will be selected to conform to the requirements dictated by the zeros of the transfer impedance $z_{12}$. The method will be explained by illustrations.

### Example 9.8.1

Realize a two-port network for which $z_{11} = (s^2 + 3s + 3)/(s^2 + 2s + 1)$, and $z_{12}$ has the zero $(s^2 + 2)$.

### Solution

$z_{11}$ is the same function given in Example 9.1.1. Its even part is given by

$$\text{Ev } z_{11} = \frac{s^4 - 2s^2 + 3}{(s^2 + 1)^2 - 4s^2} \qquad \textbf{9.8.2}$$

This function may be split as follows:

$$\text{Ev } z_{11} = \frac{1}{4}\frac{s^4}{(s^2 + 1)^2 - 4s^2} + \frac{5}{4}\frac{-4s^2}{(s^2 + 1)^2 - 4s^2} + \frac{3}{4}\frac{(s^2 + 2)^2}{(s^2 + 1)^2 - 4s^2}$$

$$\qquad \textbf{9.8.3}$$

$$= \frac{1}{4}\text{ Ev } Z_1 + \frac{5}{4}\text{ Ev } Z_2 + \frac{3}{4}\text{ Ev } Z_3$$

The impedances $\frac{1}{4}Z_1$, $\frac{5}{4}Z_2$, and $\frac{3}{4}Z_3$ may all be synthesized by the Darlington procedure. The last impedance, $\frac{3}{4}Z_3$, will serve to provide the required $z_{12}$. The first two impedances have already been realized (within a constant) in Figs. 9.1 and 9.2, respectively. Applying the Darlington synthesis to Ev $Z_3$, we get

$$z_{22} = \frac{s^2 + 1}{2s} = \frac{s}{2} + \frac{1}{2s} \qquad \textbf{9.8.4a}$$

and

$$z_{12} = \frac{\sqrt{\text{num. Ev } Z(s)}}{2s} = \frac{s^2 + 2}{2s} = \frac{s}{2} + \frac{1}{s} \qquad \textbf{9.8.4b}$$

Thus, satisfying the residue condition with the equal sign gives $z_{11} = \frac{s}{2} + \frac{2}{s}$. The final network is shown on Fig. 9.10.

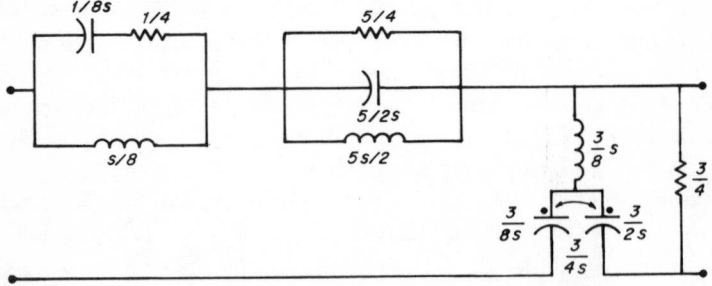

**Fig. 9.10. A network with** $z_{11} = \dfrac{s^2 + 3s + 3}{s^2 + 2s + 1}$ **and with** $z_{12}$ **having the zero** $s^2 + 2$

The shunting two-port network carries the required zero.

In general, the transfer impedance of a two-port network terminated in $\zeta$ is given by

$$z_{12} = \frac{z'_{12}\zeta}{z'_{22} + \zeta}$$

9.8.5

where the primes denote the parameters of the original two-port network. Consequently the transfer impedance of a general Darlington network is

$$z_{12} = \frac{\dfrac{\sqrt{m_1 m_2 - n_1 n_2}}{n_2}}{1 + \dfrac{m_2}{n_2}} = \frac{\sqrt{m_1 m_2 - n_1 n_2}}{m_2 + n_2}$$

9.8.6

This means that the precise value of the transfer impedance of Fig. 9.10 is

$$z_{12} = \frac{s^2 + 2}{s^2 + 2s + 1}$$

9.8.7

Thus, inasmuch as the zeros are arbitrary, the method outlined above leads to transfer impedance functions with the same denominator as that of $z_{11}$. Moreover, $z_{22}$ of the final network comes out to be $m_2/(m_2 + n_2)$. That is, $z_{22} = (s^2 + 1)/(s^2 + 2s + 1)$ for the network in Fig. 9.10.

### Example 9.8.2

Realize a two-port network for which $z_{11} = (s^2 + s + 2)/(2s^2 + s + 1)$, and $z_{12}$ has the zeros $s^2 + 4$.

### Solution

Calculation of Ev $z_{11}$ gives

$$\text{Ev } z_{11} = \frac{2(s^2 + 1)^2}{(2s^2 + 1) - s^2}$$

9.8.8

This expression has a minimum value of zero at $s = \pm j$ which means that it cannot be split unless surplus factors are used. Furthermore, the real-part condition (Eq. 9.8.1) requires that Re $z_{12}$ be zero at $s = \pm j$. This will be achieved by forcing $z_{12}$ to have the numerator factor $s^2 + 1$. Thus one possible surplus factor is $(s^2 - 4)^2$ which permits the following rearrangement of Eq. 9.8.8:

$$\text{Ev } z_{11} = 2\,\frac{(s^2 + 1)^2(s^2 - 4)^2}{((2s^2 + 1)^2 - s^2)(s^2 - 4)^2}$$

$$= 2\,\frac{(s^2 + 1)^2((s^2 + 4)^2 - 16s^2)}{(2s^4 + 13s^2 + 4)^2 - s^2(9s^2 + 8)^2}$$

$$= \frac{1}{2}\,\frac{-64s^2(s^2 + 1)^2}{(2s^4 + 13s^2 + 4)^2 - s^2(9s^2 + 8)^2}$$

$$\qquad + 2\,\frac{(s^2 + 1)^2(s^2 + 4)^2}{(2s^4 + 13s^2 + 4)^2 - s^2(9s^2 + 8)^2}$$

9.8.9

Note that upon realizing the second term on the right of Eq. 9.8.9, by the method illustrated by the first example, $z_{12}$ of the associated Darlington network (corresponding to Eq. 9.8.6) will be—within a multiplying constant—

$$z_{12} = \frac{(s^2 + 1)(s^2 + 4)}{2s^4 + 9s^3 + 13s^2 + 8s + 4} \qquad \textbf{9.8.10}$$

This transfer impedance has the required zero plus the factor $(s^2 + 1)$, which is necessary to satisfy the real-part condition. The final network, corresponding to Eq. 9.8.9, is given in Fig. 9.11 where: $a = \frac{1}{4}(9 + 85/\sqrt{137})$, $b = \frac{1}{4}(9 - 85/\sqrt{137})$, $c = 2(1 - 9/\sqrt{137})$, $d = 2(1 + 9/\sqrt{1370})$, $\omega_1^2 = \frac{1}{4}(13 - \sqrt{137})$, and $\omega_2^2 = \frac{1}{4}(13 + \sqrt{137})$. Note that the series impedance in Fig. 9.11

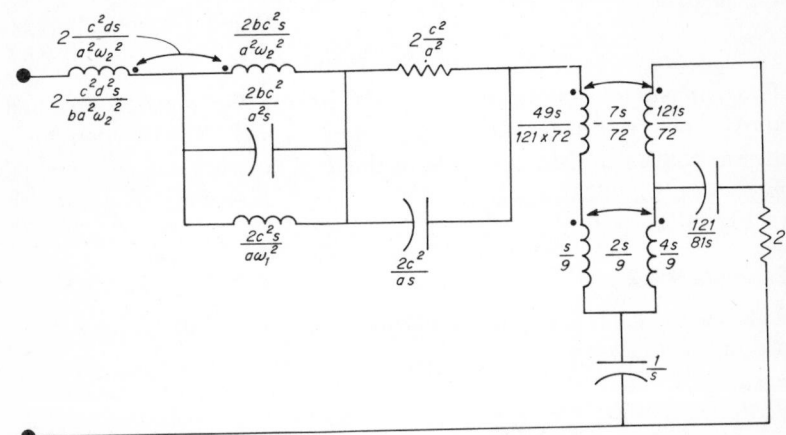

**Fig. 9.11. A network with $z_{11} = \dfrac{s^2 + s + 2}{2s^2 + s + 1}$ with $z_{12}$ having the zero $s^2 + 4$**

can be synthesized without transformers by first computing its driving point impedance function and then realizing this impedance function by transformerless methods.

The fact that $z_{12}$ has additional zeros, $(s^2 + 1)$, when $z_{11}$ is minimum resistive, is a drawback of the method. The method possesses another drawback when the $z_{12}$ zeros specified are not along the $j$ axis. For example, if it is required to have the zero $s - 1$, an additional zero (surplus zero) $s + 1$ must also be provided. This is necessary so that each numerator in the even-part split will be a squared even or odd function. This is not a requirement if gyrators are used. Hence $(s - 1)^2$ cannot belong to an even-part split and still give realizable networks unless it is accompanied by the factor $(s + 1)^2$, yielding a combined factor $(s^2 - 1)^2$.

## Example 9.8.3

Realize a network having $z_{11} = (s^2 + s + 2)/(2s^2 + s + 1)$ and for which $z_{12}$ has the zero $s - 1$.

### Solution

Construct Ev $z_{11}$, which is

$$\text{Ev } z_{11} = \frac{2(s^2 + 1)^2}{(2s^2 + 1)^2 - s^2} \qquad \textbf{9.8.8}$$

This is now multiplied by the surplus factor $(s^2 - 1)^2/(s^2 - 1)^2$ to yield

$$\text{Ev } z_{11} = \frac{2(s^2 + 1)^2(s^2 - 1)^2}{((2s^2 + 1)^2 - s^2)(s^2 - 1)^2}$$

$$= \frac{2(s^2 + 1)^2(s^2 - 1)^2}{(2s^4 + 5s^2 + 1)^2 - s^2(5s^2 + 3)^2} \qquad \textbf{9.8.11}$$

There is no need here to break the even part, since the required zero may be achieved with one network. This is due, in part, to the fact that Ev $z_{11}$ already has a perfect-square numerator. The transfer impedance function will be of the form of Eq. 9.8.6, yielding

$$z_{12} = \frac{\sqrt{2}\,(s^2 + 1)(s^2 - 1)}{(2s^2 + s + 1)(s + 1)^2} = \frac{\sqrt{2}\,(s^2 + 1)(s - 1)}{(2s^2 + s + 1)(s + 1)} \qquad \textbf{9.8.12}$$

Note that the unwanted zero in the *l.h.s* plane has been cancelled. This is no accident. If the zero is to be preserved, an alternate surplus factor must be chosen. For example, let it be $\left(s^2 - \left(\alpha + \dfrac{1}{\alpha}\right)s + 1\right)\Big/\left(s^2 - \left(\alpha + \dfrac{1}{\alpha}\right)s + 1\right)$ and let $\alpha > 0$; hence $\beta = \alpha + \dfrac{1}{\alpha} > 2$. Thus Ev $z_{11}$ may be rearranged as follows:

$$\text{Ev } z_{11} = \frac{2(s^2 + 1)^2(s^2 - 1/\alpha^2)(s^2 - \alpha^2)}{(2s^4 + (3 + \beta)s^2 + 1)^2 - s^2((2\beta + 1)s^2 + 1 + \beta)^2}$$

$$= \frac{-2(s^2 + 1)^2s^2(\alpha^2 + 1/\alpha^2 - 2)}{(2s^4 + (3 + \beta)s^2 + 1)^2 - s^2((2\beta + 1)s^2 + 1 + \beta)^2} \qquad \textbf{9.8.13}$$

$$+ \frac{2(s^2 + 1)^2(s^2 - 1)^2}{(2s^4 + (3 + \beta)s^2 + 1)^2 - s^2((2\beta + 1)s^2 + 1 + \beta)^2}$$

The second term on the right will carry the required $z_{12}$ zeros. No network realization of Eqs. 9.8.13 is given here.

Note that $\beta$ is still arbitrary (as long as it is larger than 2) and can be utilized for other purposes.

## PROBLEMS

9.1. Realize $Z(s) = \dfrac{s^2 + s + 2}{s^2 + s + 1}$

without transformers by means of an appropriate split of the even part.

9.2. Use the Miyata synthesis procedure to realize the following functions:

(a).     $\text{Ev } Z(s) = \dfrac{-s^6 + 3s^4 - 2s^2 + 1}{(2s^2 + 1)^2 - s^2(s^2 + 2)^2}$

(b).     $\text{Ev } Z(s) = \dfrac{s^4 + s^2 + 2}{(s^2 + 3)^2 - s^2}$

9.3. Realize a network from the even part of the function:

$$Z(s) = \frac{s^2 + s + 9}{s^2 + s + 4}$$

9.4. If a positive $k$ is obtained such that

$$k\zeta(k) = (D\omega_0^2 - 1)/C$$

in Eqs. 9.7.8, find the network corresponding to Fig. 9.9.

9.5. Find the maximum value of the coefficient $\alpha$ such that

$$P = s^4 + 2s^2 + 3 - \alpha(s^2 + 2)^2$$

is nonnegative on the $j$ axis.

Answer: $\alpha = \dfrac{2}{3}$ yielding $P = \dfrac{1}{3}(s^2 + 1)^2$.

9.6. Realize the network for which

(a). $z_{11} = \dfrac{s^2 + s + 2}{s^2 + s + 1}$ and $z_{12}$ has the zero $(s^2 + 1)$.

(b). $z_{12}$ is as in (a) and $z_{12}$ has the zero $(s^2 + 4)$.

(c). $z_{11}$ is as in (a) and $z_{12}$ has the zero $(s + 1)$.

In (b) and (c) use an outline form only.

9.7. $V(s)$ of Eq. 9.6.2 is a general impedance function of degree 2. Realize this function by means of the even-part split discussed in Section 7.6. This will yield a network of the type given in Fig. 7.14. Now replace terminal resistors by $\zeta$ in one of the networks and $\dfrac{1}{\zeta}$ in the other (the constant should not be deleted) to obtain a realization for the corresponding $Z(s)$. Show that one of these networks is a realization for $F(s)$ given in Eq. 8.4.2 (Section 8.4) within a constant multiplier.

Answer: If $Z_1$ is the impedance of one of the networks and $Z_2$ is that of the other then

$$Z = Z_1 + Z_2 = \frac{(s^2 + ab)^2 Z - (a + b)^2 s(abA + s^2 B)}{s^4 - (a^2 + b^2)s^2 + a^2 b^2}$$

$$+ (a + b)^2 s \frac{abA + s^2 B - sZ}{s^4 - (a^2 + b^2)s^2 + a^2 b^2}$$

where $A = \dfrac{aZ(b) - bZ(a)}{a^2 - b^2}$ and $B = \dfrac{aZ(a) - bZ(b)}{a^2 - b^2}$

## FURTHER READING

BOOKS

9.1. Balabanian, N., "Network Synthesis," Prentice-Hall, Inc., Englewood Cliffs, N. J., 1958, Chapter 3.

9.2. Guillemin, E. A., "Synthesis of Passive Networks," John Wiley & Sons, New York, 1957, Chapter 10.

9.3. Tuttle, D. F., Jr., "Network Synthesis," John Wiley & Sons, New York, 1958, Chapter 9.

9.4. Van-Valkenburg, M. E., "Introduction to Modern Network Synthesis," John Wiley & Sons, New York, 1960, Chapter 8.

RELATED PAPERS

9.5. Miyata, F., "A New System of Two-Terminal Synthesis," *IRE Trans on Circuit Theory*, Vol. CT-2, pp. 297–302, Dec., 1955.

9.6. Kuh, E. S., "Special Synthesis Techniques for Driving Point Impedance Functions," *IRE Trans. on Circuit Theory*, Vol. CT-2, pp. 302–308, Dec., 1955.

# CHAPTER 10

# Constant Immittance*
# 2-Port Networks

## 10.1. INTRODUCTION

General methods for the realization of 2-port networks require coupling elements. For example, in the previous chapter (Section 9.8) it was shown that a network can be realized if $z_{11}$ and the zeros of $z_{12}$ are specified. However, a more desirable situation would be that which, in addition to eliminating transformers, would permit a common ground; that is, the network is then a three-terminal network. This chapter will be devoted to networks where $z_{11}$ (or $y_{22}$) is a constant and where $z_{12}$ (or $-y_{12}$) is completely specified. These networks are called constant immittance networks. They are relatively simple to construct and to expand; also, they provide familiarity with techniques necessary for the forthcoming chapters. If zeros of the respective transfer immittance function do not lie on the positive real axis, common ground realization will be shown. The networks are useful in voltage transfer function synthesis, since $E_2/E_1$ (for zero $I_2$) is completely specified by $z_{12}$ (or $y_{12}$) when $z_{11}$ (or $y_{22}$) is constant.

## 10.2. ORIGIN AND INFINITY TRANSMISSION ZEROS—REAL POLES

Transmission zeros are the zeros of $z_{12}$ (or $y_{12}$). For the sake of simplicity $z_{12}$ is temporarily restricted to have only real axis poles. The subject may be introduced by recalling that $Z(s) = 1$ may be expanded as follows:

$$Z(s) = 1 = \frac{s}{s+k} + \frac{k}{s+k}$$

$$(k > 0)$$

5.1.4
10.2.1

---
*An immittance may stand for either an admittance or an impedance.

172

This expansion now can be realized in an $L$ form (Fig. 10.1) as a four-terminal network whose $z_{11} = Z(s) = 1$ and $z_{12} = \dfrac{k}{s + k}$.

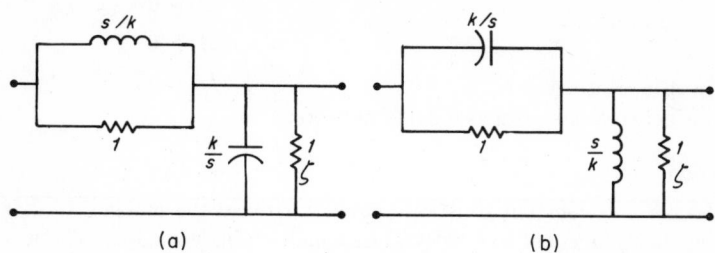

(a)                              (b)

Fig. 10.1. *Constant impedance networks ($z_{11} = 1$) and $z_{12}$ have the values (a) $k/(s + k)$ and (b) $s/(s + k)$ respectively*

At this point, the 1-ohm termination (marked $\delta$) may be replaced with another network, just like the original, with another arbitrary constant $k_1$ (Fig. 10.2).

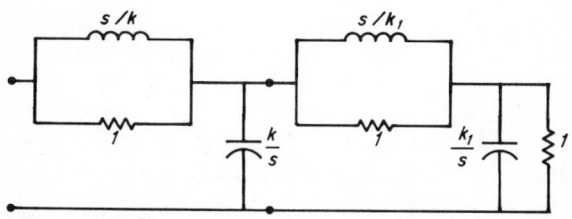

Fig. 10.2. *A network whose $z_{11} = 1$ and $z_{12} = kk_1/(s + k)(s + k_1)$*

The input impedance ($z_{11}$) has not changed, since the 1 ohm was replaced with another impedance whose $z_{11}$ is 1 ohm. The transfer impedance may be obtained from the equivalent relation for a cascade connection

$$z_{12} = \frac{z_{12}^{(1)} \times z_{12}^{(2)}}{z_{22}^{(1)} + z_{11}^{(2)}} = \frac{\dfrac{k}{s} \times \dfrac{k_1}{s + k_1}}{\dfrac{k}{s} + 1} = \frac{kk_1}{(s + k)(s + k_1)} \qquad 10.2.2$$

This process may be continued to yield a network whose $z_{11}$ is a constant, but $z_{12} = \Pi_p k_p/(s + k_p)$.

### Example 10.2.1

Realize a network with the specification that

$$T_{12} = \frac{E_2}{E_1}\bigg|_{I_2=0} = \frac{z_{12}}{z_{11}} = Ae^{-sT} \qquad\qquad \textbf{10.2.3}$$

$$T > 0$$
$$A > 0$$

where $A$ is arbitrary.

This network is known as a delay network.

### Solution

The use of a constant resistance network reduces the problem to that of forcing $z_{12}$ to be equal to $e^{-sT}$ (within a multiplying constant). The rest of the problem will be solved by approximation. Recall that the $n^{\text{th}}$ order approximation of $e^{-sT}$ may be given by

$$e^{-sT} = \frac{1}{e^{sT}} = \frac{1}{\left(1 + \dfrac{sT}{n}\right)^n} \qquad \text{for } n \to \infty$$

$$= \frac{\left(\dfrac{n}{T}\right)^n}{\left(s + \dfrac{n}{T}\right)^n} \qquad \text{for } n \to \infty \qquad\qquad \textbf{10.2.4}$$

Hence the required network is given by an $n$-section network (Fig. 10.3).

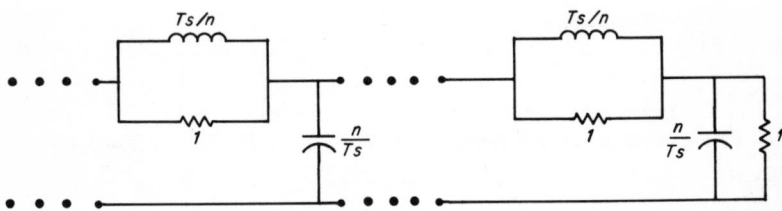

**Fig. 10.3. A delay network**

However, this network is not better than the approximation performed in Eq. 10.2.4. For a finite number of elements the approximation improves as $s$ approaches zero.

So far all the zeros of $z_{12}$ were at infinity. They may be placed at the origin if the sections of the type shown in Fig. 10.1b are connected in cascade. If it is desired to have a number of the zeros at the origin, that number of type $b$ sections should be used. These results now may be formalized.

## Theorem 10.2.1

If $z_{11}$ is a constant, $m + n$ is Hurwitz of degree $d$, and $z_{12}$ is given by

$$z_{12} = \frac{s^\alpha}{m + n} \qquad \text{10.2.5}$$

where $\alpha$ is a positive integer ($\alpha \leq d$); then the respective network is realizable as a three-terminal network.

So far this theorem has been proved for a denominator with real roots only; the rest of the theorem will be proved in the following section.

## ORIGIN AND INFINITY TRANSMISSION ZEROS—COMPLEX POLES 10.3

So far all the poles of $z_{12}$ have been real. If they are complex, the network in Fig. 10.4 is useful to realize each complex pole pair.

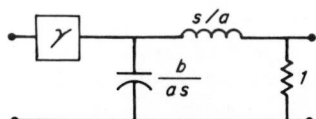

Fig. 10.4. A network whose $z_{11}$ is constant and $z_{12} = b/(s^2 + as + b)$

Here $\gamma$ is given by

$$\gamma = z_{11} - \frac{b(s + a)}{a(s^2 + as + b)} \qquad \text{10.3.1a}$$

$z_{11}$ is an arbitrary constant sufficiently large that $\gamma$ is prf. We shall prove that it is always possible to find such a constant. Let $z_{11} = \beta$ and solve for $\gamma$

$$\gamma = \frac{\beta s^2 + s(\beta a - b/a) + b(\beta - 1)}{s^2 + as + b} \qquad \text{10.3.1b}$$

Hence $\dfrac{b}{a^2} < \beta > 1$. Furthermore (after some algebra), the positive reality constraint along the $j\omega$ axis requires that $\beta > b^2/[(b - \omega^2)^2 + a^2\omega^2]$. These three conditions can be met by making $\beta$ large enough. An exception occurs if $a = 0$. Then the pole in question is on the $j$ axis. Indeed, this particular case has to be handled by other methods.

### Example 10.3.1

Realize a low-pass filter which is specified by the attenuation frequency curve of Fig. 10.5 by means of constant resistance networks.

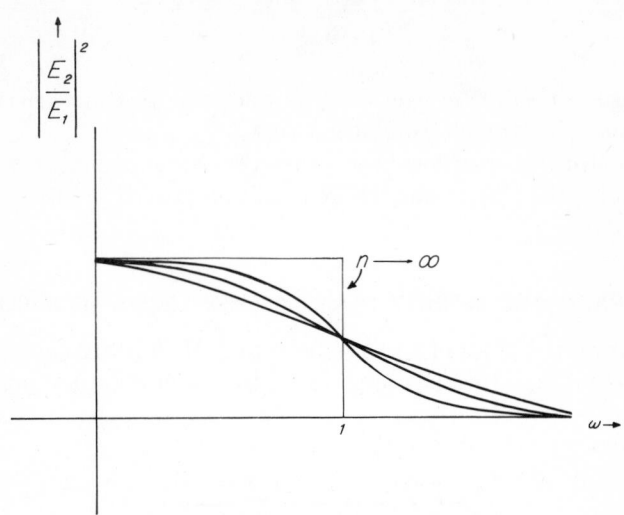

**Fig. 10.5. Characteristics of a low-pass filter**

### Solution

The problem has two parts. The first part is that of approximating the curve in Fig. 10.5 and the second is that of realizing the corresponding network. The figure can be approximated by means of a function

$$\left|\frac{E_2}{E_1}\right|^2 = \frac{1}{1 + \omega^{2n}} = \frac{1}{1 + (-s^2)^n}\bigg|_{s=j\omega} \qquad 10.3.2$$

along the $j$ axis. If $n$ is chosen as 3, Eq. 10.3.2 becomes

$$\frac{E_2}{E_1} \times \left(\frac{\bar{E}_2}{\bar{E}_1}\right) = \frac{1}{1 - s^6}$$

$$= \left(\frac{1}{(s + 1)(s^2 + s + 1)}\right)\left(\frac{1}{(1 - s)(s^2 - s + 1)}\right) \qquad 10.3.3$$

Hence $E_2/E_1$ is chosen as

$$\frac{E_2}{E_1} = \frac{1}{(s + 1)(s^2 + s + 1)} \qquad 10.3.4$$

since the conjugate of this quantity is given by

$$\frac{\bar{E}_2}{\bar{E}_1} = \frac{1}{(1 - s)(s^2 - s + 1)} \qquad 10.3.5$$

along the $j$ axis. Hence $|E_2|^2/|E_1|^2$ is given by Eq. 10.3.3 along the $j$ axis as desired.

Now it remains to realize the constant resistance network corresponding to Eq. 10.3.4. The simple pole may be realized as shown in Fig. 10.6. The complex pole may be realized by means of a network of the type in Fig. 10.4 given in Fig. 10.7. However the impedance, $\gamma$, is yet to be determined from

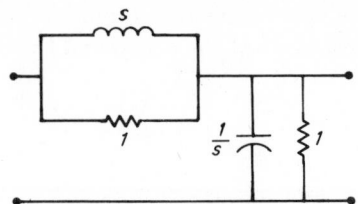

Fig. 10.6. A network with $z_{11} = 1$ and $z_{12} = 1/(s + 1)$

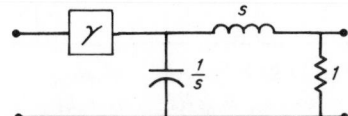

Fig. 10.7. A constant resistance net- work with $z_{12} = 1/(s^2 + s + 1)$

Eq. 10.3.1$b$. Thus

$$\gamma = \frac{\beta s^2 + s(\beta - 1) + \beta - 1}{(s^2 + s + 1)} \qquad 10.3.6$$

The minimum value of $\beta$ that will render $\gamma$ prf is $\beta = 4/3$. Then $\gamma = \frac{1}{3}$ $(4s^2 + s + 1)/(s^2 + s + 1)$, which is minimum resistive. Presumably eight elements will be necessary for its realization. However, if $\beta$ is chosen as 2, $\gamma$ becomes

$$\gamma = \frac{2s^2 + s + 1}{s^2 + s + 1} = \frac{s^2 + 1}{s^2 + s + 1} + \frac{s^2 + s}{s^2 + s + 1} \qquad 10.3.7$$

Thus the number of elements is reduced by 2 (see Fig. 10.8), but the network gain is reduced from $E_2/E_1 = \frac{3}{4}(s + 1)(s^2 + s + 1)$ to $E_2/E_1 = \frac{1}{2}(s + 1)$ $(s^2 + s + 1)$.

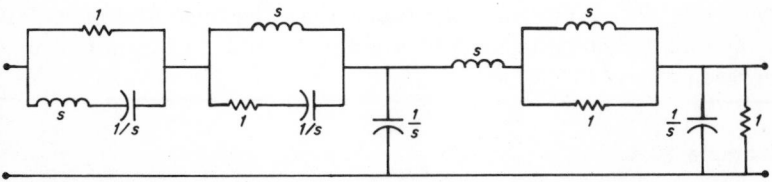

Fig. 10.8. A network with $z_{11} = 2$ and $z_{12} = 1/(s + 1)(s^2 + s + 1)$

This network represents the required approximation for the low-pass filter of Fig. 10.5, and is called a Butterworth filter. The approximation given by Eq. 10.3.2 is called the Butterworth approximation.

If $z_{12}$ has zeros at the origin instead of at infinity, the inductor and the capacitor are interchanged in Fig. 10.4. The problem is even simpler if one of the zeros is at the origin and the other is at infinity. Then $z_{12}$ is prf (Fig. 10.9).

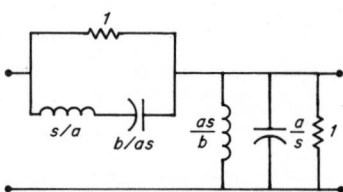

**Fig. 10.9. A network with $z_{11} = 1$ and $z_{12} = as/(s^2 + as + b)$**

Each of the networks discussed in Figs. 10.4 and 10.9 can be connected in cascade instead of the terminal resistor of any of the networks of Fig. 10.1 (proper scaling may be necessary if $z_{11} = \beta \neq 1$). Furthermore, they have complex poles. It follows that any complex poles are acceptable. This completes the proof of Theorem 10.2.1.

## 10.4. TRANSFER IMPEDANCE WITH POSITIVE COEFFICIENTS

The ideas of the last two sections may be extended to some cases where $z_{12}$ has zeros which are not at the origin and at infinity. For example, a constant resistance network can be obtained using the following grouping of terms:

$$Z(s) = 1 = \frac{(s + a) + b}{(s + a) + b} = \frac{b}{(s + a) + b} + \frac{s + a}{(s + a) + b} \qquad 10.4.1$$

The second term on the right of Eq. 10.4.1 has a real axis zero. However, this zero is closer to the origin than the respective pole. To avoid this difficulty one might attempt to add four-terminal networks in series.

**Example 10.4.1**

Realize a constant resistance network where $z_{12} = (s + a)/(s + b)$.

*Solution*

First construct two constant resistance networks having $z_{12}^{(1)} = s/(s + b)$ and $z_{12}^{(2)} = a/(s + b)$, respectively (Fig. 10.10). This is accomplished by choosing $z_{11}^{(1)} = 1$ and $z_{11}^{(2)} = a/b$.

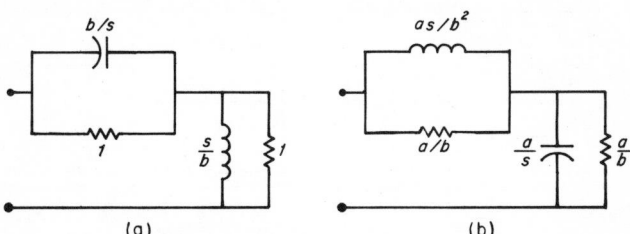

(a)                          (b)

**Fig. 10.10.** Constant impedance networks where (a) $z_{11} = 1$ and $z_{12} = s/(s + b)$, and (b) $z_{11} = a/b$ and $z_{12} = a/(s + b)$

These two can be connected in series in several ways (Fig. 10.11). The first combination (Fig. 10.11a) produces a short across the series part of one of the networks. This means that the combined $z_{11}$ will be $1 + a/(s + b)$ which is not a constant resistance. This situation can be corrected by means of an ideal transformer (Fig. 10.11b). The third combination avoids the transformer, but the common ground character of the network is lost (hence only two such networks can be connected in this manner).

One might attempt to connect these two networks in parallel (if only to preserve the common ground feature). The results are rewarding (Fig. 10.12). The parameters of the combined network are computed readily if the $Y$ matrices are added algebraically. However, for the purpose of this chapter, it is enough to find $y_{12} = y_{12}^{(1)} + y_{12}^{(2)}$ and $y_{22} = y_{22}^{(1)} + y_{22}^{(2)}$. These may be obtained by inspection of Fig. 10.10. They are:*

$$-y_{12}^{(1)} = 1 + s/b \qquad = (s + b)/b \qquad \text{10.4.2a}$$

$$y_{22}^{(1)} = 1 + s/b + 1 + b/s = (s + b)^2/bs \qquad \text{10.4.2b}$$

and

$$-y_{12}^{(2)} = b/a + b^2/as \qquad = (s + b)b/as \qquad \text{10.4.2c}$$

$$y_{22}^{(2)} = b/a + b^2/as + s/a + b/a = (s + b)^2/as \qquad \text{10.4.2d}$$

Hence

$$-y_{12} = (s + b)(1/b + b/as) \qquad \text{10.4.3a}$$

$$y_{22} = (s + b)^2(1/bs + 1/as) \qquad \text{10.4.3b}$$

---

* The negative sign of the $-y_{12}$ term is due to the sign convention adopted throughout the text. It arises when $[Y(s)]$ is computed from $[Z(s)]$. That is, $-y_{12} = (z_{21})/|z|$. It follows that $-y_{12}$ has all positive coefficients if $z_{21}$ does.

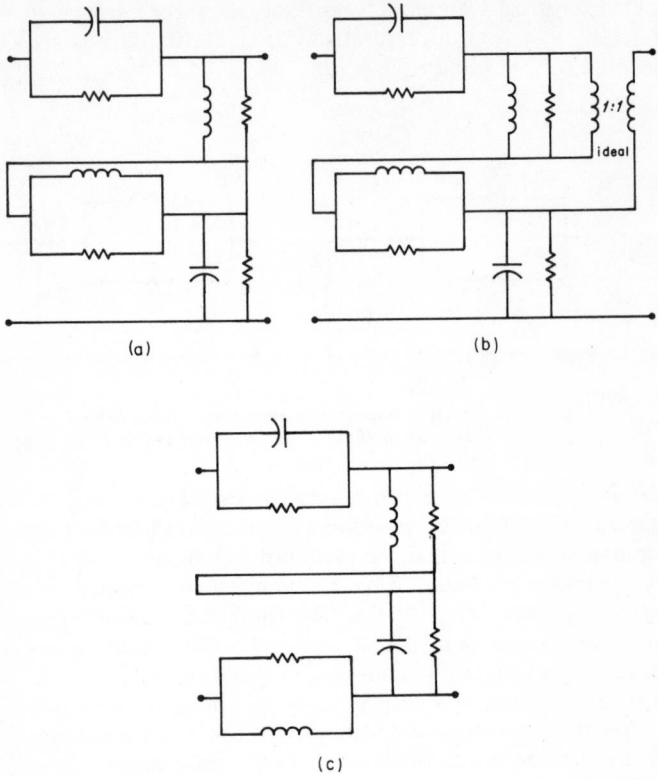

(a)          (b)

(c)

*Fig. 10.11. Several ways of connecting the networks of Fig. 10.10 in series*

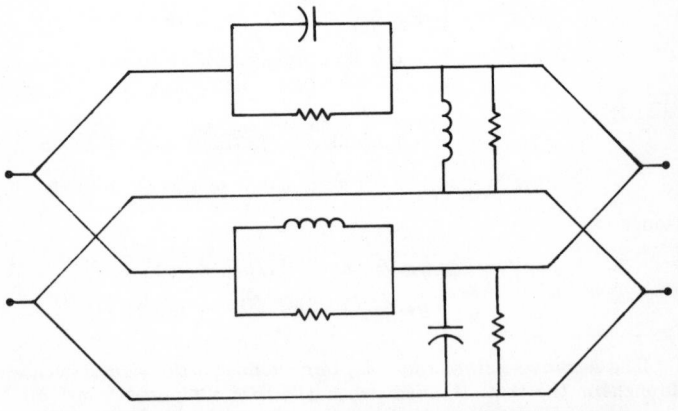

*Fig. 10.12. A parallel connection of the network of Fig. 10.10*

In comparing the results of the series connection (say Fig. 10.11c) vs. that of parallel connection, construct the ratio $T_{12} = z_{12}/z_{11} = -y_{12}/y_{22}$. In the first network, it is $b(s + a)/(s + b)(a + b)$, whereas in the second it is $(as + b^2)/(s + b)(a + b)$. Note that both networks are capable of producing arbitrary zeros of the transfer function. However the last network maintains a common ground without recourse to transformers. This suggests a close look at constant admittance networks.

## TRANSFER ADMITTANCE WITH POSITIVE COEFFICIENTS  10.5

The constant resistance networks in the admittance form are not very different from the corresponding ones in the impedance form. To get familiar with the rules, note that in network a (Fig. 10.13) $y_{22} = 1$ and $-y_{12} = k/(s + k)$. In a manner similar to Section 10.2, the 1-ohm resistance (marked a) may be replaced with a like network but, perhaps, with a different constant $k$ (Fig. 10.14). The transfer admittance may be obtained from the equivalent relation for a cascade connection

$$-y_{12} = -\frac{y_{12}^{(1)} \times y_{21}^{(2)}}{y_{22}^{(1)} + y_{11}^{(2)}} = \frac{\dfrac{1}{1 + s/k'} \times \dfrac{k}{s}}{1 + \dfrac{k}{s}} = \frac{kk'}{(s + k)(s + k')}$$

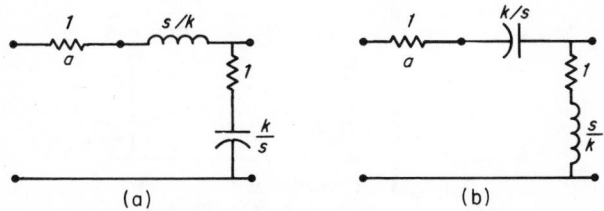

Fig. 10.13. Constant admittance networks where $-y_{12}$ equals $k/(s + k)$ and $s/(s + k)$ respectively

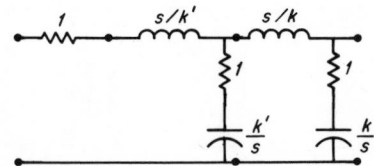

Fig. 10.14. A network with $y_{22} = 1$ and $-y_{12} = kk'/(s + k)(s + k')$

This process may be continued to produce any $-y_{12}$ with zeros at infinity (or at the origin if networks 10.13b are used) and with any real axis poles. Furthermore, by appropriately adding sections with zeros at the origin, we can produce a network which has as many zeros at the origin as desired. Note that the system cannot produce a higher-degree numerator than the denominator, since then $y_{12}$ has a pole at infinity which $y_{22}$ has not. This violates the residue condition (Eq. 6.6.8).

### Example 10.5.1

Realize a network with a constant $y_{22}$ and where $-y_{12}$ is given by

$$-y_{12} = \frac{1 + s^3}{(s + 1)(s + 2)(s + 3)} \qquad 10.5.1$$

### Solution

$-y_{12}$ in Eq. 10.5.1 may be split into two:

$$-y_{12} = \underbrace{\frac{1}{(s + 1)(s + 2)(s + 3)}}_{-y_{12}{}^{(1)}} + \underbrace{\frac{s^3}{(s + 1)(s + 2)(s + 3)}}_{-y_{12}{}^{(2)}} \qquad 10.5.2$$

For the sake of synthesis it is assumed that the desired network is made up of two networks connected in parallel. Each of these has a constant $y_{22}$, and their respective transfer impedance is given by $y_{12}{}^{(1)}$ and $y_{12}{}^{(2)}$ of Eq. 10.5.2. Hence, the desired networks are of the type given by Figs. 10.13 and 10.14 The network corresponding to $y_{12}{}^{(1)}$ of Eq. 10.5.2 is shown in Fig. 10.15.

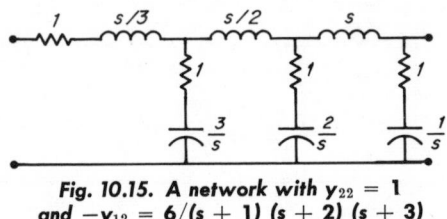

**Fig. 10.15. A network with $y_{22} = 1$
and $-y_{12} = 6/(s + 1)(s + 2)(s + 3)$**

Similarly, the network corresponding to $y_{12}{}^{(2)}$ is given by Fig. 10.16.

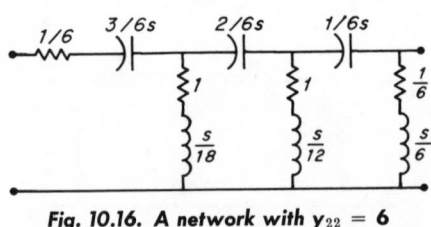

**Fig. 10.16. A network with $y_{22} = 6$
and $-y_{12} = 6s^3/(s + 1)(s + 2)(s + 3)$**

The final network (corresponding to Eq. 10.5.1) is obtained by connecting the networks of Figs. 10.15 and 10.16 in parallel. They represent Eq. 10.5.1 within a constant multiplier. Note the scaling constant 1/6 used in Fig. 10.16.

The presence of complex poles does introduce some difficulty. The problem is essentially the same as with the constant resistance network (Section 10.3). A satisfactory network is given in Fig. 10.17.

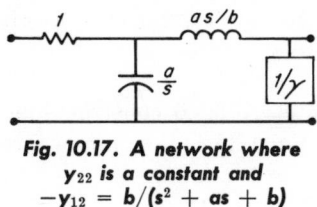

**Fig. 10.17. A network where**
**$y_{22}$ is a constant and**
**$-y_{12} = b/(s^2 + as + b)$**

Here $\gamma$ is given by

$$\gamma = y_{22} - \frac{b(s + a)}{a(s^2 + as + b)}$$

It was shown in Section 10.3 (the parallel section on constant impedance networks) that it is always possible to find a sufficiently large constant, $y_{22}$, that $\gamma$ is prf.

Interchanging the capacitor with the inductor in Fig. 10.17 would yield

$$-y_{12} = \frac{s^2}{s^2 + as + b}$$

Furthermore if we specify that

$$-y_{12} = \frac{as}{s^2 + as + b}$$

the problem is considerably simpler, since this function is prf. A satisfactory constant admittance network is given in Fig. 10.18.

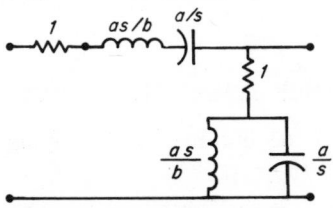

**Fig. 10.18. A network with $y_{22} = 1$**
**and $-y_{12} = as/(s^2 + as + b)$**

Hence a theorem, a sequel to Theorem 10.2.1 for constant impedance networks, now may be stated for constant admittance networks.

**Theorem 10.5.1**

If $y_{22}$ is a constant, $m + n$ is Hurwitz of degree $d$, and $-y_{12}$ is given by

$$-y_{12}{}^{(\alpha)} = \frac{s^\alpha}{m + n} \qquad \textbf{10.5.3}$$

where $\alpha$ is a positive integer ($\alpha \leq d$); then the respective network is realizable as a three-terminal network.

This fact makes it possible to construct networks in which the transfer admittance (Eq. 10.5.4) is a sum of terms of the type given in Eq. 10.5.3:

$$-y_{12} = \frac{\displaystyle\sum_{p=0}^{d} a_p s^p}{m + n} \qquad a_p > 0 \qquad \textbf{10.5.4}$$

and whose $y_{22}$ is a constant. Furthermore, the use of auxiliary Hurwitz polynomials would make it possible to make all the coefficients ($a_p$) positive as long as no zeros lie along the positive real axis (Section 9.4). This suggests the following theorem.

**Theorem 10.5.2**

If $y_{22}$ is constant, and if $-y_{12}$ has poles in the *l.h.s* plane and zeros everywhere in the complex plane except along the positive real axis, then the corresponding network (within a constant multiplier) may be realized as a three-terminal network.

**Corollary 10.5.1**

$T_{12}$, the voltage transfer ratio, $T_{12} = -y_{12}/y_{22}$, may be realized as a three-terminal network (within a constant multiplier) if its poles are in the *l.h.s* plane and its zeros do not lie along the positive real axis ($j$ axis poles are excluded).

## 10.6. A CONSTANT RESISTANCE SYMMETRIC LATTICE

These networks can be obtained by applying Darlington's synthesis to functions of the type

$$Z(s) = 1 = \frac{(s + k)^2}{(s + k)^2} = \frac{s^2 + 2sk + k^2}{s^2 + 2sk + k^2} \qquad \textbf{10.6.1}$$

Hence

$$z_{11} = \frac{m_1}{n_2} = \frac{k^2 + s^2}{2sk} = \begin{bmatrix} \dfrac{s}{2k} \end{bmatrix} \begin{bmatrix} \dfrac{k}{2s} \end{bmatrix}$$

$$z_{12} = \frac{\sqrt{m_1 m_2 - n_1 n_2}}{2sk} = \begin{bmatrix} \dfrac{-s}{2k} \end{bmatrix} + \begin{bmatrix} \dfrac{k}{2s} \end{bmatrix} \qquad 10.6.2$$

$$z_{22} = \frac{m_2}{n_2} = \frac{k^2 + s^2}{2sk} = \begin{bmatrix} \dfrac{s}{2k} \end{bmatrix} \begin{bmatrix} \dfrac{k}{2s} \end{bmatrix}$$

The first column to the right of Eq. 10.6.2 can be realized by means of a perfectly coupled $1: -1$ transformer, whereas the second represents a series capacitor Fig. 10.19. However Eq. 10.6.2 also may be realized by means of a lattice shown in Fig. 10.20. In both of these networks the equivalent transfer function $z_{12}$ of the complete 2-port network is

$$z_{12} = \frac{\dfrac{(k^2 - s^2)}{2sk} \times 1}{\dfrac{k^2 + s^2}{s} + 1} = \frac{k - s}{k + s} \qquad 10.6.3$$

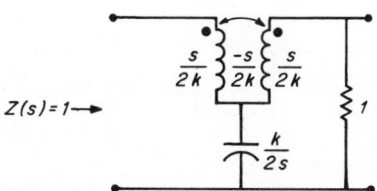

Fig. 10.19. A Darlington network for Eq. 10.6.1

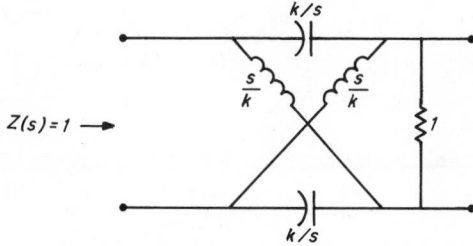

Fig. 10.20. An equivalent network to Fig. 10.19

The numerator becomes $s - k$ if the capacitors are interchanged with the inductors in Fig. 10.20. In Fig. 10.19 the change will require a capacitive transformer (or the respective capacitor loaded ideal transformer).

### Example 10.6.1

Realize a constant impedance network where $z_{12}$ is given by

$$z_{12} = \frac{(2 - s)}{(s + 1)(s + 3)} \qquad 10.6.4$$

*Solution*

Before the network is realized, it is advantageous to use the surplus factor $(s + 2)$. Hence

$$z_{12} = \underbrace{\frac{1}{s + 1}}_{(a)} \times \underbrace{\frac{(s + 2)}{(s + 3)}}_{(b)} \times \underbrace{\frac{(2 - s)}{(2 + s)}}_{(c)} \qquad 10.6.5$$

Following the techniques of Section 10.2, we get a network for element (a) in Eq. 10.6.5. Similarly the second term may be obtained by expanding

$$Z(s) = 1 = \frac{s + 3}{s + 3} = \frac{1}{(s + 2) + 1} + \frac{s + 2}{(s + 2) + 1} \qquad 10.6.6$$

(Section 10.4.). The final term may be obtained by the use of Eq. 10.6.3, corresponding to Fig. 10.20. The resulting network is given in Fig. 10.21.

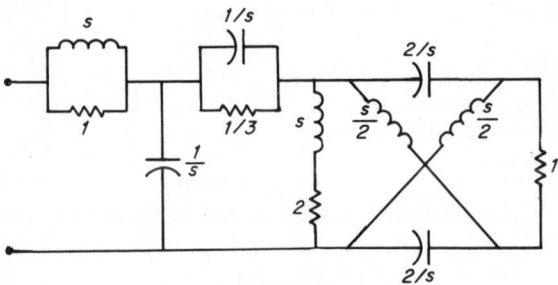

**Fig. 10.21. A network where** $z_{11} = 1$
**and** $z_{12} = (2 - s)/(s + 1)(s + 3)$

### Example 10.6.3

Realize a constant impedance network where $z_{12}$ is given by

$$z_{12} = \frac{4 - s}{(s + 1)(s + 3)} \qquad 10.6.7$$

*Solution*

This function cannot be realized in the same way as $z_{12}$ in Example 10.6.2, since a similar grouping does not yield obvious networks (Eq. 10.6.8):

$$z_{12} = \underbrace{\frac{1}{s + 1}}_{(a)} \times \underbrace{\frac{s + 4}{s + 3}}_{(b)} \times \underbrace{\frac{4 - s}{4 + s}}_{(c)} \qquad 10.6.8$$

The terms (a) and (c) in Eq. 10.6.8 are the same kind as in Eq. 10.6.5. The second term (b) in Eq. 10.6.8 is not of the type that can be handled directly (as in Eq. 10.6.6). However it is prf and may be written as follows:

$$\frac{3}{4} Z_{(b)} = \frac{\dfrac{s}{4}+1}{\dfrac{s}{3}+1} = \frac{1}{\dfrac{s}{3s+12}+1} \qquad 10.6.9$$

The scaling factor, 3/4, was used in Eq. 10.6.9 in order to produce a 1-ohm termination in the following circuit shown in Fig. 10.22.*

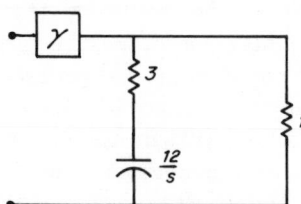

Fig. 10.22. A network where

$$z_{12} = \frac{3}{4} \times \frac{s+4}{s+3}$$

The impedance $\gamma$ was inserted in series for the purpose of producing a constant input impedance as prescribed by the statement of the problem. Choosing $\gamma = s/(4s+12)$ would render $z_{11}$ unity as desired. Then the final network is shown in Fig. 10.23.

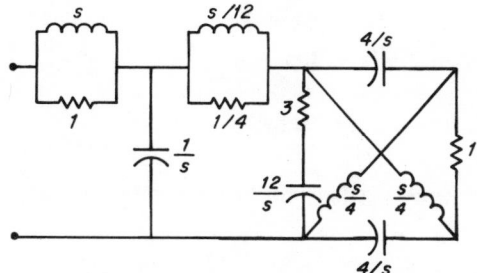

Fig. 10.23. A network where $z_{11} = 1$

and $z_{12} = \dfrac{3}{4} \times \dfrac{4-s}{(s+1)(s+3)}$

---

* An equally satisfactory approach would be along the lines of Section 10.4.

Our development of Eq. 10.6.9 was motivated by the necessity to realize a network with a resistive termination (and with a prescribed transfer function). There are many approaches to this problem, several of which will be described in the next chapter.

In concluding the discussion on a constant resistance lattice, note that, in general, if the additional pole ($s + k$ in Eq. 10.6.3) is not objectionable, the zero ($k - s$) can be obtained without using surplus factors by replacing the 1-ohm terminal impedance with the lattice of Fig. 10.20.

The constant resistance nature of the lattice is maintained as long as the product of the horizontal member ($Z_{(a)}$) and the diagonal member is unity. Then the resulting transfer impedance is $(Z_{(a)} - 1)/(Z_{(a)} + 1)$. This network may be very useful in synthesis except that the loss of common ground property is very objectionable. There are many methods today which make it possible to convert the lattice into an equivalent three-terminal device (called "unbalancing"). However, the methods either use transformers (see Fig. 10.19) or are not general. But a lattice is the only transformerless, passive device capable of handling positive real axis zeros of $z_{12}$.

### PROBLEMS

10.1. Realize the following four-terminal immittance function (no transformers):

(a). $z_{11} = 1$

$z_{12} = 15/(s + 3)(s + 5)$

(b). $z_{11} = 1$

$z_{12} = s^2/(s + 3)(s + 5)$

(c). $z_{11} = 2$

$z_{12} = (s^2 + 15)/(s + 3)(s + 5)$

(d). $y_{22} = 1$

$- y_{12} = 15/(s + 3)(s + 5)$

(e). $y_{22} = 1$

$- y_{12} = s^2/(s + 3)(s + 5)$

(f). $y_{22} = 2$

$- y_{12} = (s^2 + 15)/(s + 3)(s + 5)$

10.2. Realize the fourth Butterworth approximation to the low-pass filter given by

$$|T_{12}|^2 = \left|\frac{E_2}{E_1}\right|^2 = \frac{1}{1 + \omega^8}$$

in terms of a constant resistance network.

10.3. Give transformerless realizations of the following immittance functions:

(a). $z_{11} = $ constant

$$z_{12} = (s^2 + 1)/(s^2 + s + 2)$$

(b). $y_{11} = $ constant

$$- y_{12} = (s^2 + 1)/(s^2 + s + 2)$$

(c). $z_{22} = $ constant

$$z_{12} = (3 - s)/(s + 1)(s + 2)$$

10.4. Realize the following transfer voltage ration $(T_{12})$ with the largest $k$ you can:

(a). $T_{12} = \dfrac{k}{s^2 + s + 2}$      (b). $T_{12} = \dfrac{k}{s^2 + s + 9}$

Hint: Evaluate $\gamma$ of Section 10.3 with the lowest $\beta$ possible.

## FURTHER READING

Books

10.1. Balabanian, M.," Network Synthesis," Prentice-Hall, Inc., Englewood Cliffs, N. J., 1958, Chapter 8.
10.2. Guillemin, E. A., "Synthesis of Passive Networks," John Wiley & Sons, New York, 1957, Chapter 11.
10.3. Kuh, E. S., and Pederson, D. O., "Principles of Circuit Synthesis," McGraw-Hill Book Co., Inc., New York, 1959, Chapter 12.
10.4. Tuttle, D. F., Jr., "Network Synthesis," John Wiley & Sons, New York, 1958, Chapter 10.
10.5. Van Valkenburg, M. E., "Introduction to Modern Network Synthesis," John Wiley & Sons, New York, 1960, Chapter 12.

Related Papers

10.6. Fialkow, A., and Gerst, I., "The Transfer Function of Networks Without Mutual Reactance," *Quarterly of Appl. Math.*, Vol. 12, pp. 117–131, July, 1954.
10.7. Fialkow, A., "Networks Without Mutual Reactance," *Proc. Symp. Modern Network Synthesis*, Polytechnic Inst. Brooklyn, Vol. 5, pp. 79–97, April, 1955.

# CHAPTER 11

# Problems in Two-Element-Kind 2-Port Synthesis

The problem of 2-port synthesis is relatively complex. It will be considered as a part of $n$-port synthesis in Chapter 13. However since the two-element-kind networks have relatively simple synthesis procedures, these will be taken up in the following two sections. It is important to note that for two-element-kind 2-port synthesis the corresponding networks require transformers unless constraints are imposed on the functions. For example, it is possible to realize without transformers both $z_{12}$ and $z_{22}$ within a positive constant of $z_{12}$ for lossless networks if the zeros of $z_{12}$ are along the $j$ axis. Because of this fact and some variations on it, satisfactory networks can be produced for many important current problems. The last section is devoted to a discussion of the splitting of a Hurwitz polynomial into a sum of Hurwitz polynomials for synthesis purposes.

## 11.1 LOSSLESS 2-PORT NETWORKS

Lossless, reciprocal, 2-port networks can be realized quite readily by the use of partial fraction expansion, if transformers are used. In fact, this kind of network synthesis was utilized in Chapter 7 to realize the 2-port lossless networks associated with the Darlington synthesis. However, there the residue condition is satisfied with the equal sign. If this is not so, a part of each pole is removed from either $z_{11}$ or $z_{22}$ such that the residue condition (Eq. 6.6.8) is satisfied. In Eqs. 11.1.1 the coefficient of the removed part of the pole is $\beta^{(p)}$, and it is removed from $z_{11}^{(p)}(s)$

$$z_{11} = \left(k_{11}^{(0)} - \beta^{(0)}\right)s + \sum_p \frac{\left(k_{11}^{(p)} - \beta^{(p)}\right)s}{s^2 + \omega_p^2} + \beta^{(0)}s + \sum_p \frac{\beta^{(p)}s}{s^2 + \omega_p^2}$$

$$z_{12} = k_{12}^{(0)}s + \sum_p \frac{k_{12}^{(p)}s}{s^2 + \omega_p^2} \qquad\qquad 11.1.1$$

$$z_{22} = k_{22}^{(0)}s + \sum_p \frac{k_{22}^{(p)}s}{s^2 + \omega_p^2}$$

where $\beta^{(p)} = k_{11}^{(p)} - (k_{12}^{(p)})^2/k_{22}^{(p)}$. Note that since all the poles lie along the $j$ axis, the residue condition must be fulfilled and $\beta^{(p)}$ must be positive. The typical element representing Eqs. 11.1.1 may be of the forms illustrated in Figs. 11.1a and b. The final network—known as the Cauer 2-port network—is made up of elements of the type shown in Fig. 11.1 in the series-series connection.

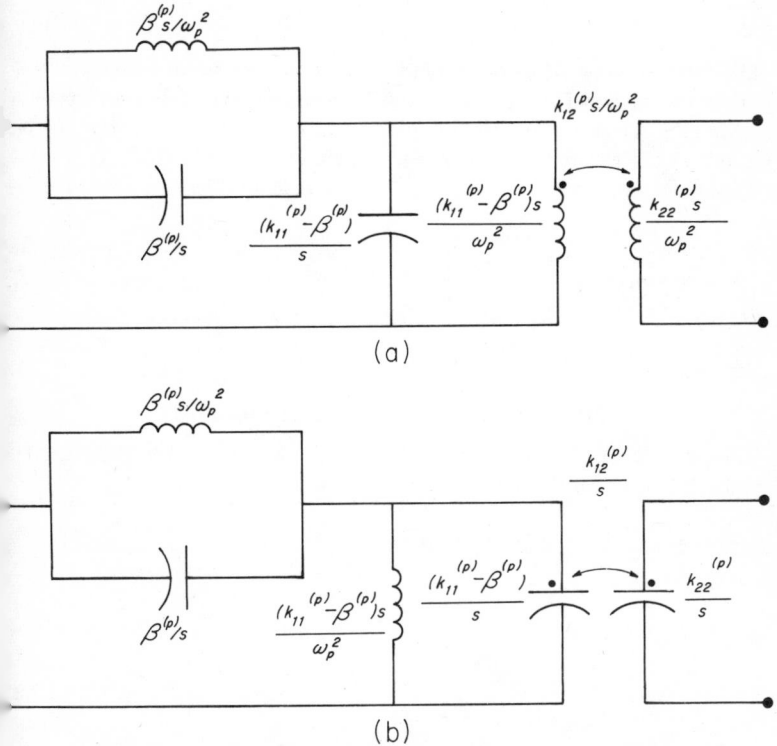

Fig. 11.1. Two realizations of a typical element of Eqs. 11.1.1. A simple transformer due to the zero term in Eq. 11.1.1 and the corresponding inductor due to $\beta^{(0)}s$ are not indicated

## 11.2. RC AND RL 2-PORT NETWORKS

In Chapter 4 it was pointed out that two-element-kind impedance functions are very similar to each other. In fact, a lossless network function may be constructed from that of an $RC$ network by performing a change of variable as follows

$$Z_{RC}(x) = \left.\frac{Z_{LC}(s)}{s}\right|_{s^2=x} \qquad 11.2.1$$

whereas for $RL$ networks

$$Z_{RL}(x) = \left. s\, Z_{LC}(s)\right|_{s^2=x}$$

### Example 11.2.1

Realize $Z(s) = (s^2 + 1)/s(s^2 + 2)$ by synthesizing the appropriate $RC$ impedance function.

### Solution

The appropriate $RC$ impedance function is obtained from Eq. 11.2.1:

$$Z_{RC}(x) = \left.\frac{Z(s)}{s}\right|_{s^2=x} = \frac{x+1}{x(x+2)} = \frac{1}{2x} + \frac{1}{2(x+2)} \qquad 11.2.2$$

The corresponding $RC$ network (Fig. 11.2a) is converted into the respective $LC$ network by first letting $x = s^2$ and then scaling every element up by a factor $s$ (Fig. 11.2b). The only difference between the two networks of Fig. 11.2 is that the resistor in (a) is replaced by an inductor in (b).

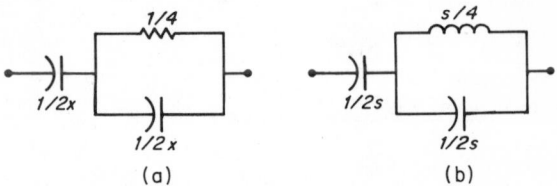

**Fig. 11.2. Networks associated with Example 11.2.1**

This result can be extended to 2-port networks. Corresponding to Eq. 11.1.1, one may write

$$z_{11RC}(x) = \left.\frac{z_{11}(s)}{s}\right|_{x=s^2} = (k_{11}^{(0)} - \beta^{(0)})$$
$$+ \sum_p \frac{k_{11}^{(p)} - \beta^{(p)}}{x + \omega_p{}^2} + \beta^{(0)} + \sum_p \frac{\beta^{(p)}}{x + \omega_p{}^2}$$

$$z_{12RC}(x) = \left.\frac{z_{12}(s)}{s}\right|_{x=s^2} = k_{12}^{(0)} + \sum_p \frac{k_{12}^{(p)}}{x + \omega_p{}^2} \qquad 11.2.3$$

$$z_{22RC}(x) = \left.\frac{z_{22}(s)}{s}\right|_{x=s^2} = k_{22}^{(0)} + \sum_p \frac{k_{22}^{(p)}}{x + \omega_p{}^2}$$

where $\beta^{(p)} = k_{11}^{(p)} - (k_{12}^{(p)})^2/k_{22}^{(p)}$. Note that by virtue of the correspondence between $RC$ networks and $LC$ networks $\beta$ must be positive. This means that the residue condition holds at the poles (real axis) of $RC$ (or $RL$) networks. The typical element of Eqs. 11.2.3 may be realized as in Fig. 11.3.

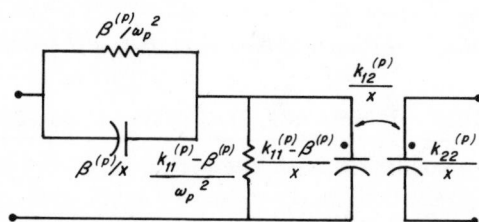

**Fig. 11.3. A realization of the typical element of Eqs. 11.2.3**

Again note the similarity between this circuit and that of Fig. 1.1b. They differ only in that all resistors are replaced with inductors. Figure 11.3 was modeled after Fig. 11.1b, but it could have been modeled after Fig. 11.1a except that resistive transformers would be needed. Resistive transformers may exist in nature; however, they may also be approximated by means of a resistor shunting an ideal transformer.

In concluding this section, observe that the same approach might be used to arrive at $RL$ networks from $LC$ networks. Rewriting Eq. 11.2.3 in accordance with Eq. 11.2.1 for $Z_{RL}(x)$, we get

$$z_{11RL}(x) = sZ_{11}(s)\Big|_{x=s^2} = (k_{11}^{(0)} - \beta^{(0)})x$$

$$+ \sum_p \frac{(k_{11}^{(p)} - \beta^{(p)})x}{x + \omega_p^2} + \beta^{(0)}x + \sum_p \frac{\beta^{(p)}x}{x + \omega_p^2} \qquad \textbf{11.2.4a}$$

$$z_{12RL}(x) = sz_{12}(s)\Big|_{x=s^2} = k_{12}^{(0)}x + \sum_p \frac{k_{12}^{(p)}x}{x + \omega_p^2} \qquad \textbf{11.2.4b}$$

$$z_{22RL}(x) = sz_{22}(s)\Big|_{x=s^2} = k_{22}^{(0)}x + \sum_p \frac{k_{22}^{(p)}x}{x + \omega_p^2} \qquad \textbf{11.2.4c}$$

The typical element representing Eqs. 11.2.4 is shown in Fig. 11.4. This element is similar to that of Fig. 11.1a except that all capacitors are replaced by resistors.

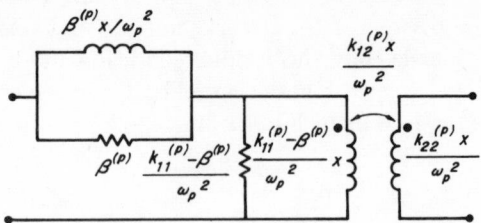

**Fig. 11.4.** *A realization of the typical element of Eqs. 11.2.4*

## 11.3. COMMON GROUND IMPEDANCE SYNTHESIS—LOSSLESS NETWORK?

Here we are concerned with the synthesis of $z_{12}$ when either $z_{11}$ or $z_{22}$ is also prescribed. Further, at this stage, the zeros of $z_{12}$ are at the origin and at infinity. Driving point immittance functions of two-element-kind networks belong to a class of functions which can be realized by means of continued fraction expansion. The resulting networks can be grouped into the first or the second Cauer form or in any combination of the two. All of these possible Cauer form variations do not alter the value of the driving point immittance function, although there is an effect on the values of the transfer functions involved.

### Example 11.3.1

Synthesize $z_{11} = (s^5 + 6s^3 + 8s)/(s^4 + 4s^2 + 3)$ by means of variations of the Cauer forms.

### Solution

Expand $z_{11}$ in a continued fraction expansion; there results (these do not exhaust all the possibilities)

$$
\begin{array}{cc}
\text{(a)} & \text{(b)} \\
\end{array}
$$

$$
z_{11} = \varepsilon + \cfrac{1}{\cfrac{s}{2} + \cfrac{1}{\cfrac{4s}{3} + \cfrac{1}{\cfrac{3s}{2} + \cfrac{3}{s}}}} = s + \cfrac{1}{\cfrac{3}{5s} + \cfrac{1}{\cfrac{25}{14s} + \cfrac{1}{\cfrac{196}{15s} + \cfrac{14s}{3}}}}
$$

$$
\begin{array}{cc}
\text{(c)} & \text{(d)} \\
\end{array}
$$

$$
= s + \cfrac{1}{\cfrac{3}{5s} + \cfrac{s}{2} + \cfrac{1}{\cfrac{50}{3s} + \cfrac{20s}{3}}} = s + \cfrac{1}{\cfrac{3}{5s} + \cfrac{s}{2} + \cfrac{1}{\cfrac{20s}{3} + \cfrac{50}{3s}}}
$$

(e)

(f)

**11.3.1**

$$= \cfrac{1}{\dfrac{3}{8s} + \cfrac{1}{\dfrac{32}{7s} + \cfrac{1}{\dfrac{49}{88s} + \cfrac{1}{\dfrac{968}{21s} + \dfrac{44s}{3}}}}}$$

$$= \cfrac{1}{\dfrac{3}{8s} + \cfrac{1}{\dfrac{32}{7s} + \cfrac{1}{\dfrac{49}{88s} + \cfrac{1}{\dfrac{44s}{3} + \dfrac{968}{21s}}}}}$$

(g)

(h)

$$= \cfrac{1}{\dfrac{3}{8s} + \cfrac{1}{\dfrac{8s}{5} + \cfrac{1}{\dfrac{25s}{128} + \cfrac{1}{\dfrac{256s}{15} + \dfrac{128}{3s}}}}}$$

$$= \cfrac{1}{\dfrac{3}{8s} + \cfrac{1}{\dfrac{8s}{5} + \cfrac{1}{\dfrac{25s}{128} + \cfrac{1}{\dfrac{128}{3s} + \dfrac{256s}{15}}}}}$$

The corresponding networks (and the resulting transfer impedances) are given in Fig. 11.5 (pages 195 and 196).

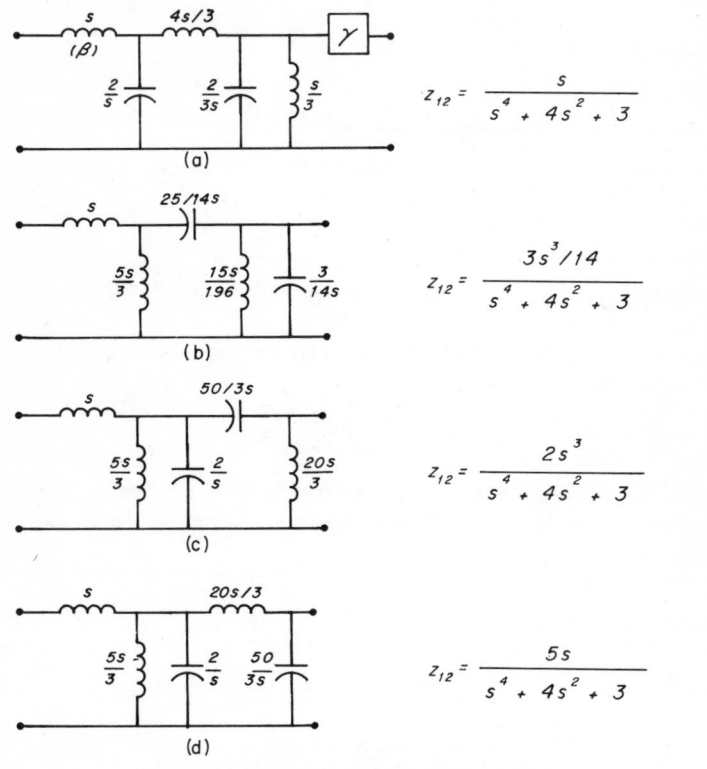

$$z_{12} = \frac{s}{s^4 + 4s^2 + 3}$$

(a)

$$z_{12} = \frac{3s^3/14}{s^4 + 4s^2 + 3}$$

(b)

$$z_{12} = \frac{2s^3}{s^4 + 4s^2 + 3}$$

(c)

$$z_{12} = \frac{5s}{s^4 + 4s^2 + 3}$$

(d)

**Fig. 11.5. Variations on the Cauer network for**
$$z_{11} = \frac{s^5 + 6s^3 + 8s}{s^4 + 4s^2 + 3} \text{ and the resulting } z_{12}$$

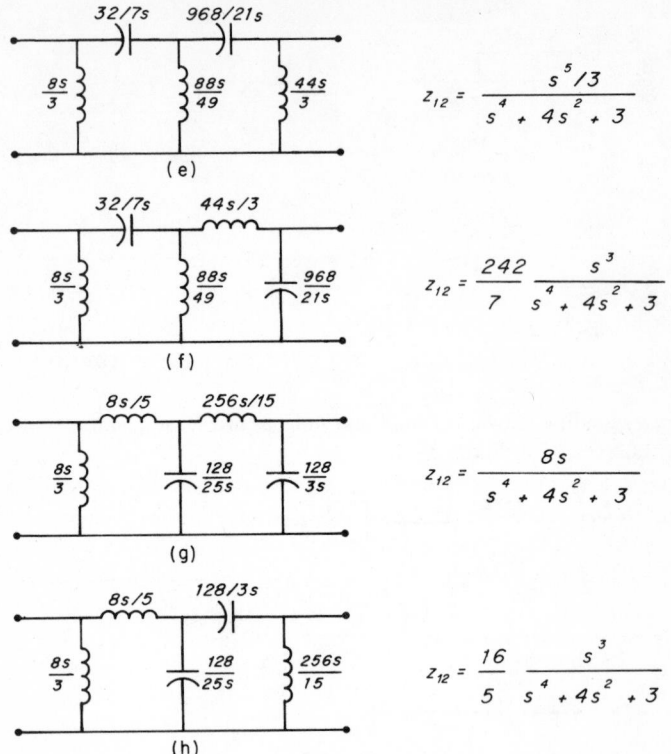

Fig. 11.5. (continued)

A useful tool for computing the transfer impedance functions for the networks above is

$$z_{12} = \frac{z_{12}^{(1)} \times z_{12}^{(2)}}{z_{22}^{(1)} + z_{11}^{(2)}}$$ 11.3.2

where the superscripts denote the respective networks. Thus the network of Fig. 11.5a can be split into two 2-port networks as shown in Fig. 11.6.

For network a $z_{12}^{(1)} = \dfrac{2}{s}$ and $z_{22}^{(1)} = \dfrac{2}{s} + \dfrac{4s}{3}$, whereas in network

b $z_{12}^{(2)} = z_{11}^{(2)} = \dfrac{2s/3}{s^2 + 2}$. Hence the corresponding $z_{12}$ is

$$z_{12} = \frac{\dfrac{2}{s} \times \dfrac{2s/3}{s^2 + 2}}{\dfrac{2}{s} + \dfrac{4s}{3} + \dfrac{2s/3}{s^2 + 2}} = \frac{s}{s^4 + 4s^2 + 3}$$

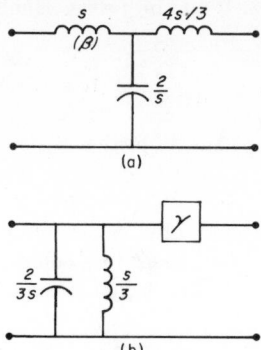

**Fig. 11.6. Splitting a net-
work for the computation
of the transfer impedance**

These results may be extended to $RC$ networks as well. The final results will be the replacement of the inductor with resistors (see Section 11.2). Note that neither the first-series element ($\beta$) nor the last-series element ($\gamma$) are included in the computation. This and some other computation rules for $z_{12}$ follow. (These rules apply to all two-element-kind networks.)

(1). Series elements, before the first and past the last parallel elements, are not included in the calculation of $z_{12}$. The rest of the elements are called participating elements.

(2). Shunt inductors produce zeros at the origin, whereas shunt capacitors produce zeros at infinity. Similarly participating series inductors produce zeros at infinity, and participating series capacitors produce zeros at the origin.

(3). $z_{12}$ of an $LC$ network is an odd function of $s$.

Rule (1) was demonstrated by the sample calculation above. Rule (2) may be demonstrated by noting that the secondaries of a ladder 2-port network may be isolated from the primaries in either of two ways: a series element is open circuited, or a parallel element is shorted. A capacitor becomes an open circuit at zero frequency. Hence, in series it isolates the secondaries (i.e., it produces a zero) at the origin. This argument may be continued to prove the rest of rule (2).

To prove rule (3) note that the real part condition (for $LC$)

$$\text{Re } z_{11} \text{ Re } z_{22} - (\text{Re } z_{12})^2 \geqslant 0 \qquad \text{Re } s = 0 \qquad \textbf{6.4.17}$$
$$> 0 \qquad \text{Re } s > 0 \qquad \textbf{11.3.3}$$

reduces to $-(\text{Re } z_{12})^2 \geqslant 0$ on the $j$ axis. Hence Ev $z_{12} = 0$ and $z_{12}$ is an odd function of $s$.*

### Example 11.3.2

Realize the transfer impedance function $Z_{12} = 1/(s + 1) (s^2 + s + 1)$.

*Solution*

Since $z_{11}$ is not specified, $z_{12}$ will be realized in two forms: (a) as a lossless network shunted with a 1-ohm resistance shunting the primaries; (b) as a lossless network terminated with a 1-ohm resistance. Hence for case (a):

$$Z_{12} = \frac{z_{12}}{1 + z_{11}(s)} = \frac{1}{s^3 + 2s^2 + 2s + 1} = \frac{1/(s^3 + 2s)}{1 + (2s^2 + 1)/(s^3 + 2s)} \quad 11.3.4$$

Thus the problem has been reduced to that of realizing a lossless network where

$$z_{11} = \frac{2s^2 + 1}{s^3 + 2s} \text{ and } z_{12} = \frac{1}{s^3 + 2s} \quad 11.3.5$$

Furthermore, in accordance with rule (2), and since all the zeros are at infinity, then all the inductors must be in series and the capacitors in shunt. Hence $z_{11}$ is developed as follows:

$$z_{11} = \frac{1}{(s^3 + 2s)/(2s^2 + 1)} = \frac{1}{\dfrac{s}{2} + \dfrac{1}{\dfrac{4s}{3} + \dfrac{2}{3s}}}$$

The final network is given in Fig. 11.7.

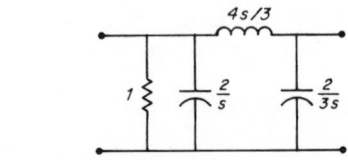

**Fig. 11.7. A network with** $Z_{12} = \dfrac{1}{(s + 1)(s^2 + s + 1)}$

For the second part of the problem (b) Eq. 11.3.4 becomes

$$Z_{12} = \frac{z_{12}}{1 + z_{22}} \quad 11.3.6$$

Hence $z_{11}$ in Eq. 11.3.4 will become $z_{22}$, and the final network will be a mirror image (left side-right) of Fig. 11.7.

---

* Rule (3) is stronger than rule (2). See Fig. 11.5h where rules (1) and (2) would predict three zeros at the origin and two at infinity. There $z_{12}$ should have been $(s^3 + \cdots +)/(s^5 + \cdots +)$. This violates rule (3).

Example 11.3.1 served as a basis for formulating the three rules above. The corresponding networks were constructed from the continued fraction expansion of $z_{11}$ ($= n/m$), and then the resulting $z_{12}$ was computed. However, these networks may also be realized by a different method related to that by Miyata. Suppose, for example, that it is desired to synthesize a network where $z_{22}$ and $z_{12}$ are prescribed and that $z_{12}$ is in the form of Eq. 11.3.7 ($a_p > 0$).

$$z_{12} = \sum \frac{a_p s^p}{n_2}, \qquad\qquad z_{12} = \sum \frac{a_p s^p}{m_2}$$

and

$$z_{22} = \frac{m_2}{n_2}, \qquad\qquad z_{22} = \frac{n_2}{m_2} \qquad\qquad \textbf{11.3.7}$$

$$\text{(for even } p) \qquad\qquad \text{(for odd } p)$$

Now suppose that we wish to solve a different problem, namely, that of realizing a driving point impedance function from its even part (Section 9.2)

$$\text{Ev } Z(s) = \sum_p \frac{a_p{}^2(-s^2)^p}{m_2{}^2 - n_2{}^2} \qquad\qquad \textbf{11.3.8}$$

realizing each member of the sum separately as a lossless network with a resistive termination.

But the input impedance of a 2-port network with a 1-ohm termination is given by

$$Z(s) = \frac{z_{11} + |z|}{1 + z_{22}} \qquad\qquad \begin{matrix}\textbf{7.2.2}\\ \textbf{11.3.9}\end{matrix}$$

Calculating its even part and making use of the fact that $z_{11}$, $z_{12}$, and $z_{22}$ are odd functions of $s$, we get

$$\text{Ev } Z(s) = \frac{|z| - z_{11}z_{22}}{1 - z_{22}{}^2} = \frac{-z_{12}{}^2}{1 - z_{22}{}^2} \qquad\qquad \textbf{11.3.10}$$

Hence the problem is reduced to that of performing the identity

$$\text{Ev } Z_p(s) = \frac{-z_{p12}{}^2}{1 - z_{p22}{}^2} = \frac{a_p{}^2(-s^2)^p}{m_2{}^2 - n_2{}^2} = \underbrace{\frac{-(a_p s^p)^2/n_2{}^2}{1 - \left(\dfrac{m_2}{n_2}\right)^2}}_{p \text{ even}} = \underbrace{\frac{-(a_p s^p)^2/m_2{}^2}{1 - \left(\dfrac{n_2}{m_2}\right)^2}}_{p \text{ odd}} \qquad \textbf{11.3.11}$$

resulting in $z_{22} = m_2/n_2$ and $z_{12} = a_p s^p/n_2$ for even $p$, and $z_{22} = n_2/m_2$ and $z_{12} = a_p s^p/m_2$ for odd $p$. These results are identical with the parameters of Eq. 11.3.7. They also may be obtained by applying a Darlington-like process (Section 9.1). Thus the method of continued fraction expansion yields a solution to the Miyata's function (Eq.

11.3.8). This solution is the same as that using the Miyata synthesis procedure, since both use the same canonic forms and since (as is possible to show) both have the same number of possible equivalent networks. This fact was mentioned (but not proved) in the last paragraph of Section 9.2.

In all the networks discussed in this section, the zeros of $z_{12}$ were either at infinity or at the origin. If they are along the $j$ axis, the process of zero shifting may be utilized.

## 11.4. ZERO SHIFTING TECHNIQUES

In the last section it was pointed out that it is possible to produce zeros at the origin by placing an inductor in a parallel position in a ladder network, since this isolates the primaries from the secondaries for $s = 0$. The same may be obtained for a $j$ axis zero, (say at $s = j\omega_0$) if a series resonant circuit is placed in a parallel position, since at resonance it presents a short across the ladder. Similar effects will be obtained if a parallel resonant circuit is placed in a series position, since at resonance this represents an open circuit and the ladder is effectively split into two disjointed sections. The process of zero shifting involves the introduction of some additional elements (without effecting $z_{11}$) in order to either produce a series resonance circuit in a parallel position or a parallel resonance circuit in a series position in the ladder. Consider, for example, a typical tail end of a Cauer network (Fig. 11.8a). It is possible to obtain any possible $j$ axis zero by utilizing the right one of the first two circuits, (b) and (c), or the third circuit (d).

Hence if it is desired to add a single $j$ axis zero pair to any of the networks of Fig. 11.5 it is sufficient to select the networks (e) and (g). Their last two elements are in the form of network (a) in Fig. 11.8. These elements are replaced by the corresponding ones in network (d) above. The results are given in Fig. 11.9. Note that realizability does not permit terms like $s^5(s^2 + \omega_0^2)$ in $z_{12}$ when the denominator is of degree 4, since then $z_{12}$ has a higher order pole at infinity. In turn the real part condition (Eq. 6.4.17) would require that either $z_{11}$ or $z_{22}$ have a higher order pole at infinity. This is impossible since $z_{11}$ and $z_{22}$ are prf. Thus the network in Fig. 11.8d may handle all possible requirements on $z_{12}$ with one $j$ axis zero pair. Focusing our attention on Fig. 11.8b, we see that like Fig. 11.8d it can be used for zero shifting, but only when $\omega_0^2 \geqslant \dfrac{\beta}{\alpha}$. On the other hand, the

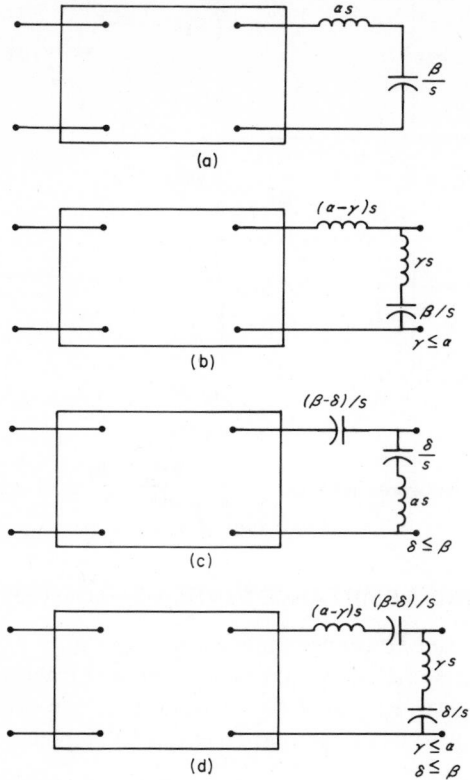

**Fig. 11.8.** Networks for production of $j$ axis zeros in $z_{12}$

...etwork of Fig. 11.8c is useful when $\omega_0{}^2 \leqslant \dfrac{\beta}{\alpha}$. Thus between Figs. 11b

...nd 11c the whole range $0 \leqslant \omega_0 \leqslant \infty$ is covered. The results may be ...eneralized to say that any lossless impedance function $z_{11}$ may be ...ealized by means of a common ground ladder network such that ...$_{12}$ has one $j$ axis zero pair and an arbitrary number of zero at the ...rigin or at infinity (as prescribed by general realizability ...onsiderations).

If additional $j$ axis zeros are required, it is no longer possible to ...ork on the tail end of the Cauer form, though no change in the ...pproach is necessary. This approach may be extended to $RC$ (or ...$L$) networks by interchanging inductors (or capacitors) with resis-...ors. Then the technique applies to zero shifting of real axis zeros.

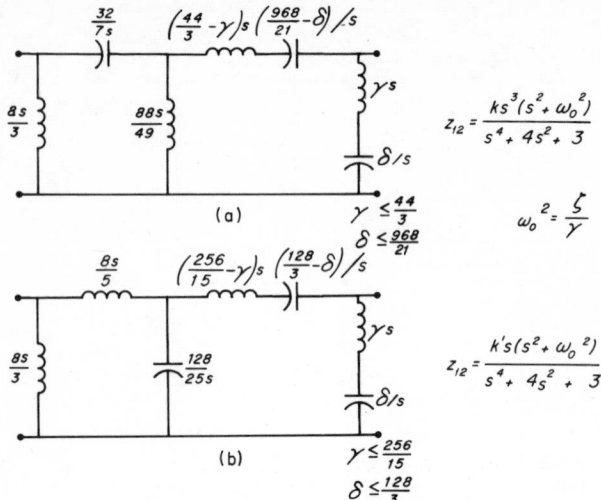

$$z_{12} = \frac{ks^3(s^2 + \omega_0{}^2)}{s^4 + 4s^2 + 3}$$

$$\omega_0{}^2 = \frac{\zeta}{\gamma}$$

$$\gamma \leq \frac{44}{3}$$

$$\delta \leq \frac{968}{21}$$

$$z_{12} = \frac{k's(s^2 + \omega_0{}^2)}{s^4 + 4s^2 + 3}$$

$$\gamma \leq \frac{256}{15}$$

$$\delta \leq \frac{128}{3}$$

**Fig. 11.9. Networks with** $z_{11} = \dfrac{s^5 + 6s^3 + 8s}{s^4 + 4s^2 + 3}$ **with arbitrary**
**j axis zero of** $z_{12}$

## 11.5. COMMON GROUND ADMITTANCE SYNTHESIS—LOSSLESS NETWORK

Following a similar development for impedance functions, the principle tool of synthesis would be a continued fraction expansion. The resulting network would be a variation of the Cauer network. The rules of synthesis are similar to those for impedance functions

### Example 11.5.1

Realize the driving point admittance function $y_{22}$ (Eq. 11.5.1), by means of variations of the Cauer network:

$$y_{22} = \frac{s(s^2 + 2)(s^2 + 4)}{(s^2 + 1)(s^2 + 3)} \qquad 11.5.1$$

### Solution

$y_{22}$ is the same function of $s$ as that used in Section 11.3 for $z_{11}$. Hence the same expansions (Eq. 11.3.1) will be used. The following are the first two:

(a)       (b)

$$y_{22} = s + \cfrac{1}{\cfrac{s}{2} + \cfrac{1}{\cfrac{4s}{3} + \cfrac{1}{\cfrac{3s}{2} + \cfrac{3}{s}}}} = s + \cfrac{1}{\cfrac{3}{5s} + \cfrac{1}{\cfrac{25}{14s} + \cfrac{1}{\cfrac{196}{15s} + \cfrac{14s}{3}}}} \qquad 11.5.2$$

The realizations corresponding to all these expansions and the resuiting $-y_{12}$ are given in Fig. 11.10. The letters a, b, c, etc. correspond to Eq. 11.3.1, where $y_{22}$ replaces $z_{11}$.

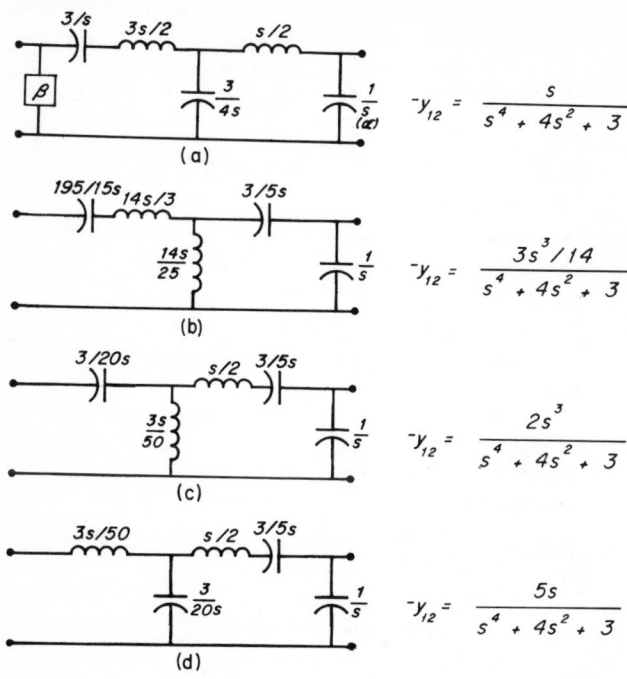

$$-y_{12} = \frac{s}{s^4 + 4s^2 + 3}$$

(a)

$$-y_{12} = \frac{3s^3/14}{s^4 + 4s^2 + 3}$$

(b)

$$-y_{12} = \frac{2s^3}{s^4 + 4s^2 + 3}$$

(c)

$$-y_{12} = \frac{5s}{s^4 + 4s^2 + 3}$$

(d)

Fig. 11.10. Variations on the Cauer network for $y_{22} = \dfrac{s^5 + 6s^3 + 8}{s^4 + 4s^2 + 3}$ and the resulting $-y_{12}$

A useful tool for computing $-y_{12}$ in the networks in Fig. 11.10 (pages 203 and 204) is the formula

$$-y_{12}(s) = -\frac{y_{12}^{(1)} \times y_{12}^{(2)}}{y_{22}^{(1)} + y_{11}^{(2)}} \qquad 11.5.3$$

where the superscripts denote the respective 2-port networks. One way to divide Fig. 11.10a into two networks is shown in Fig. 11.11. Hence for network (1)

$$-y_{12}^{(1)} = \frac{1}{\dfrac{3}{s} + \dfrac{3s}{2}} = \frac{2s}{3s^2 + 6}$$

and                                                                                           11.5.4

$$y_{22}^{(1)} = \frac{1}{\dfrac{3}{s} + \dfrac{3s}{2}} + \frac{4s}{3}$$

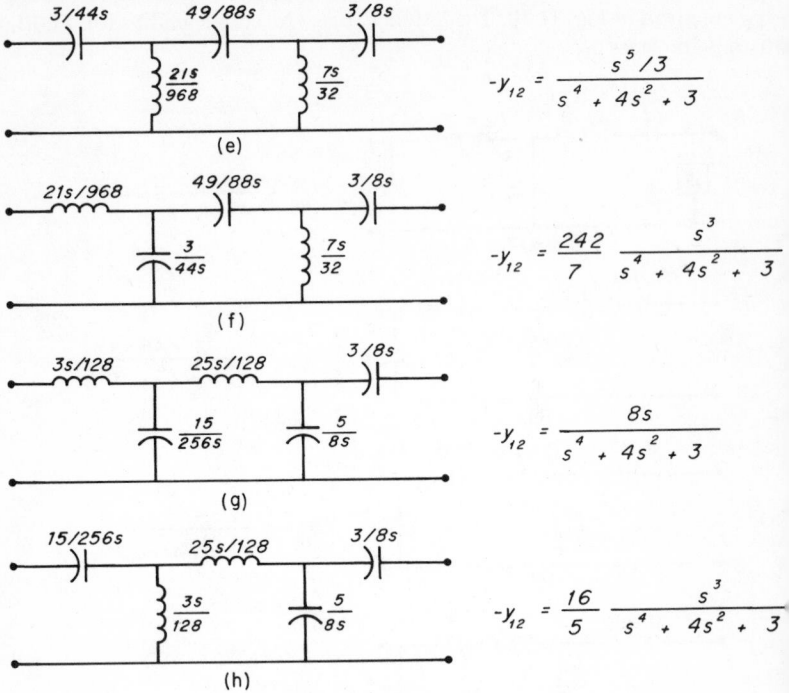

Fig. 11.10. (continued)

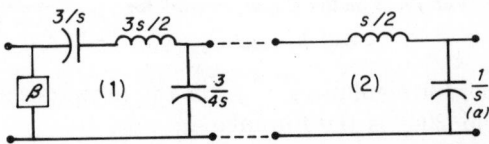

**Fig. 11.11.** *The network of Fig. 11.10a is split up for the computation of the transfer admittance*

whereas for the second network (2)

$$-y_{12}^{(2)} = y_{11}^{(2)} = \frac{2}{s}$$ 11.5

Putting these values into Eq. 11.5.3, we get

$$-y_{12} = \frac{\dfrac{2s}{3s^2 + 6} \times \dfrac{2}{s}}{\dfrac{2s}{3s^2 + 6} + \dfrac{4s}{3} + \dfrac{2}{s}} = \frac{s}{s^4 + 4s^2 + 3}$$ 11.5

These results now may be extended to $RL$ and $RC$ networks by first noting that $Y_{RL}(x) = \dfrac{Y_{LC}(s)}{s}\Big|_{s^2=x}$ and that $Y_{RC}(x)$
$= sY_{LC}(s)\Big|_{s^2=x}$. The final effect on the network is that all the capacitors in an $LC$ network become resistors in the $RL$ networks, and similarly all the inductors in $LC$ networks become resistors in $RC$ networks (Section 11.2).

Thus the following rules may be observed concerning the value of $-y_{12}$.

(1). Parallel elements before the first and past the last series elements are not included in the computation. (Follow the sample calculation above.)

(2). Participating shunt inductors produce zeros at the origin, whereas participating shunt capacitors produce zeros at infinity. Similarly, series inductors produce zeros at infinity, and series capacitors produce zeros at the origin.

(3). $-y_{12}$ is an odd function of $s$.

Note the similarity between these rules and those (Section 11.3) for transfer impedances. Rules (2) and (3) are identical. To prove that this is so, note that $-y_{12} = z_{12}/|z|$; hence $y_{12}$ is zero when $z_{12}$ is zero (except for special cases where some of them are cancelled). Rule (3) may also be substantiated by applying the real part condition for lossless networks along the $j$ axis:

$$\operatorname{Re} y_{11} \times \operatorname{Re} y_{22} - (\operatorname{Re} y_{12})^2 = 0$$
$$\operatorname{Re} s = 0 \qquad\qquad \textbf{11.5.7}$$

(This condition may be derived in the same manner as Eq. 4.17.) Hence as $\operatorname{Re} y_{11} = 0 = \operatorname{Re} y_{22}$ on the $j$ axis, $\operatorname{Re} y_{12}$ is also zero and $-y_{12}$ is an odd function of $s$ (see Footnote p. 198).

### Example 11.5.1

Realize $T_{12} \equiv \dfrac{E_2}{E_1}\Big|_{I_2=0} = 1/(s+1)(s^2+s+1)$ as a lossless network terminating in 1 ohm.

### Solution

Writing $T_{12}$ in the following manner

$$T_{12} = \frac{-y_{12}}{1+y_{22}} = \frac{1/(s^3+2s)}{1+\dfrac{2s^2+1}{s^3+2s}} \qquad\qquad \textbf{11.5.8}$$

permits selecting $-y_{12} = 1/(s^3 + 2s)$ and $y_{22} = (2s^2 + 1)/(s^3 + 2s)$. Expanding $y_{22}(s)$ in a continued fraction expansion, we get

$$y_{22} = \cfrac{1}{(s^3 + 2s)/(2s^2 + 1)} = \cfrac{1}{\cfrac{s}{2} + \cfrac{1}{\cfrac{4s}{3} + \cfrac{2}{3s}}} \qquad \text{11.5.9}$$

resulting (after termination with 1 ohm) in the network shown in Fig. 11.12.

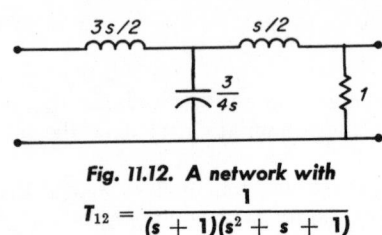

**Fig. 11.12. A network with**
$$T_{12} = \frac{1}{(s + 1)(s^2 + s + 1)}$$

Observe that all the zeros are at infinity as required. Furthermore, note that this network is a precise solution to the lossless filter (third-degree approximation) of Example 10.3.1.

## Example 11.5.2

Realize $T_{12} = e^{-s}$, a delay line.*

### Solution

Since $y_{22}$ is not specified, let $T_{12}$ be given by

$$T_{12} = \frac{-y_{12}}{1 + y_{22}} = \frac{1}{e^s} = \frac{\dfrac{1}{\sinh s}}{1 + \coth s} \qquad \text{11.5.10}$$

yielding $-y_{12} = 1/\sinh s$ and $y_{22} = \coth s$.

The fact that $\coth s$ is a reactance function can be demonstrated by expanding $y_{22}$ in a continued fraction expansion:

$$y_{22} = \cfrac{1}{s} + \cfrac{1}{\cfrac{3}{s} + \cfrac{1}{\cfrac{5}{s} + \cfrac{1}{\cfrac{7}{s} + \cdots}}} \qquad \text{11.5.11}$$

$\cdots$

---

* Storch, L., "Synthesis of Constant-Time-Delay Ladder Networks Using Bessel Polynomials," *Proc. IRE*, Vol. 42, pp. 1666–1676, November, 1954.

Constructing the corresponding Cauer network does not yield the desired $-y_{12}$, since all the resulting zeros are at the origin and not at infinity. It is not very clear how other Cauer forms may be arrived at unless the sequence is truncated first (i.e., the sequence is approximated). The first four approximations yield

$$y_{22} = \frac{1}{s} \qquad \text{(a)}$$

$$y_{22} = \frac{s}{3} + \frac{1}{s} \qquad \text{(b)}$$

$$y_{22} = \frac{6s^2 + 15}{s(s^2 + 15)} \qquad \text{(c)}$$

$$y_{22} = \frac{s^4 + 45s^2 + 105}{s(10s^2 + 105)} \qquad \text{(d)}$$

11.5.12

Now (the fourth approximation) $y_{22}$ may be expanded in a continued fraction expansion such that $y_{12}$ of the resulting Cauer network will have all its zeros at infinity (Eq. 11.5.13)

$$y_{22} = \frac{s}{10} + \cfrac{1}{\frac{20}{69}s + \cfrac{1}{\frac{1497}{3430}s + \frac{69}{49s}}} \qquad \text{11.5.13}$$

resulting in the final network of Fig. 11.13.

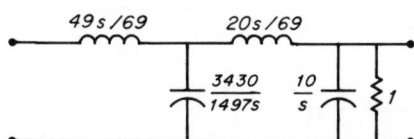

**Fig. 11.13. A network for Example 11.5.2**

## ZERO SHIFTING TECHNIQUES FOR $-y_{12}$ 11.6

A typical possible ending of a Cauer network of a driving point lossless admittance function is given in Fig. 11.14a. The process of producing a finite $j$ axis zero pair is similar to that used for producing $j$ axis zeros for $z_{12}$ (Section 11.4). It involves introducing redundant elements in strategic positions such that the effective $y_{22}$ is not altered. In networks (b), (c), and (d) of Fig. 11.14 the zero is produced in the transfer admittance by creating a parallel resonance section in a series position of the ladder network. At resonance the section becomes an "open circuit." The primaries are isolated from the secondaries, and hence $y_{12}$ has a zero at that frequency. The network of Fig. 11.14d is superior to those of (b) and (c) in being able to produce any zero from the origin to infinity. The others divide the range (for network (b), $0 \leqslant \omega_0{}^2 \leqslant \dfrac{\alpha}{\beta}$ and for (c), $\dfrac{\alpha}{\beta} \leqslant \omega_0{}^2 \leqslant \infty$).

That the ending of network (a) is always possible may be observed by examining networks (e) and (g) of Fig. 11.10; hence these become the networks of Fig. 11.15.

These results are also applicable to $RL$-$RC$ networks. In $RL$ networks, circuits corresponding to Fig. 11.14 will have the capacitors

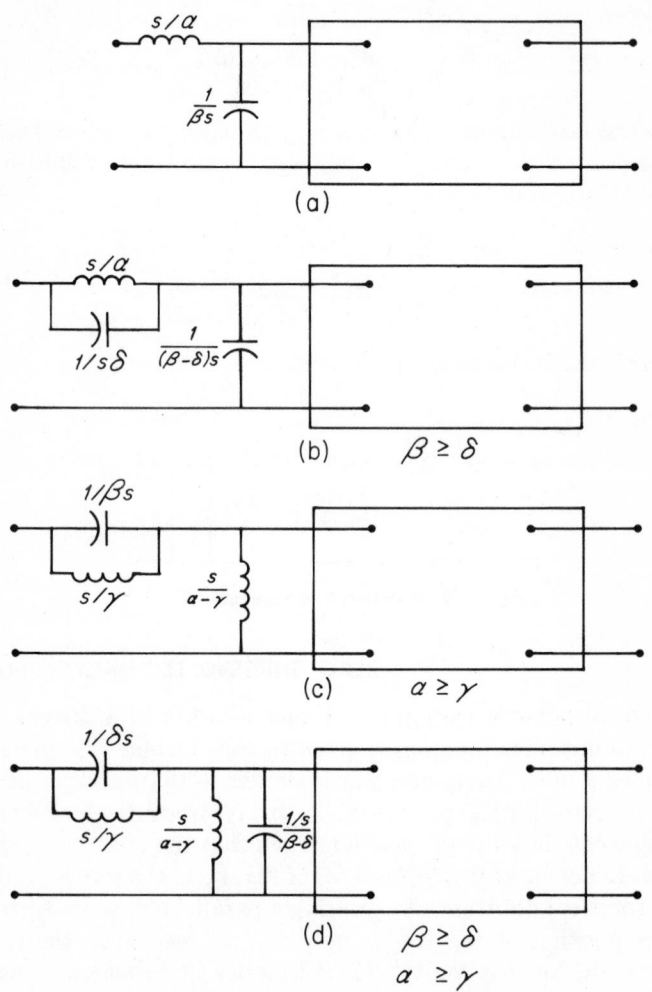

Fig. 11.14. **Networks for production of j axis zeros on** $-y_{12}$

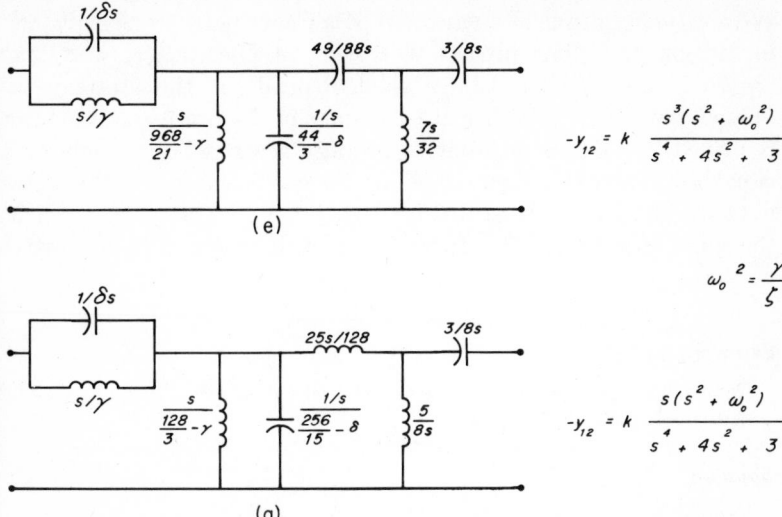

**Fig. 11.15.** *Networks with* $y_{22} = \dfrac{s^5 + 6s^3 + 8s}{s^4 + 4s^2 + 3}$ *with arbitrary j axis zeros of* $-y_{12}$

interchanged with resistors, whereas in $RC$ networks the inductor above would degenerate into resistors.

Note that realizability requirements do not permit any other permutation of zeros at the origin and infinity and the term ($s^2 + \omega_0^2$); that is, $s^5(s^2 + \omega_0^2)$ is forbidden. This can be generalized to say that any lossless admittance function $y_{22}$ may be realized in a ladder network such that $-y_{12}$ has a $j$ axis zero pair in addition to an arbitrary number of zeros at the origin and infinity (as prescribed by general realizability requirements). No change in strategy is involved if additional $j$ axis zeros are present, although it is not enough to use the front end alone.

## GUILLEMIN'S TRANSFER ADMITTANCE SYNTHESIS   11.7

If the numerator of $-y_{12}$ is a polynomial with all positive coefficients, it is possible to realize the network by attacking each term of $-y_{12}$ separately. Thus let $-y_{12}$ be given by

$$-y_{12} = \frac{a_1 s + a_3 s^3 + \cdots + a_{(2p+1)} s^{(2p+1)} \cdots +}{m}$$

and                                                                                 **11.7.1**

$$y_{22} = \frac{n}{m} \text{ (where } m + n \text{ is Hurwitz)}$$

The typical term, $s^{(2p+1)}/m$, may be realized as $-y_{12}^{(2p+1)}$ from $y_{22} = n/m$ by means of a variation on a Cauer network as explained in Section 11.5. The process will yield, in effect, $\beta_{(2p+1)}s^{(2p+1)}/m$. [$\beta_{(2p+1)}$ is a positive constant which depends on the strategy involved, namely on whether at each stage of the process an inductor is placed in parallel in order to produce a zero at the origin or a capacitor in series.] Hence, to obtain the coefficient $a_{(2p+1)}$ the whole network of $y_{22}$ must be scaled by $a_{(2p+1)}/\beta_{(2p+1)}$. Thus, $-y_{12}$ will be the same as in Eq. 11.7.1. However, $y_{22}$ will be scaled by a positive constant.

### Example 11.7.1

Realize the network where $-y_{12} = (s^5 + s)/(s^4 + 4s^2 + 3)$ and $y_{22} = (s^5 + 6s^3 + 8s)/(s^4 + 4s^2 + 3)$.

### Solution

Express $-y_{12}$ as a sum of two terms:

$$-y_{12} = \frac{s}{s^4 + 4s^2 + 3} + \frac{s^5}{s^4 + 4s^2 + 3} = -y_{12}^{(1)} + -y_{12}^{(2)} \quad \textbf{11.7.2}$$

Now $y_{22}$ is realized by means of a variation of the Cauer network (Section 11.5). This is done twice (once for each term in Eq. 11.7.2). Hence $-y_{12}^{(1)}$ is obtained in the network shown in Fig. 11.16.

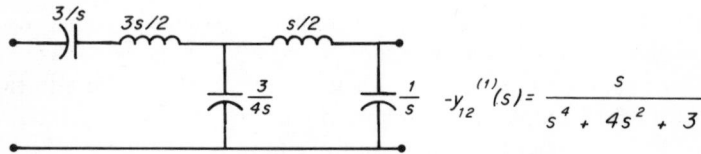

$$-y_{12}^{(1)}(s) = \frac{s}{s^4 + 4s^2 + 3}$$

**Fig. 11.16. A network with** $y_{22} = \dfrac{s^5 + 6s^3 + 8s}{s^4 + 4s^2 + 3}$

whereas $-y_{12}^{(2)}$ is obtained in Fig. 11.17.

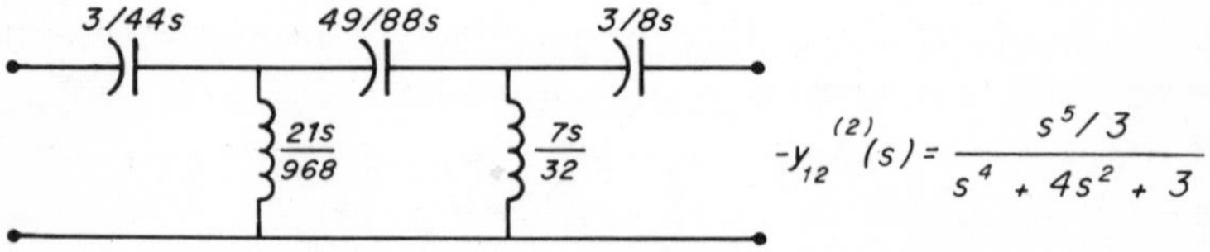

$$-y_{12}^{(2)}(s) = \frac{s^5/3}{s^4 + 4s^2 + 3}$$

**Fig. 11.17. A second network with** $y_{22} = \dfrac{s^5 + 6s^3 + 8s}{s^4 + 4s^2 + 3}$

Note that $-y_{12}^{(2)}$ is smaller than required in Eq. 11.7.2. Hence this network has to be scaled down by 3. Therefore, the final $y_{22}$ will be four times larger than in the original statement of the problem. The required network is given in Fig. 11.18.

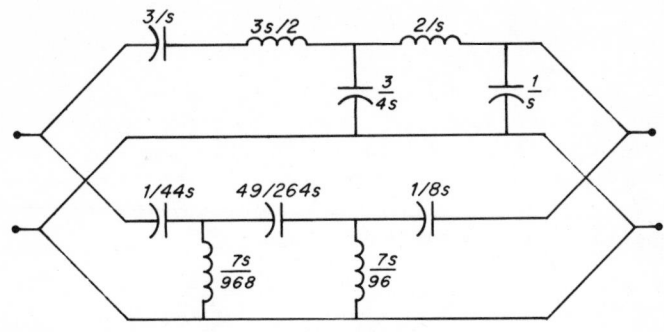

**Fig. 11.18. A network where** $y_{22} = \dfrac{4(s^5 + 6s^3 + 8s)}{s^4 + 4s^2 + 3}$ **and** $-y_{12} = \dfrac{s^5 + s}{s^4 + 4s^2 + 3}$

## Example 11.7.2

Realize the transfer admittance function $-y_{12} = (s^4 - s^2 + 1)/s(s^2 + 3)$.

### Solution

$-y_{12}$ (as specified) is not synthesizable by Guillemin's method, since one of the coefficients is negative. However, if a surplus factor $(s^2 + 1)$ is used, $-y_{12}$ becomes

$$-y_{12} = \frac{s^6 + 1}{s(s^2 + 1)(s^2 + 3)} \qquad \textbf{11.7.3}$$

(see Section 9.4 for details). Now $-y_{12}$ is in the proper form. However, $y_{22}$ is not specified, and therefore it may be selected at will. Choosing $y_{22}$ as

$$y_{22} = \frac{(s^2 + 1/2)(s^2 + 2)(s^2 + 4)}{s(s^2 + 1)(s^2 + 3)} \qquad \textbf{11.7.4}$$

would give a satisfactory network.

Observe that the Guillemin technique can handle zeros which do not lie on the $j$ axis (numerator of Eq. 11.7.3), although breaking the numerator into parts with $j$ axis zeros would lend itself to zero shifting with possible economy in number of elements. For example, if num. $-y_{12} = s^6 + s^4 + s^2 + 1$, it can be written in pairs $-y_{12} = s^4(s^2 + 1) + (s^2 + 1)$. Each of these terms can be realized by means of one ladder network (Section 11.6). The final result would be two parallel networks instead of four.

### Example 11.7.3

Realize the transfer function $T_{12} = (E_2)/E_1)\big|_{I_2=0} = \dfrac{s^2 + 1}{2s^2 + 10s + 11}$ in terms of $RC$ networks.

*Solution*

$T_{12} = \dfrac{-y_{12}}{1 + y_{22}}$ in a 2-port network terminated with a 1-ohm resistor. Hence, if the denominator is broken into two parts so that the ratio between these two parts would yield an $RC$ network, the problem would be reduced to that of synthesizing a 2-port network when both $y_{22}$ and $-y_{12}$ are specified. The denominator of $T_{12}$ may be written as $(s + 1)(s + 3) + (s + 2)(s + 4)$. (There is a great deal of arbitrariness in the split. This will be shown in Theorem 11.8.1.) Then $T_{12}$ can be rewritten as

$$T_{12} = \frac{(s^2 + 1)/(s + 2)(s + 4)}{1 + \dfrac{(s + 1)(s + 3)}{(s + 2)(s + 4)}} \qquad \text{11.7.5}$$

yielding $-y_{12} = \dfrac{(s^2 + 1)}{(s + 2)(s + 4)} = \dfrac{s^2}{(s + 2)(s + 4)} + \dfrac{1}{(s + 2)(s + 4)}$ and

$$y_{22} = \frac{(s + 1)(s + 3)}{(s + 2)(s + 4)} \qquad \text{11.7.6}$$

The use of Guillemin's procedure entails the realization of $y_{22}$ in two forms In one case, $-y_{12}$ has to have two zeros at the origin; hence the two capacitors (in a canonic realization) must be in the series position in a Cauer network. In the second case, $-y_{12}$ (Eq. 11.7.6) must have the two capacitors in the shunting position in the Cauer network.

The two respective expressions for $y_{22}$ are as follows:

$$y_{22} = \frac{3}{8} + \cfrac{1}{\dfrac{32}{7s} + \cfrac{1}{\dfrac{49}{88} + \cfrac{1}{\dfrac{968}{21s} + \dfrac{44}{3}}}} = \cfrac{1}{1 + \cfrac{1}{\dfrac{s}{2} + \cfrac{1}{\dfrac{4}{3} + \cfrac{1}{\dfrac{3s}{2} + 3}}}} \qquad \text{11.7.7}$$

$$\text{(a)} \qquad\qquad\qquad \text{(b)}$$

The corresponding networks are shown in Fig. 11.19.

Examination of the resulting transfer admittance in Fig. 11.20 shows that the admittance of each member of Fig. 11.20a must be scaled up by a factor of 44; then the sum of the transfer admittance functions will have the factor $(s^2 + 1)$. Furthermore, the sum of the two $y_{22}$ must be equal to $(s^2 + 4s + 3)/(s^2 + 6s + 8)$ so that the result would conform with Eq. 11.7.5. This requires additional scaling. Thus

$$k\big(\underbrace{44\,y_{22}}_{(a)} + \underbrace{y_{22}}_{(b)}\big) = 1 \times y_{22} \qquad \text{11.7.8}$$

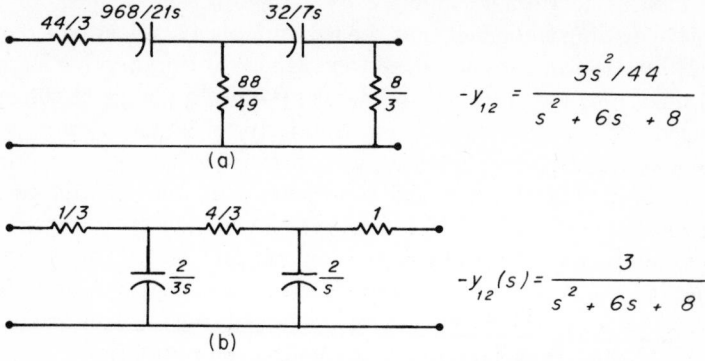

$$-y_{12} = \frac{3s^2/44}{s^2 + 6s + 8}$$

(a)

$$-y_{12}(s) = \frac{3}{s^2 + 6s + 8}$$

(b)

**Fig. 11.19. Two networks where** $y_{22} = \dfrac{s^2 + 4s + 3}{s^2 + 6s + 8}$

where $k$ is the new scaling constant. The coefficient, 44, is there to insure that the sum of the two transfer functions has the factor $s^2 + 1$. Hence $k = 1/45$. The final network is given in Fig. 11.20.

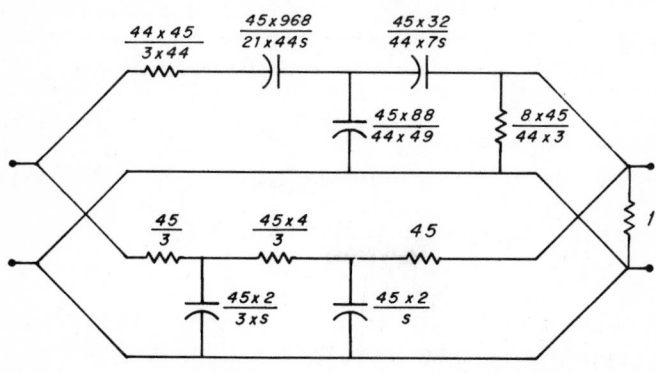

**Fig. 11.20. An RC network where** $T_{12} = \dfrac{(s^2 + 1)}{15(2s^2 + 10s + 11)}$

Example 11.7.3 can serve to show that any $T_{12}$ can be realized in terms of $RC$ networks if its numerator has only positive coefficients and if its denominator has only negative real axis zeros. If some of the coefficients are negative, it may be still possible to utilize auxiliary polynomials to hide them. This will be shown in Section 12.5.

## DOUBLE-RESISTIVE-TERMINATED LOSSLESS 2-PORT NETWORKS 11.8

In Section 11.5 a function of the type $T_{12} = \dfrac{E_2}{E_1}\Big|_{I_2=0}$ was realized as a lossless network terminated by a resistor. One reason for the resistive loading is the fact that the network always is loaded to some extent by the element connected to it. Hence, if the effective loading is lumped into the terminal resistance, the performance of the synthesized network is unimpaired. Similarly, it is also desirable to have a series resistance associated with the synthesized network as illustrated in Fig. 11.21 which represents a double-resistive-terminated lossless network. $Z_1(s)$ is the input impedance as seen from the input terminals of the lossless network terminated in $R_2$. The value of $T_{12}(s)$ will be derived from power consideration. The method is from Darlington. Thus, with sinusoidal excitation assumed, the power delivered into $R_2$ can be computed from

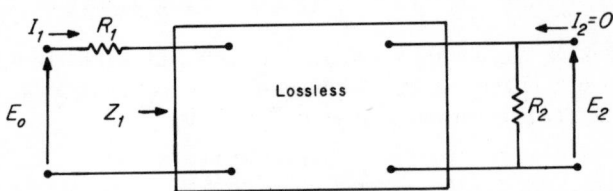

**Fig. 11.21. A double-resistive-terminated lossless network**

$$P_{in} = |E_2|^2/R_2 \qquad \text{11.8.1a}$$

and

$$P_{in} = |I_1|^2 \operatorname{Re} Z_1(j\omega) \qquad \text{11.8.1b}$$

From these $\left|\dfrac{E_2}{I_1}\right|^2$ can be computed to be

$$\left|\frac{E_2}{I_1}\right|^2 = R_2 \operatorname{Re} Z_1(j\omega) \qquad \text{11.8.2}$$

Now it is possible to make use of the fact that

$$I_1 = \frac{E_0}{R_1 + Z_1(j\omega)} \qquad \text{11.8.3}$$

to put Eq. 11.8.2 into the form

$$\left|\frac{E_2}{E_0}\right|^2_{s=j\omega} = |T_{12}(s)|^2\Big|_{s=j\omega} = \frac{R_2 \operatorname{Re} Z_1(s)}{|R_1 + Z_1(s)|^2}\Big|_{s=j\omega} \qquad \text{11.8.4}$$

Next we shall introduce the quantity $s_{11}(s)$ which is called the reflection coefficient:

$$|s_{11}(s)|^2\Big|_{s=j\omega} = 1 - \frac{4R_1}{R_2}|T_{12}(s)|^2\Big|_{s=j\omega} = 1 - \frac{4R_1 \operatorname{Re} Z_1(s)}{|R_1 + Z_1(s)|^2}\Big|_{s=j\omega}$$

$$= \left|\frac{R_1 - Z_1(s)}{R_1 + Z_1(s)}\right|^2_{s=j\omega} \qquad \text{11.8.5}$$

$s_{11}(s)$ arises in terminated 2-port and transmission-line theory.* Furthermore, a close look at the mapping properties of $s_{11}(s)$ shows that it maps the $r.h.Z_1(s)$ plane to a unit circle (see Section 2.6). Thus, for $Z_1(s)$ to be prf, it is required that

$$|s_{11}(s)|^2 \leq 1 \qquad \text{for Re } s = 0 \qquad \text{11.8.6a}$$

$$|s_{11}(s)|^2 < 1 \qquad \text{for Re } s > 0 \qquad \text{11.8.6b}$$

But Eq. 11.8.6a can be maintained if $T_{12}(s)$ is realizable. The truth of this is shown by noting that the maximum possible power delivered to $Z_1$ (and hence to $R_2$), $P_{\max}$ is

$$P_{\max} = \frac{|E_0|^2}{4R_1} \qquad \text{11.8.7}$$

Thus for $T_{12}(s)$ to be passive (and hence possibly realizable)† the following must be obeyed:

$$\frac{4R_1}{R_2} |T_{12}(s)|^2 \Big|_{s=j\omega} = \frac{P(R_2)}{P_{\max}(R_2)} \leq 1 \qquad \text{11.8.8}$$

This quantity now may be substituted in Eq. 11.8.5 to show that condition 11.8.6a is maintained. To show that condition 11.8.6b is maintained note that the combination of Eqs. 11.8.8 and 11.8.5 have quadrantal symmetry (Theorem 7.2.1). Thus, by selecting $s_{11}(s)$ from Eq. 11.8.5 such that it has all *l.h.s.* plane poles would make it analytic in *r.h.s.* plane. This is sufficient, according to the maximum modulus theorem, to show that 11.8.6b is maintained. Selecting $s_{11}(s)$ accordingly one may write (using Eq. 11.8.5)

$$s_{11}(s)s_{11}(-s) = \left( \pm \frac{R_1 - Z_1(s)}{R_1 + Z_1(s)} \right)\left( \pm \frac{R_1 - Z_1(-s)}{R_1 + Z_1(-s)} \right) \qquad \text{11.8.9}$$

and therefore choose

$$s_{11}(s) = \pm \frac{R_1 - Z_1(s)}{R_1 + Z_1(s)} \qquad \text{11.8.10}$$

This is now solved for $Z_1(s)/R_1$ to give

$$\frac{Z_1(s)}{R_1} = \frac{1 - s_{11}(s)}{1 + s_{11}(s)} \qquad \text{(or its reciprocal)} \qquad \text{11.8.11}$$

In conclusion note that the problem of realizing $T_{12}(s)$ in terms of a double-terminated lossless network was reduced to that of realizing a positive real function $Z_1(s)/R_1$ (as given in Eq. 11.8.11) as a loss-

---

* The term is also used in another network theory formalism where it is called the scattering coefficient (see Carlin, H. J., "The Scattering Matrix in Network Theory," *IRE Trans. on Circuit Theory*, Vol. CT-3, pp. 88–97, June, 1956).

† As a double-resistive-terminated lossless network.

less network terminated with a resistor. This always can be done by means of the Darlington procedure of Chapter 7. However, if the zeros of the even part of $Z_1(s)$ do not lie along the positive real axis, other techniques developed in this chapter for three-terminal networks may be applied.

At this point it is important to note that the zeros of Ev $Z_1(s)$ are determined by the zeros of $T_{12}(s)$ as may be seen in Eq. 11.8.4.

### Example 11.8.1

Realize the function $T_{12}(s)$ as a double-terminated lossless network with $R_1 = R_2 = 1$ ohm. The function is given by

$$|T_{12}(s)|^2 = \frac{k}{1 + s^6} \qquad \text{11.8.12}$$

where $k$ is a positive constant that is to be selected to be as large as possible. This relation describes a third-order approximation of the low-pass filter (Example 10.3.1). The constant $k$ can be determined from Eq. 11.8.8:

$$4|T_{12}(s)|^2 \Big|_{s=j\omega} = \frac{4k}{1 + \omega^6} \leq 1 \qquad \text{11.8.13}$$

Then $k_{max} = 1/4$. $s_{11}(s)$ can be determined from Eq. 11.8.5:

$$s_{11}(s)s_{11}(-s) = 1 - \frac{1}{1 - s^6} = \frac{-s^6}{1 - s^6} \qquad \text{11.8.14}$$

which yields

$$s_{11}(s) = \frac{+s^3}{s^3 + 2s^2 + 2s + 1}$$

whereas $Z_1(s)$ can be obtained from Eq. 11.8.11. From Eq. 11.8.4 we see that the zeros of Ev $Z_1(s)$ all lie at infinity. Hence we may realize $Z_1(s)$ by continued fraction expansion to yield a lossless ladder terminated in a resistance (Section 11.3). Proceeding accordingly we get

$$Z_1(s) = \frac{2s^3 + 2s^2 + 2s + 1}{2s^2 + 2s + 1} = s + \cfrac{1}{2s + \cfrac{1}{s + 1}} \qquad \text{11.8.15}$$

The final realization is given in Fig. 11.22.

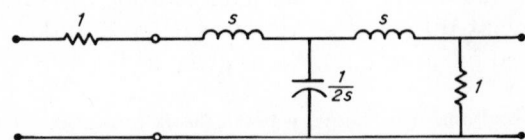

**Fig. 11.22. A double-resistive-terminated lossless network for Example 11.8.1**

## DENOMINATOR PARTITIONING 11.9

In Example 11.7.3 a polynomial with negative real zeros was broken into two with alternating negative real zeros. This was done for the purpose of forming a two-element kind impedance function by taking the ratio of the two polynomials. The manner of performing this split depends (so far) upon the individual investigator. To prove that this can be done, we shall use the following argument.

### Theorem 11.9.1

If $P$ is a Hurwitz polynomial whose zeros are simple and lie on the negative real axis, then it may be split into two parts $(P_1 + P_2)$ such that $P_1/P_2$ or its inverse is an $RC$ driving point impedance function.

### Proof

Construct an auxilliary polynomial $P_0$ such that $P/P_0$ is an $RC$ driving point impedance function (this can be done by selecting the zeros of $P_0$ to alternate with the zeros of $P$). In addition let $P_0$ be of the same degree as $P$. Hence $P/P_0$ may be expanded in a partial fraction expansion as follows:

$$Z_{RC} = \frac{P}{P_0} = R + \sum_p \frac{a_p}{s + b_p} \qquad \text{11.9.1}$$

Now $R$ is split into two positive parts $R = \dfrac{R}{2} + \dfrac{R}{2}$. It follows that

$$Z_{RC} = \frac{P}{P_0} = \underbrace{\frac{R}{2} + \sum_p \frac{a_p}{s + b_p}}_{Z_{1RC}} + \underbrace{\frac{R}{2}}_{Z_{2RC}} \qquad \text{11.9.2}$$

Notice that $Z_{1RC}$ has the same poles as $Z_{RC}$. Then Eq. 11.9.2 may be written as

$$\underbrace{\frac{P}{P_0}}_{Z_{RC}} = \underbrace{\frac{P_1}{P_0}}_{Z_{1RC}} + \underbrace{\frac{P_2}{P_0}}_{Z_{2RC}} = \frac{P_1}{P_0} + \frac{R}{2}\frac{P_0}{P_0} \qquad \text{11.9.3}$$

Hence $P_1$ and $P_2 \left( = \dfrac{R}{2} P_0 \right)$ are the required polynomials.

*Proof completed*

### Example 11.9.1

Split $P = (s + 2)(s + 4)$ into two polynomials of the same degree such that their ratio is an $RC$ impedance function.

*Solution*

Select $P_0 = (s + 1)(s + 3)$. $P/P_0$ is expanded in a partial fraction expansion to give

$$Z(s) = \frac{P}{P_0} = \frac{(s + 2)(s + 4)}{(s + 1)(s + 3)} = 1 + \frac{3/2}{s + 1} + \frac{1/2}{s + 3}$$

$$= \frac{1}{2}\left(1 + \frac{3}{s + 1} + \frac{1}{s + 3}\right) + \frac{1}{2}$$

$$= \frac{1}{2}\left(\frac{s^2 + 8s + 13}{s^2 + 4s + 3} + \frac{s^2 + 4s + 3}{s^2 + 4s + 3}\right) \quad \text{11.9.4}$$

Thus $P_1 = \dfrac{1}{2}(s^2 + 8s + 13)$ and $P_2 = \dfrac{1}{2}(s^2 + 4s + 3)$.

## PROBLEMS

11.1. Realize the following impedance matrices:

(a).
$$[Z(s)] = \begin{bmatrix} \dfrac{5s^3 + 6s}{s^2 + 1} & 2\dfrac{s^3}{s^2 + 1} \\[3mm] 2\dfrac{s^3}{s^2 + 1} & \dfrac{s^3 + 6s}{s^2 + 1} \end{bmatrix}$$

(b).
$$[Z(s)] = \begin{bmatrix} \dfrac{3s + 1}{s(s + 1)} & \dfrac{-1}{s(s + 1)} \\[3mm] \dfrac{-1}{s(s + 1)} & \dfrac{2s + 1}{s(s + 1)} \end{bmatrix}$$

11.2. Realize a three-terminal network such that

$$\text{(a).}\quad z_{12} = \frac{ks}{s^2 + 1}$$

$$z_{11} = \frac{s(s^2 + 2)}{(s^2 + 1)(s^2 + 3)} \qquad \text{(b).}\quad z_{12} = \frac{ks}{(s^2 + 1)(s^2 + 3)}$$

$$\text{(c).}\quad z_{12} = \frac{ks^3}{(s^2 + 1)(s^2 + 3)}$$

where $k$ is positive but otherwise arbitrary. Determine $k$ for each network.

11.3. Use zero shifting to realize three-terminal networks $(3T.N)$ such that

$$\text{(a).}\quad z_{12} = \frac{ks(s^2 + 4)}{(s^2 + 1)(s^2 + 3)}$$

$$z_{11} = \frac{s(s^2 + 2)}{(s^2 + 1)(s^2 + 3)} \qquad \text{(b).}\quad z_{12} = \frac{ks(s^2 + \frac{1}{2})}{(s^2 + 1)(s^2 + 3)}$$

where $k$ is any positive constant. Determine the value of $k$ in each network.

11.4. Realize a three terminal network such that

$$\text{(a).} \quad -y_{12} = \frac{ks}{s^2 + 1}$$

$$y_{22} = \frac{s(s^2 + 2)}{(s^2 + 1)(s^2 + 3)} \qquad \text{(b).} \quad -y_{12} = \frac{ks}{(s^2 + 1)(s^2 + 3)}$$

$$\text{(c).} \quad -y_{12} = \frac{ks^3}{(s^2 + 1)(s^2 + 3)}$$

$k$ is any positive constant. Determine the value of $k$ in each network.

11.5. Determine the fifth approximation for $y_{22}$ in Example 11.5.1.

11.6. Use Guillemin's method to obtain a 3 T.N such that

$$\text{(a).} \quad -y_{12} = \frac{ks(s^2 + 4)}{(s^2 + 1)(s^2 + 3)}$$

$$y_{22} = \frac{s(s^2 + 2)}{(s^2 + 1)(s^2 + 3)} \qquad \text{(b).} \quad -y_{12} = \frac{ks(s^2 + \frac{1}{2})}{(s^2 + 1)(s^2 + 3)}$$

where $k$ is an arbitrary positive constant. Determine the maximum value of this constant in each network.

11.7. Realize a double-resistive-terminated lossless 3 T.N such that if $R_1 = R_2$

$$T_{12} = \frac{b/2}{s^2 + as + b}$$

Are $a$ and $b$ arbitrary?

11.8. Split the following polynomials into two parts such that the ratio between the two respective parts of each polynomial will be an $RC$ impedance function:

(a). $\qquad P = s^2 + 5s + 5$

(b). $\qquad P = s^2 + 8s + 14.$

## FURTHER READING

BOOKS

11.1. Balabanian, N., "Network Synthesis," Prentice-Hall, Inc., Englewood Cliffs, N. J. 1958, Chapters 8 and 9.

11.2. Guillemin, E. A., "Synthesis of Passive Networks," John Wiley & Sons, New York, 1957, Chapters 11 and 13.

11.3. Kuh, E. S., and Pederson, D. O., "Principles of Circuit Synthesis," McGraw-Hill Book Co., Inc., New York, 1959, Chapters 5, 7, 9, and 11.

11.4. Van Valkenburg, M. E., "Introduction to Modern Network Synthesis," John Wiley & Sons, New York, 1960, Chapters 11, 14, and 15.

A RELATED PAPER

11.5. Weinberg, L., and Slepian, Paul, "Takahasi's Results on Tchebycheff and Butterworth Ladder Networks," *IRE Trans on Circuit Theory*, Vol. CT-7, pp. 88–101, June, 1960.

# CHAPTER 12

# Three-Terminal RC Networks With an Arbitrary Gain

## 12.1. INTRODUCTION

In the previous chapters a synthesis of the transfer function $T_{12}(s) \left( = \left. \dfrac{E_2}{E_1} \right|_{I_2=0} \right)$ was qualified with the statement "within a multiplying constant." $T_{12}$ was always synthesized as prescribed, but with a constant multiplier governed by the particular method chosen. Now we will discuss a synthesis procedure that can produce a desired realization that does not depend on the "constant multiplier" (usually called the "gain constant") as long as it is bounded in accordance with a specified realizability criterion.

This method of synthesis was essentially formulated by Fialkow and Gerst who discovered the necessary and sufficient conditions for the realization of $RC$ three-terminal networks,* and the following section (Section 12.2) develops this procedure. In Section 12.3, the analysis of three-terminal $RC$ networks is presented to demonstrate that the transfer function synthesized in Section 12.2 was not only sufficient but also necessary for all $RC$ three-terminal networks. The fourth section is devoted to the proof of a lemma (the Fialkow-Gerst lemma) needed for establishing the validity of Section 12.3. The last section gives a method for determining surplus factors for improving the numerator of the transfer function $T_{12}$. Sometimes this numerator may have some negative coefficients. These can be made to vanish if an appropriate surplus factor is

---

* Fialkow, A., and Gerst, I., "The Transfer Function of General Two Terminal-Pair $RC$ Networks," *Quarterly of Appl. Math.*, Vol. 10, pp. 113–127, April, 1952.

used and if the numerator has no positive real zero. The method presented here is different from the one presented in Section 9.4, since only real zeros are involved.

The chapter is devoted to $RC$ synthesis only. However, as was pointed out earlier, the results apply equally well for other two-element-kind networks. For example, $LC$ networks can be obtained from $RC$ networks by making the transformation $s = s'^2$ and then multiplying each element by $s'$ (see, for example, Section 11.2). This chapter ends our treatment of $RC$ networks.

## THE FIALKOW-GERST NETWORKS 12.2

The Fialkow-Gerst synthesis procedure applies to the synthesis of $RC$ networks for which the transfer functions are of the type

$$T_{12} = \frac{E_2}{E_1}\bigg|_{I_2=0}$$

$$= \frac{z_{12}}{z_{11}} \qquad\qquad \textbf{12.2.1}$$

$$= -\frac{y_{12}}{y_{22}}$$

This section will be devoted to the Fialkow-Gerst synthesis of three-terminal networks (3T.N). Unlike the restrictions imposed in previous chapters, it is no longer necessary to specify that the results satisfy Eqs. 12.2.1 within a multiplying constant. Now, however, $T_{12}$ is constrained as follows. Write $T_{12}$ in the usual polynomial ratio form

$$T_{12} = \frac{a_0 s^n + a_1 s^{n-1} + \cdots + a_{n-1} s + a_n}{b_0 s^n + b_1 s^{n-1} + \cdots + b_{n-1} s + b_n} = \frac{\displaystyle\sum_{i=0}^{n} a_i s^{n-i}}{\displaystyle\sum_{i=0}^{n} b_i s^{n-i}} \qquad \textbf{12.2.2}$$

here we have

(a) The poles of $T_{12}$ are distinct and lie along the negative real axis.

(b)
$$0 \le a_i \le b_i; \qquad b_0 \ne 0 \ne b_n$$

In case that some of the $a_i$ are negative, it may be still possible to augment $T_{12}$ by using auxiliary polynomials such that condition (b) is satisfied. This will be discussed later (Section 12.5). If both conditions (a) and (b) of Eq. 12.2.2 are satisfied, $T_{12}$ is called an $R$ function.

The essence of the Fialkow-Gerst procedure will be outlined through an example. The procedure given differs somewhat from the original, but the philosophy is essentially unchanged.

**Illustrative Example**

Realize a 3T.N which possesses the following transfer function, $T_{12}$:

$$T_{12} = \frac{s^2 + s + 1}{s^2 + 4s + 3} \qquad \text{12.2.3}$$

*Solution*

The principal tool of the procedure is the relation

$$T_{12} = -\frac{y_{12}}{y_{22}} = -\frac{y_{12}^{(1)} + y_{12}^{(2)}}{y_{22}^{(1)} + y_{22}^{(2)}} \qquad \text{12.2.4}$$

which can be represented simply as

$$T_{12} = \frac{P}{Q}$$

Equation 12.2.4 is associated with a network (Fig. 12.1) made up of two 3T.N networks in the parallel parallel connection, denoted as $\Gamma_1$ and $\Gamma_2$, respectively.

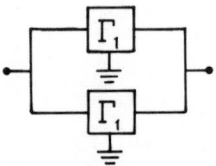

Fig. 12.1. The Fialkow-
Gerst 3 terminal network

The superscripts 1 and 2 in Eq. 12.2.4 refer to networks $\Gamma_1$ and $\Gamma_2$, respectively. But if the resulting network is that illustrated, then it will follow that the respective transfer functions of the two networks may be written as

$$T_{12}^{(1)} = -\frac{y_{12}^{(1)}}{y_{22}^{(1)}} \qquad \text{and } T_{12}^{(2)} = -\frac{y_{12}^{(2)}}{y_{22}^{(2)}}$$

For the sake of the continued development, it is further assumed that $y_{22}$ of the original network is also specified (hence also $y_{12}$ is known) and that it is given by the form $\dfrac{Q}{S}$, where $S$ is a polynomial of degree $n-1$ in $s$. Furthermore, since $y_{22}$ is an $RC$ admittance function, it can be expanded in the following canonical form:

$$y_{22} = \frac{Q}{S} = s + c + \sum_{i=1}^{n-1} \frac{sc_i}{s + \sigma_i} \qquad \textbf{12.2.5}$$

The corresponding expansion, for the example under consideration, depends on the choice of $S$. Let $S$ be given by $S = s + 2$ (remember that the zeros and poles must alternate). Thus

$$y_{22} = \frac{s^2 + 4s + 3}{s + 2} = s + \frac{3}{2} + \frac{\dfrac{s}{2}}{s + 2} \qquad \textbf{12.2.6}$$

Now it is necessary to split $y_{22}$ into two parts, as indicated in Eq. 12.2.4. The process selected to accomplish this is very arbitrary. Consider the following split:

$$y_{22} = y_{22}^{(1)} + y_{22}^{(2)}$$

$$\equiv \left( s + \sum_{i=1}^{n-1} \frac{\alpha_i c_i s}{s + \sigma_i} \right) + \left( c + \sum_{i=1}^{n-1} \frac{(1 - \alpha_i)c_i s}{s + \sigma_i} \right); \ 0 < \alpha_i < 1 \qquad \textbf{12.2.7}$$

Thus in the particular example under survey $\left( \text{take } \alpha = \dfrac{1}{2} \right)$

$$y_{22} = y_{22}^{(1)} + y_{22}^{(2)} \qquad \textbf{12.2.8a}$$

$$y_{22}^{(1)} + y_{22}^{(2)} = \left( s + \frac{\dfrac{s}{4}}{s + 2} \right) + \left( \frac{3}{2} + \frac{\dfrac{s}{4}}{s + 2} \right) \qquad \textbf{12.2.8b}$$

which may be put into the form

$$y_{22}^{(1)} + y_{22}^{(2)} = \frac{s\left( s + \dfrac{9}{4} \right)}{s + 2} + \frac{\dfrac{7}{4}s + 3}{s + 2} \qquad \textbf{12.2.8c}$$

Note that both $y_{22}^{(1)}$ and $y_{22}^{(2)}$ are $RC$ admittance functions by construction. Reexamination of Eq. 12.2.5, reveals that multiplying $y_{22}^{(1)} + y_{22}^{(2)}$ by the polynomial $S$ decomposes $Q$:

$$y_{22}S = Q = Sy_{22}^{(1)} + Sy_{22}^{(2)} \qquad \textbf{12.2.9}$$

or more specifically

$$Q = s \sum_{i=0}^{n-1} b'_i s^{n-1-i} + \sum_{i=1}^{n} b''_i s^{n-i}$$

In the example

$$Q = s\left(s + \frac{9}{4}\right) + \frac{7}{4}s + 3 \qquad \text{12.2.10}$$

Now it is necessary to decompose the numerator of $T_{12}$. Here, too, there is a great deal of arbitrariness, although a systematic method will be given later. The final decomposition should be of the following form (which is always possible)

$$P = s\sum_{i=0}^{n-1} a'_i s^{n-1-i} + \sum_{i=1}^{n} a''_i s^{n-i} \qquad \text{12.2.11}$$

where

$$0 \leq a'_i \leq b'_i \quad 0 \leq a''_i \leq b''_i$$

One satisfactory possibility for the example is the expression

$$P = s(s + 1) + 1 \qquad \text{12.2.12}$$

Now we are in a position to tell what the transfer functions are of each network in Fig. 12.1. Our formal decomposition permits them to be written as

$$T_{12}^{(1)} = \frac{s\displaystyle\sum_{i=0}^{n-1} a'_i s^{n-1-i}}{s\displaystyle\sum_{i=0}^{n-1} b'_i s^{n-1-i}} = \frac{s(a'_0 s^{n-1} + \cdots + a'_{n-1})}{s(b'_0 s^{n-1} + \cdots + b'_{n-1})} \qquad \text{12.2.13a}$$

and

$$T_{12}^{(2)} = \frac{\displaystyle\sum_{i=0}^{n} a''_i s^{n-1}}{\displaystyle\sum_{i=1}^{n} b''_i s^{n-i}} = \frac{a''_1 s^{n-1} + \cdots + a''_n}{b''_1 s^{n-1} + \cdots + b''_n} \qquad \text{12.2.13b}$$

In the example under study these become

$$T_{12}^{(1)} = \frac{s(s + 1)}{s\left(s + \dfrac{9}{4}\right)} = \frac{s + 1}{s + \dfrac{9}{4}}$$

and

$$T_{12}^{(2)} = \frac{1}{\dfrac{7}{4}s + 3} \qquad \text{12.2.14}$$

It is important to notice that both transfer functions are $R$ functions, and are at least 1 less in degree than the original $T_{12}$. At this stage, for further reduction, the problem may be attacked in many ways. Fialkow and Gerst suggest that $y_{22}^{(1)}$ and $y_{22}^{(2)}$ be first reduced in the manner illustrated in Fig. 12.2.

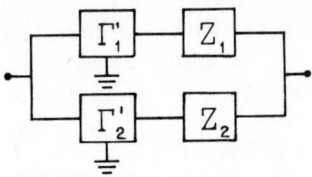

**Fig. 12.2. A development of the Fialkow-Gerst network**

Note that since $T_{12} = \dfrac{E_2}{E_1}\bigg|_{I_2=0}$, then both $\Gamma'_1$ and $\Gamma'_2$ have the same respective transfer functions as $\Gamma_1$ and $\Gamma_2$. Hence the final transfer admittance function, $-y_{12}^{(1)}$, (or $-y_{12}^{(2)}$) can be determined from the reduced $y_{22}^{(1)}$ (or $y_{22}^{(2)}$) and the original $T_{12}^{(1)}$ (or $T_{12}^{(2)}$).

To proceed along these lines, $y_{22}^{(1)}$ and $y_{22}^{(2)}$ are expanded as follows:

$$\frac{1}{y_{22}^{(1)}} = \frac{S}{s\displaystyle\sum_{i=0}^{n-1} b'_i s^{n-1-i}} = \frac{d}{s} + \frac{1}{Y_{22}^{(1)}}$$

$$\text{12.2.15a}$$

and

$$\frac{1}{y_{22}^{(2)}} = \frac{S}{\displaystyle\sum_{i=1}^{n} b''_i s^{n-i}} = r + \frac{1}{Y_{22}^{(2)}}$$

$$\text{12.2.15b}$$

where $r$ is the minimum resistance of $1/y_{22}^{(2)}$. Hence, both $Y_{22}^{(1)}$ and $Y_{22}^{(2)}$ are less in degree than $y_{22}^{(1)}$ and $y_{22}^{(2)}$, respectively, and furthermore $Z_1$ may be taken as $\dfrac{d}{s}$, and $Z_2$, as $r$. Identifying these values in Eq. 12.2.8c, we get

$$Z_1 = \frac{8}{9s}, \qquad Z_2 = \frac{4}{7}$$

and

$$Y_{22}^{(1)} = 9\left(s + \frac{9}{4}\right),$$
$$Y_{22}^{(2)} = \frac{7}{2}\left(\frac{7}{4}s + 3\right)$$

$$\text{12.2.16}$$

It is observed at this point that a synthesis cycle is complete. Both $T_{12}{}^{(1)}$ and $Y_{12}{}^{(1)}$ are given for the network $\Gamma'_1$, and likewise the corresponding terms for $\Gamma'_2$ are given. Furthermore, the final transfer functions are of reduced degree (Eqs. 12.2.14), and the final admittances $Y_{22}$ (Eqs. 12.2.16) are also reduced in degree in addition to being in the proper form (like Eq. 12.2.5) necessary for the continuation of the process. However, here the problem is simple enough to be carried out by ladder expansions. Towards this end the transfer admittances ($Y_{12}$) are computed first:

$$-Y_{12}{}^{(1)} = T_{12}{}^{(1)} \times Y_{22}{}^{(1)} = \frac{s+1}{s+\dfrac{9}{4}} \times 9\left(s+\frac{9}{4}\right) = 9(s+1)$$

and

$$-Y_{12}{}^{(2)} = T_{12}{}^{(2)} \times Y_{22}{}^{(2)} = \frac{1}{\dfrac{7}{4}s+3} \times \frac{7}{2}\left(\frac{7}{4}s+3\right) = \frac{7}{2}$$

12.2.17

The final network is given in Fig. 12.3.

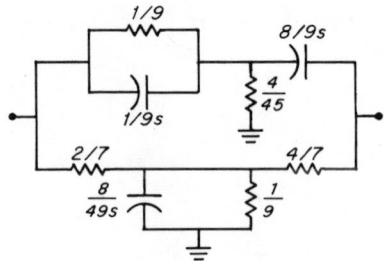

**Fig. 12.3. A Fialkow-Gerst network for**
$$T_{12} = \frac{s^2 + s + 1}{s^2 + 4s + 3}$$

To complete the development of the procedure it is still necessary to prove that the decomposition of the numerator $P$ (Eq. 12.2.11) is always possible. Towards this end the coefficients of $P$ and $Q$ (Eq. 12.2.9) are compared as follows. The coefficients of $Q$ are

$$b'_0 \qquad = b_0$$

$$\cdot \qquad \cdot \qquad \cdot$$

$$b'_i + b''_i = b_i$$

12.2.18

$$\cdot \qquad \cdot \qquad \cdot$$

$$b''_n = b_n$$

and similarly the coefficients of $P$ are

$$a'_0 \qquad = a_0$$

$$\cdot \qquad \cdot$$

$$a'_i + a''_i = a_i \qquad\qquad \text{12.2.19}$$

$$\cdot \qquad \cdot \qquad \cdot$$

$$a''_n = a_n$$

Thus as $T_{12}$ is an $R$ function, $0 \le a_i \le b_i$, and it is possible to select the $a$'s by choosing $a'_0 = a_0$ and $a''_n = a_n$ (as before) and $a'_i < b'_i$ and $a''_i < b''_i$ such that $a'_i + a''_i = a_i$. One such choice, for example, would be $(a_i/b_i) = (a'_i/b'_i) = (a''_i/b''_i)$.

*Proof completed*

We digress to discuss the possibility of a resistive loading. Split $T_{12}$ (Eq. 12.2.2) as follows:

$$T_{12} = \frac{\displaystyle\sum_{i=0}^{n} a_i s^{n-i}}{\displaystyle\sum_{i=0}^{n} b_i s^{n-i}} = \frac{P}{Q} = \frac{-y_{12}}{y_{22} + \eta} \qquad\qquad \text{12.2.20}$$

where $\eta^{-1}$ is the resistive load. Note that the development deletes one term of the numerator in the corresponding expansion of Eq. 12.2.4. This means that $\Gamma_1$ of Fig. 12.1 will be deleted. Then $\eta^{-1}$ will be in position $P$ in Fig. 12.4.

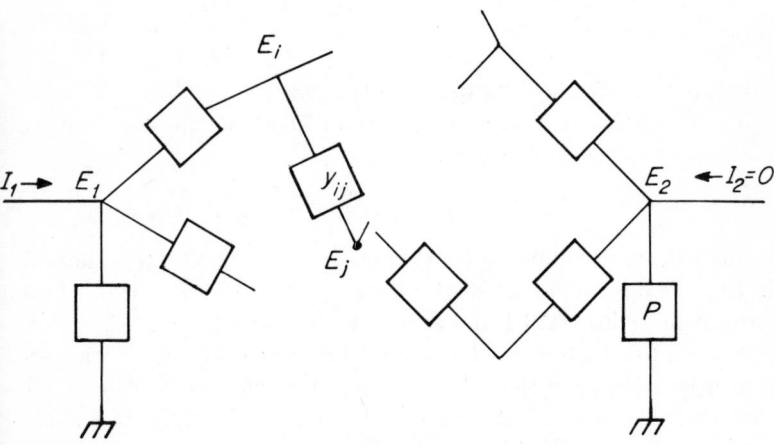

Fig. 12.4. A three-terminal RC network

$Q$ is now divided by an auxilliary polynomial $S$ such that $Q/S$ is an $RC$ admittance function. Furthermore, let $S$ be 1 less in degree than $Q$. This permits expanding $Q/S$ in the following canonical form:

$$\frac{Q}{S} = \left( as + (1 - \alpha)c + \sum \frac{sc_i}{s + \sigma_i} \right) + \alpha c; \quad 0 < \alpha < 1 \quad \textbf{12.2.21}$$

Dividing through by $\alpha c/\eta$ we define $y_{22}$ and $\eta$ as follows:

$$\frac{\eta Q}{\alpha c S} = y_{22} + \eta \qquad \textbf{12.2.22}$$

Eq. 12.2.21 indicates that $\alpha$ is not arbitrary; $\alpha$ is further restricted since the following must be an $R$ function:

$$\frac{-y_{12}}{y_{22}} = \frac{P}{Q - \alpha c S} \qquad \textbf{12.2.23}$$

However it is clear that if $0 < a_i < b_i$, it is always possible to find an $\alpha$ different from zero such that the above is satisfied.

## 12.3. $T_{12}$ OF THREE-TERMINAL RC NETWORKS

In the last section it was demonstrated that any $T_{12}$ can be realized in terms of three-terminal networks. Recall that $T_{12}$ is given by

$$T_{12} = \left. \frac{E_2}{E_1} \right|_{I_2=0} = \frac{\displaystyle\sum_{i=0}^{n} a_i s^{n-i}}{\displaystyle\sum_{i=0}^{n} b_i s^{n-i}} \qquad \textbf{12.3.1}$$

$$b_0 \neq 0 \neq b_n$$

and must satisfy the following contraints:

(a). The poles of $T_{12}$ are distinct and lie along the negative real axis.

(b).

$$0 \leq a_i \leq b_i$$

In this section it will be shown that the converse is also true, namely all $RC$ three-terminal networks have the transfer function of the form given in Eq. 12.3.1 and satisfy restrictions (a) and (b). However, common factors in $T_{12}$ should be cancelled only with care, since otherwise condition (b) may be violated (see Section 12.5).

In trying to prove the above statements, analyze the three-terminal $RC$ network shown in Fig. 12.4.

In this network all series elements are separated by nodes so that the final admittance between two adjacent nodes is due to parallel elements only. The network functions will be determined on the basis of nodal analysis. It is important to note that because of the way the nodes were designated, the admittance between nodes $i$ and $j$($y_{ij}$) in the following set of equations (Eqs. 12.3.3) must be of the form $cs + d$. Also observe that the self-admittance $y_{ii}$ at node $i$ contains all admittance terms to node $i$:

$$y_{ii} = \sum_{\substack{j=0 \\ j \neq i}}^{n} y_{ij} = y_{i0} + y_{i1} + y_{i2} + \cdots + y_{in} \qquad \text{12.3.2}$$

Furthermore, the general nodal set of equations is

$$
\begin{aligned}
I_1 &= y_{11}E_1 - y_{12}E_2 - \cdots - y_{1n}E_n \\
I_2 &= -y_{21}E_1 + y_{22}E_2 - \cdots - y_{2n}E_n \\
&\;\cdot \quad \cdot \quad \cdot \quad \cdot \quad \cdot \quad \cdot \quad \cdot \quad \cdot \quad \cdot \quad \cdot \\
0 &= -y_{n1}E_1 - y_{n2}E_2 - \cdots + y_{nn}E_n
\end{aligned}
\qquad \text{12.3.3}
$$

It follows from these equations that

$$T_{12} = \frac{E_2}{E_1}\Big|_{I_2=0} = \frac{\Delta_{12}}{\Delta_{11}} \qquad \text{12.3.4}$$

where

$$
\Delta_{12} = 
\begin{vmatrix}
y_{21} & y_{23} & \cdots & y_{2m} \\
-y_{31} & y_{33} & \cdots & -y_{3m} \\
\cdot & \cdot & \cdot & \cdot \\
-y_{m1} & -y_{m3} & \cdots & y_{mm}
\end{vmatrix}
= a_0 s^n + a_1 s^{n-1} + \cdots + a_n \qquad \text{12.3.5}
$$

and

$$
\Delta_{11} = 
\begin{vmatrix}
y_{22} & -y_{23} & \cdots & -y_{2m} \\
-y_{32} & y_{33} & \cdots & -y_{3m} \\
\cdot & \cdot & \cdot & \cdot \\
-y_{m2} & -y_{m3} & \cdots & y_{mm}
\end{vmatrix}
= b_0 s^n + b_1 s^{n-1} + \cdots + b_n \qquad \text{12.3.6}
$$

While $\Delta_{11}$ and $\Delta_{12}$ may have a common factor, these should not be cancelled. (This point is explained in Section 12.5.)

To prove statement (a) of Eq. 12.3.1 we shall use the following property which is proved in Section 13.8:

> *If $[Z(s)]$ represents an immittance matrix of a two-element-kind network (RL, RC), then all its poles are simple and lie on the negative real axis.*     12.3.7

### Lemma 12.3.1

If $[A(s)]$ represents an immittance matrix of a two-element-kind network $(RL, RC)$, then the zeros of det. $[A(s)]$ lie on the negative real axis.

*Proof*

Suppose that det. $[A(s)]$ has a zero which is off the real axis, say at $s = s_0$. Then the inverse of $[A(s)]$ has a pole at $s_0$ unless each minor has this zero. Property 12.3.7 dictates that $[A(s)]^{-1}$ may not have a pole at $s_0$; hence all the minors of $[A(s)]$ have this zero. Focusing our attention at one of the principal matrix minors, say $[A]_{pp}$, we note :

(1). $[A]_{pp}$ represents an $n$-port network in which one of the ports is open circuited. Hence it is an $RC$, $RL$ impedance matrix if $[A(s)]$ is one.

(2). Following the same argument as above, if det. $[A]_{pp}$ has the zero $s_0$, then all of its minors must have this zero.

Continuing this line of reasoning we conclude that each member of the principal diagonal of $[A(s)]$ has a zero at $s_0$. But this is impossible, since each member of the principal diagonal is an $RC$, $RL$ driving point impedance function.

*Proof completed*

Now we are in a position to prove statement (a) of the beginning of the section. The proof will be given in two parts. In the first part it will be shown that the poles of $T_{12}$ lie along the negative real axis. In the second part it will be shown that the poles are distinct.

### Part 1

The poles of $T_{12}$ lie along the negative real axis.

*Proof*

The poles of $T_{12}$ are determined by the zeros of $\Delta_{11}$. But $z_{11}(= \Delta_{11}/|Y|)$ is an $RC$ driving point impedance function, and therefore all its zeros lie along the negative real axis. Because of Lemma 12.3.1, the zeros of $|Y|$ are also along the negative real axis. Hence zeros common to $\Delta_{11}$ and $|Y|$ are of the same type. It follows that all the zeros of $\Delta_{11}$ are along the negative real axis.

*Proof completed*

### Part 2

The poles of $T_{12}$ are distinct.

*Proof*

Consider the following impedance matrix:

$$\begin{bmatrix} z_{11} & z_{12} \\ z_{12} & z_{22} \end{bmatrix} = \frac{1}{|Y|} \begin{bmatrix} \Delta_{11} & \Delta_{12} \\ \Delta_{12} & \Delta_{22} \end{bmatrix} \qquad \textbf{12.3.8}$$

By 12.3.7 all the poles are simple. Then if $|Y|$ has a higher-order zero, say $(s + \rho)^n$, the elements $\Delta_{11}$, $\Delta_{22}$, and $\Delta_{12}$ must have the zero $(s + \rho)^{n-1}$. Furthermore, $z_{11} = \Delta_{11}/|Y|$ has distinct zeros since it is an RC driving point impedance function. Thus all zeros of $\Delta_{11}$ are distinct except those of the form $(s + \rho)$.

It follows that we have three possibilities concerning the order of the zeros of $\Delta_{11}$ and $\Delta_{12}$:

(1). $\Delta_{11}$ has the zero $(s + \rho)^{n-1}$

then

$$\Delta_{12} \text{ has the zero } (s + \rho)^{n-1+i} \qquad i \geqslant 0$$

(2). $\Delta_{11}$ has the zero $(s + \rho)^n$

then

$$\Delta_{12} \text{ has the zero } (s + \rho)^{n-1+i} \qquad i \geqslant 1$$

(3). $\Delta_{11}$ has the zero $(s + \rho)^{n+1}$

then

$$\Delta_{12} \text{ has the zero } (s + \rho)^{n-1+i} \qquad i \geqslant 1$$

In (2) and (3) $i \geqslant 1$, since otherwise $z_{12}\left( = \dfrac{\Delta_{12}}{|Y|} \right)$ will have a pole where $z_{11}$ does not. This would violate the residue condition. Taking the ratio $T_{12} = \dfrac{\Delta_{12}}{\Delta_{11}}$, we get simple poles only.

*Proof completed*

Now we are in a position to prove (b) of Eq. 12.3.1 stated early in this section. Certain standard procedures in the theory of determinants are used. Determinant $\Delta_{11}$ is now evaluated. First add all the columns of Eq. 12.3.6 $(3 + 4 + \cdots + n)$ to the first (recall the term $y_{ii}$ as given in Eq. 12.3.2). This yields

$$\Delta_{11} = \begin{vmatrix} (y_{20} + y_{21}) & -y_{23} & \cdots & -y_{2m} \\ (y_{30} + y_{31}) & y_{33} & \cdots & -y_{3m} \\ \cdot & \cdot & \cdots & \cdot \\ (y_{m0} + y_{m1}) & -y_{m3} & \cdots & y_{mm} \end{vmatrix} \qquad \textbf{12.3.9}$$

This can be split into two parts as follows:

$$
\Delta_{11} =
\begin{vmatrix}
y_{21} - y_{23} & \cdots & -y_{2m} \\
y_{31} & y_{33} & \cdots & -y_{3m} \\
\cdot & \cdot & \cdot & \cdot & \cdot & \cdot \\
y_{m1} - y_{m3} & \cdots & y_{mm}
\end{vmatrix}
+
\begin{vmatrix}
y_{20} & -y_{23} & \cdots & -y_{2m} \\
y_{30} & y_{33} & \cdots & -y_{3m} \\
\cdot & \cdot & \cdot & \cdot & \cdot & \cdot \\
y_{m0} & -y_{m3} & \cdots & y_{mm}
\end{vmatrix}
\qquad 12.3.10
$$

These two determinants are now defined as $\Delta'_{11}$ and $\Delta''_{11}$, respectively. Hence

$$\Delta_{11} = \Delta'_{11} + \Delta''_{11} \qquad 12.3.11$$

Observe that $\Delta'_{11}$ is equal to $\Delta_{12}$ in Eq. 12.3.5. This can be shown by multiplying the first row and then the first column of $\Delta'_{11}$ by $(-1)$. Hence Eq. 12.3.4 can be rewritten as follows

$$T_{12} = \frac{\Delta_{12}}{\Delta_{11}} = \frac{\Delta_{12}}{\Delta_{12} + \Delta_{11}''^t} \qquad 12.3.12$$

where $\Delta''_{11}{}^t$ which is the transposed determinant equals $\Delta''_{11}$ with the rows and columns interchanged. This does not change the value of the determinant, however.

It will be shown in the following section (Section 12.4) that each of the terms in Eq. 12.3.11 is a determinant of a special form. Explicitly, each one is composed of sums and products of the admittance functions $y_{ij}$. Hence, since each of the admittance functions is of the form $cs + d$, and since the product of positive terms yields positive terms, $T_{12}$ can be put in the form

$$T_{12} = \sum_{i=0}^{n} \frac{a_i s^{n-i}}{(a_i + \beta_i)s^{n-i}} \qquad 12.3.13$$

$$a_i \geq 0 < \beta_i$$

where the $a_i$ terms are due to $\Delta_{12}$ and the $\beta_i$ terms are due to $\Delta''_{11}$ in Eq. 12.3.12.

Thus $0 \leq a_i \leq b_i = a_i + \beta_i$ in Eq. 12.3.1.
This completes the proof.

## 12.4. THE FIALKOW-GERST LEMMA

The lemma, which was important in the work of the preceding section, follows:

**Lemma 12.4.1**

If $a_{ij}$ $(i \neq j)$ as well as $a_{11}$ are independent quantities and

$$a_{ii} = a_{i0} + a_{i1} + a_{i2} + \cdots + a_{i\,i-1} + a_{i\,i+1} + \cdots + a_{in}$$

$$= \sum_{\substack{j=0 \\ j \neq i}}^{n} a_{ij} \qquad i = 2, 3, 4, \cdots, n \qquad \qquad \text{12.4.1}$$

then the expansion of the determinant

$$|A| = \begin{vmatrix} a_{11} & a_{12} & a_{13} & \cdots & a_{1n} \\ -a_{21} & a_{22} & -a_{23} & \cdots & -a_{2n} \\ -a_{31} & -a_{32} & a_{33} & \cdots & -a_{3n} \\ \cdot & \cdot & \cdot & \cdot\ \cdot\ \cdot & \cdot \\ -a_{i1} & -a_{i2} & -a_{i3} & \cdots & -a_{in} \\ \cdot & \cdot & \cdot & \cdot\ \cdot\ \cdot & \cdot \\ -a_{n1} & -a_{n2} & -a_{n3} & \cdots & a_{nn} \end{vmatrix} \qquad \text{12.4.2}$$

is composed of sums of products of the $a_{ij}$ $(i \neq j)$ and of $a_{11}$ with positive coefficients.

The validity of this lemma is apparent for $n = 1$ and $n = 2$. Hence, it will suffice to show that the statement is true for any $n$ if it is also true for $n - 1$. Thus it will be shown that $|A|$ can be expressed as a sum of terms of the same form as itself but of reduced degree (degree $= n$).

**Proof**

Expand $|A|$ in terms of its cofactors (cofactors are signed minors) as follows:

$$|A| = a_{11}\Delta_{11} + a_{12}\Delta_{12} + \cdots + a_{in}\Delta_{in} = \sum_{i=1}^{n} a_{1i}\Delta_{1i} \qquad \text{12.4.3}$$

where $A_{1i}$ is the cofactor which is determined by crossing out the $1_i$ row and column from the determinant $|A|$. To complete the induction it will suffice to show that each one of the cofactors in Eq. 12.4.3 is of the same form of $|A|$ in Eq. 12.4.2. This will be done by attacking them sequentially as follows:

(1). Proof that $\Delta_{11}$ can be put in the form of $|A|$

$$\Delta_{11} = \begin{vmatrix} a_{22} & -a_{23} & \cdots & -a_{2n} \\ -a_{32} & a_{33} & \cdots & -a_{3n} \\ \cdot & \cdot & \cdots & \cdot \\ -a_{i2} & -a_{i3} & \cdot \; a_{ii} \; \cdot & -a_{in} \\ \cdot & \cdot & \cdots & \cdot \\ -a_{n2} & -a_{n3} & \cdots & a_{nn} \end{vmatrix} \qquad 12.4.4$$

adding all the columns $(3 + 4 + \cdots + n)$ to the first yields (remember that $a_{22} = a_{20} + a_{21} + a_{23} + \cdots + a_{2n}$)

$$\Delta_{11} = \begin{vmatrix} (a_{20} + a_{21}) & -a_{23} & \cdots & -a_{2n} \\ (a_{30} + a_{31}) & a_{33} & \cdots & -a_{3n} \\ \cdot & \cdot & \cdots & \cdot \\ (a_{i0} + a_{i1}) & -a_{i3} & \cdots & -a_{in} \\ \cdot & \cdot & \cdots & \cdot \\ (a_{n0} + a_{n1}) & -a_{n3} & \cdots & a_{nn} \end{vmatrix} \qquad 12.4.5$$

Now interchange the rows and columns of $\Delta_{11}$ in Eq. 12.4.5. This does not change the value of the determinant, but it does put $\Delta_{11}$ in the form of $|A|$. This completes the proof of (1).

(2). Evaluation of $\Delta_{12}$ gives [note that the first row does not have the term $a_{22} = (a_{20} + a_{21} + a_{23} + \cdots)$]

$$\Delta_{12} = (-1)^1 \begin{vmatrix} -a_{21} & -a_{23} & \cdots & -a_{2n} \\ -a_{31} & +a_{33} & \cdots & -a_{3n} \\ \cdot & \cdot & \cdots & \cdot \\ -a_{i1} & -a_{i3} & \cdot \; a_{ii} \; \cdot & -a_{in} \\ \cdot & \cdot & \cdots & \cdot \\ -a_{n1} & -a_{n3} & \cdots & a_{nn} \end{vmatrix} \qquad 12.4.6$$

Interchanging the minus sign in front with that of the first row puts $\Delta_{12}$ in the form of $|A|$.

(3). Before $\Delta_{13}$ is evaluated, it is noted that interchanging two adjacent rows changes the sign of the determinant. Then $\Delta_{13}$ may be written as follows:

$$\Delta_{13} = \begin{vmatrix} a_{31} & a_{32} & a_{34} \cdot \cdot & a_{3n} \\ -a_{21} & a_{22} & \cdots & -a_{21} \\ \cdot & \cdot & \cdots & \cdot \\ -a_{i1} & -a_{i2} & \cdot \; a_{ii} \; \cdot & -a_{in} \\ \cdot & \cdot & \cdots & \cdot \\ -a_{n1} & -a_{n2} & \cdots & a_{nn} \end{vmatrix} \qquad 12.4.7$$

This is in the same form of $|A|$.

Now consider the general cofactor $\Delta_{1i}$, which can be written as follows:

$$\Delta_{1i} = \begin{vmatrix} a_{i1} & a_{i2} & a_{i3} \cdots & a_{in} \\ -a_{21} & a_{22} & \cdots & -a_{2n} \\ -a_{31} & -a_{32} & \cdots & -a_{3n} \\ \cdot & \cdot & \cdot \cdot \cdot \cdot \cdot & \cdot \\ \cdot & \cdot & \cdot \cdot \cdot \cdot \cdot & \cdot \\ -a_{n1} & -a_{n2} & \cdots & a_{nn} \end{vmatrix} \qquad \text{12.4.8}$$

This also is in the form of $|A|$. This completes the proof of the lemma.

## SURPLUS FACTORS FOR RC NETWORK FUNCTIONS 12.5

If the numerator of the transfer function $T_{12}$ contains some negative coefficients, these may be removed if surplus factors are used, provided that the numerator has no positive real axis zeros. Recall that these surplus factors multiply both the numerator and the denominator and hence produce no effective change in the transfer function involved. As has already been noted, surplus factors are frequently used in synthesis problems. For example, in Section 9.4 they were used in conjunction with even-part synthesis. In that section the Poincaré method was used to determine the necessary factor. We cannot use this method for $RC$ network functions, since now factors with distinct, positive, real zeros only are required. Thus this section will be devoted to the proof of the following lemma.

### Lemma 12.5.1

Let $F(s) = s^t + a_1 s^{t-1} + \cdots$, be a real polynomial having no positive real zeros. Then there exists a polynomial $P(s) = \prod_{i=0}^{n} (s + \delta_i)$ with $\delta_i > 0$ and distinct, such that $P(s)F(s)$ is a polynomial with nonnegative coefficients.

The proof of the lemma will be given in two parts. In the first part it will be shown that a polynomial of the type $(s + 1)^n$ could produce the desired coefficients. This polynomial is not yet satisfactory as the zeros are not distinct. Thus, in the second part of the proof it will be shown that the results of the first part can be used to obtain a satisfactory polynomial.

*Proof: Part 1*

If $F(s)$ has some negative coefficients, then it must have at least one factor of the form*

$$s^2 - 2s \rho \cos \varphi + \rho^2 \qquad \text{12.5.}$$

Let this factor be normalized as follows:

$$s^2 - 2s \cos \varphi + 1$$

Clearly if $\cos \varphi$ is negative, the problem would be of no interest in the present context. Multiply this by the factor $(s + 1)^n$ in its binomial expansion form

$$(s^2 - 2s \cos \varphi + 1)\left( s^n + ns^{n-1} + \frac{n(n-1)}{2!} s^{n-2} + \cdots \right)$$

$$= s^{n+2} + s^{n+1}(n + 2\cos \varphi) + s^n \left( 1 + \frac{n(n-1)}{2!} - 2n \cos \varphi \right)$$

$$+ \cdots + \frac{n(n-1) \cdots (n - i + 2)}{i!} s^{n-i+2}[i(i-1)$$

$$+ (n - i + 1)(n - i + 2) - 2i(n - i + 2) \times \cos \varphi] + \cdots \qquad \text{12.5.}$$

where $i$ denotes a positive integer $i < n$. The problem is reduced to showing that there exists an $n$ such that the general coefficient of Eq. 12.5.2 is positive. This means that the following quantity must be positive:

$$C_i = \frac{i(i-1) + (n - i + 1)(n - i + 2)}{i(n - i + 2)} - 2 \cos \varphi \qquad \text{12.5.}$$

Now we note that

$$\frac{(n + 2)^2}{4} = \frac{(n - i + 2 + i)^2}{4}$$

$$= \frac{1}{4}\left( \frac{(n - i + 2)^2 + 2i(n - i + 2) + i^2}{i(n - i + 2)} \right) i(n - i + 2)$$

$$= \frac{1}{4}\left( 2 + \frac{(n - i + 2)}{i} + \frac{i}{n - i + 2} \right) i(n - i + 2); \qquad \text{12.5.}$$

$$\equiv \left( 2 + \alpha + \frac{1}{\alpha} \right) \times \frac{i(n - i + 2)}{4}$$

$$\geq i(n - i + 2)$$

The last result is due to the fact that $\min \left( \alpha + \dfrac{1}{\alpha} \right) = 2$ for $\alpha > 0$.

---

* The following normalized forms were also utilized in Section 9.4.

Similarly, by completing a square, we can write

$$i(i - 1) + (n - i + 1)(n - i + 2) = \frac{n(n - 2) + (n - 2(i - 1))^2}{2}$$

$$\geq \frac{n(n + 2)}{2}$$

12.5.5

Now by using Eqs. 12.5.4 and 12.5.5, $C_i$ in Eq. 12.5.3 can be put in the form

$$C_i \geq \frac{2n}{n + 2} - 2 \cos \varphi$$

12.5.6

We wish to generate positive $C_i$'s; hence $n - (n + 2) \cos \varphi > 0$. This can be solved for $n$, yielding

$$n > \frac{2 \cos \varphi}{1 - \cos \varphi}$$

12.5.7

$$(n \text{ integer} > 0)$$

One can verify by direct substitution that this value also will render the factor $n - 2 \cos \varphi$ in Eq. 12.5.2 positive.

*Proof completed*

*Proof: Part 2*

Consider the polynomial

$$f(s) = \prod_{i=1}^{n} (s + 1 + \epsilon_i)(s^2 - 2s \cos \phi + 1)$$

The coefficients of $f(s)$ are continuous functions of $\epsilon_i$. If $n$ is chosen by Eq. 12.5.7 (strict inequality), then all the coefficients of $f(s)$ are positive for each $\epsilon_i = 0$ and hence will remain positive for sufficiently small value of the $\epsilon_i$.

*Proof completed*

## PROBLEMS

12.1. Realize the following 3T.N:

(a). $\qquad T_{12} = \dfrac{s^2 + s + 1}{(s + 2)(s + 4)}$

(b). $\qquad T_{12} = \dfrac{s^2 + s + 3}{(s + 1)(s + 3)}$

(c). $\qquad T_{12} = \dfrac{s^2 + s + 1}{(s + 2a)(s + 2b)}; \; ab > 1, a > 0 < b$

Hint: try $S = s + a + b$

12.2. Find a suitable polynomial $P$ with distinct negative real zeros such that the product $PQ$ will yield a polynomial with nonnegative coefficients for each of the polynomials $Q$ below:

(a).                    $Q = s^2 - s + 1$

(b).                    $Q = s^2 - 2s + 9$

(c).                    $Q = s^2 - 6s + 25$

Compare with the results you would obtain using the Poincaré method (Section 9.4).

12.3. Realize the following 3T.N:

$$T_{12} = \frac{s^2 - s + 1}{(s + 3)(s + 5)}$$

Hint: Try a surplus factor $(s + 1)$.

12.4. Realize the following $T_{12}$ as an $RC$ 3T.N with a 1-ohm resistive termination:

$$T_{12} = \frac{s^2 + s + 1}{(2s + 1)(s + 2)}$$

12.5. The necessary and sufficient conditions (the Fialkow-Gerst conditions) for the realization of $T_{12}$ as an $RC$ 3T.N are given in Section 12.2. If we remove the constraint that the poles of $T_{12}$ are distinct and lie along the negative real axis (but still insist that denominator is Hurwitz), we lose the two-element-kind feature of the synthesis. Analyze the following network (from Togan Zeren) and show that it satisfies the Fialkow-Gerst conditions for $T_{12}$ but that the poles are arbitrary:

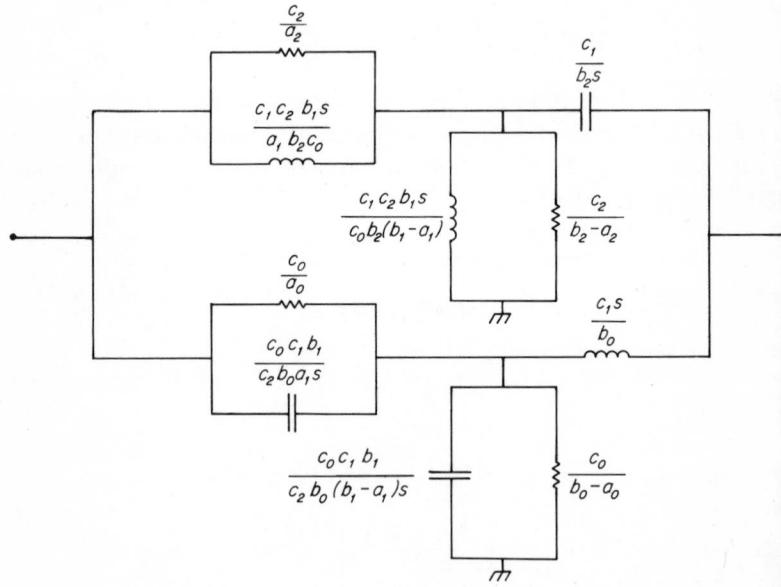

**Fig. P. 12.5**

$C_1$ and $C_2$ are positive but otherwise arbitrary. $C_0$ is given by

$$c_0 = \frac{b_1 c_1 - b_0 c_2}{b_2} > 0$$

Answer: $\qquad T_{12} = \dfrac{a_2 s^2 + a_1 s + a_0}{b_2 s^2 + b_1 s + b_0}$

## FURTHER READING

BOOKS

12.1. Balabanian, N., "Network Synthesis," Prentice-Hall, Inc., Englewood Cliffs, N. J., 1958, Chapter 7.

RELATED PAPERS

12.2. Cederbaum, I., "The Limits of Gain Attainable in Three Terminal *RC* Networks With Two Capacitors," *IRE Trans. on Circuit Theory*, Vol. CT-4, pp. 298–307, Dec., 1957.

12.3. Dasher, B. J., "Synthesis of *RC* Transfer Functions as Unbalanced Two Terminal Pair Networks," *Trans. on Circuit Theory*, Vol. CT-1, pp. 20–34, 1952.

12.4. Fialkow, A. D., and Gerst, I., "The Transfer Function of an *RC* Ladder Network," *J. Math. Phys.*, Vol. 30, pp. 49–71, Jan., 1952.

12.5. Fialkow, A. D., "Two Terminal Pair Networks Containing Two Kinds of Elements Only," *Proc. Symp. Mod. Network Synthesis*, pp. 50–65, 1952.

12.6. Fialkow, A. D., and Gerst, I., "The Transfer Function of Networks Without Mutual Reactance," *Quart. Appl. Math.*, Vol. 12, pp. 117–131, 1954.

12.7. Kuh, E. H., "Synthesis of *RC* Grounded 2 Ports," *IRE Trans. on Circuit Theory*, Vol. CT-5, pp. 55–61, March 1958.

12.8. Lucal, H. M., "Synthesis of Three Terminal *RC* Networks," *IRE Trans. on Circuit Theory*, Vol. CT-2, pp. 308–316, Dec., 1955.

12.9. Ozaki, H., "Synthesis of *RC* Three Terminal Network Without Ideal Transformer," *Tech. Rep. of the Osaka Univ.*, Vol. 3, No. 60, pp. 57–77, 1953.

12.10. Paige, A., and Kuh, E. S., "Maximum Gain Realization of an *RC* Ladder Network," *IRE Trans. on Circuit Theory*, Vol. CT-7, pp. 32–40 March, 1960.

CHAPTER 13 | # Introduction to n-Port Synthesis

At this stage, we are ready to tackle contemporary $n$-port synthesis. Hence, the necessary and sufficient conditions for the realization of an $n$-port immittance function are herein demonstrated. The material is developed by first discussing the elementary constraints, that is, what is a positive real (denoted $PR$) matrix. Paralleling the development of 1-port synthesis, the following questions are answered successively: Is the inverse of a $PR$ matrix $PR$? What is the degree of a matrix? What is an $n$-port transformer?

The $n$-port problem also has additional concepts not related to 1 port. These are: (1) the congruence transformer producing a network $[A]_t[Z][A]$ in terms of $[Z]$, (2) the singular matrix, and (3) the reduced (and partially reduced) matrices, whose even part matrix is of matrix rank 1 (and singular). The concept of two-element-kind networks extends easily from 1 to $n$ port.

The over-all philosophy of this chapter is similar to that of the "chop-chop" technique in the sense that recognizable parts of the matrix are chiseled away. When this method is no longer useful, the matrix is converted into a sum of reduced (or partially reduced) matrices which can be realized by a method of repeated inversions.

This chapter also serves as an introduction for the following two chapters. In Chapter 14 the Bott-Duffin approach as described in Chapters 5 and 8 is extended to $n$ port. The Oono synthesis procedure is described in Chapter 15. It is a Darlingtonlike synthesis. The book does not provide a complete synthesis procedure for non-reciprocal networks and for networks which do not possess an impedance matrix and an admittance matrix simultaneously.

240

## ELEMENTARY $n$-PORT CONSTRAINTS 13.1

In Section 6.4 it was shown that if $[Z(s)]$ characterizes a lumped, passive, linear, 2-port network, then the impedance function $Z(s)$ given by

$$Z(s) = n^2 z_{22} - n(z_{12} + z_{21}) + z_{11}$$
$$n = \text{real}$$

**13.1.1**

is prf for all $n$. This theorem was proved by converting the 2-port network into a 1 port by means of an ideal transformer. This theorem can be extended to $n$-port functions. In fact, we are now in a position to define a positive real $n$-port matrix as an extension of the idea of a positive real function of a 1-port network.

A positive real matrix function $[Z(s)]$ is defined as follows:

(1). $[Z(s)]$ is an $n$ by $n$ symmetric matrix.
(2). The matrix element $z_{pq}$ is a rational function of $s$ with real coefficients.
(3). For any choice of real numbers $n_1$, $n_2$, $\cdots$, $n_n$, the associate function $Z(s)$ defined by the following equation is prf:

$$Z(s) = \sum_{1}^{n}\sum_{1}^{n} z_{pq} n_p n_q \equiv [N]_t [Z(s)][N]$$

**13.1.2**

where $[N]$ is a column matrix.

Thus $Z(s)$ of Eq. 13.1.1 is the associate impedance function of a 2-port network. The fundamental theme of this chapter is that any positive real matrix can be realized by means of an $RLCT$ network (resistors, inductors, capacitors, and transformers); however, now we shall show that all such networks lead to positive real matrices.

### Theorem 13.1.1

If $[Z(s)]$ represents an $RLCT$ $n$-port network matrix, then it is a positive real matrix.

### Proof

To prove this theorem, the $n$-port network will be converted into a 1-port network in the manner illustrated (Fig. 13.1) by using a sufficient number of ideal transformers appropriately connected. The equations of the $n$-port part of Fig. 13.1 are given by the matrix set

$$[E] = [Z(s)][I]$$

**13.1.3**

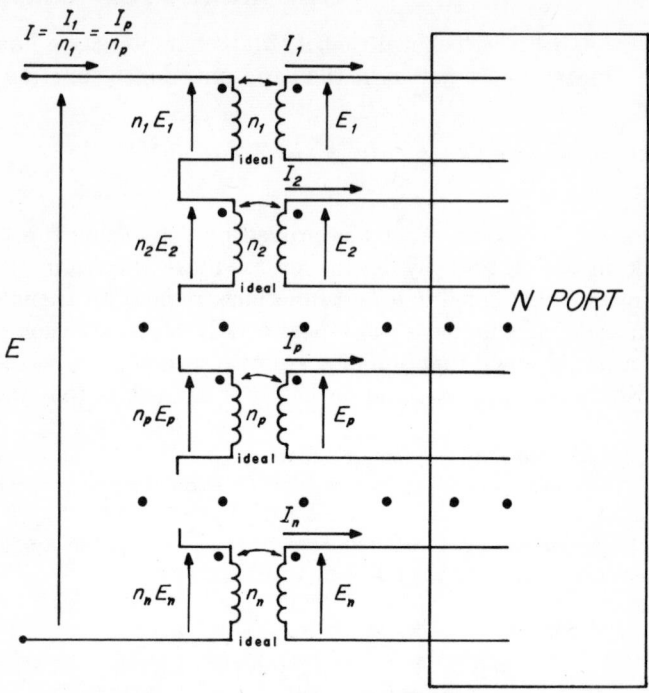

**Fig. 13.1. Conversion of an n-port network into a 1-port network**

The voltage across the 1 port is given by

$$E = n_1 E_1 + n_2 E_2 + \cdots + n_p E_p + \cdots n_n E_n \qquad 13.1.4$$

Also the current of the 1 port is related to the currents of the $n$ port by

$$I = I_1/n_1 = I_2/n_2 = \cdots = I_p/n_p = \cdots = I_n/n_n \qquad 13.1.5$$

Now, evaluating the individual voltage components of Eq. 13.1.4 from Eq. 13.1.3 and substituting the values of the currents in terms of $I$ as given in Eq. 13.1.5, we get

$$n_1 E_1 = (n_1^2 z_{11} \quad + \cdots + \qquad \qquad + n_1 n_n z_{1n})I$$

$$n_p E_p = (n_p n_1 z_{p1} + \cdots + n_p^2 z_{pp} + \cdots + n_p n_n z_{pn})I \qquad 13.1.6$$

$$n_n E_n = (n_n n_1 z_{n1} + \cdots \qquad \qquad + n_n^2 z_{nn})I$$

Adding these equations, as is required by Eq. 13.1.4, and dividing the result by $I$, we get

$$Z(s) = \frac{E}{I} = \sum_{p=1}^{n} \sum_{q=1}^{n} z_{pq} n_p n_q \qquad \text{13.1.7}$$

as in Eq. 13.1.2. Now to complete the proof of the theorem it is only necessary to note that $Z(s)$ is a driving point impedance function (1 port), and hence it is prf.

*Proof completed*

Two important corollaries follow:

## Corollary 13.1.1—Real Part Condition

The $z_{pp}$ terms in Eqs. 13.1.7 and 13.1.3 are prf, and the determinant of Re $[Z(s)]$ and of each of its principal minors (minors that are symmetric about the $z_{pp}$ axis) are positive (or zero) along the $j$ axis and are positive in the *r.h.s* plane.

*Proof*

Set all the $n$'s to zero in Eq. 13.1.7 except a particular $n_p$. This gives $Z(s) = n_p{}^2 z_{pp}$; hence $z_{pp}$ is prf. To prove that the principal minors of $|\text{Re } [Z(s)]|$ are positive, start by setting all the $n$'s to zero except $n_1$ and $n_2$. This gives

$$Z(s) = n_1{}^2 z_{11} + 2 n_1 n_2 z_{12} + n_2{}^2 z_{22} \qquad \text{13.1.8}$$

and therefore (by the Lagrange-Gauss method of completing the square)

$$\text{Re } Z(s) = r_{11} \left(n_1 + \frac{r_{12}}{r_{11}} n_2\right)^2 + \frac{n_2{}^2}{r_{11}} (r_{11} r_{22} - r_{12}{}^2); \ (r_{pq} = \text{Re } z_{pq}) \qquad \text{13.1.9}$$

This has to be true for all values of $n_1$ including the value corresponding to $n_1 + r_{12} n_2/r_{11} = 0$. Then if Re $Z(s) \geq 0$, the same is true for the determinant

$$r_{11} r_{22} - r_{12}{}^2 = \begin{vmatrix} r_{11} & r_{12} \\ r_{12} & r_{22} \end{vmatrix} \geqslant 0 \qquad \text{13.1.10}$$

It can be shown in a similar way that all the other principal minors of order 2 are positive or zero when Re $Z(s) \geq 0$. To prove the corollary for higher-order determinants, the process of completing squares will be used again; the strategy will be as follows:*

---

* Mirsky, L., "Introduction to Linear Algebra," Oxford University Press, England, Chap. 12, pp. 371–374, 1961.

Form squares such that the first square will contain all the $n$'s; the second will contain all the $n$'s but one; the third all the $n$'s but two; etc. For example, if Eq. 13.1.7 has three nonzero $n$'s, the expansion will be

$$\text{Re } Z(s) = (a_1n_1 + a_2n_2 + a_3n_3)^2 + (b_2n_2 + b_3n_3)^2 + c_3n_3^2 \qquad \textbf{13.1.11}$$

where the $a$'s, $b$'s, and $c$ are real constants to be determined. Since it always is possible to select our $n$'s to make the first and second term equal to zero in Eq. 13.1.11, it follows that $c_3$ is positive when Re $Z(s)$ is positive. Evaluating Eq. 13.1.11 for Eq. 13.1.7 where all the $n$'s are zero except the first three, we get

$$\text{Re } Z(s) = \frac{1}{r_{11}}(r_{11}n_1 + r_{12}n_2 + r_{13}n_3)^2$$

$$+ \frac{1}{(r_{11}r_{22} - r_{12}^2)r_{11}}\big((r_{11}r_{22} - r_{12}^2)n_2 + (r_{11}r_{23} - r_{12}r_{13})n_3\big)^2$$

$$\qquad\qquad\qquad\qquad\qquad\qquad\qquad\qquad\qquad \textbf{13.1.12}$$

$$+ \frac{1}{(r_{11}r_{22} - r_{12}^2)r_{11}}\big((r_{11}r_{33} - r_{13}^2)(r_{11}r_{22} - r_{12}^2)$$

$$- (r_{11}r_{23} - r_{12}r_{13})^2\big)n_3^2$$

However, the quantity

$$\frac{(r_{11}r_{33} - r_{13}^2)(r_{11}r_{22} - r_{12}^2) - (r_{11}r_{23} - r_{12}r_{13})^2}{r_{11}} \qquad \textbf{13.1.13}$$

may be identified with the determinant

$$|\text{Re } [Z(s)]| = |r| = \begin{vmatrix} r_{11} & r_{12} & r_{13} \\ r_{12} & r_{22} & r_{23} \\ r_{13} & r_{23} & r_{33} \end{vmatrix} \qquad \textbf{13.1.14}$$

as evidenced by a direct expansion. (Note that since $r_{pq}$ was made equal to $r_{qp}$, the proof is valid for reciprocal networks only.) Furthermore, since $(r_{11}r_{22} - r_{12}^2)$ is positive, if Re $Z(s) \geqslant 0$, it follows by the arguments advanced above that $|r|$ in Eq. 13.1.14 is also positive. This process now may be continued to show that the rest of Corollary 13.1.1 is correct.

*Proof completed*

## Corollary 13.1.2

If $[Z(s)]$ is a $PR$ matrix, and if $[A]$ is an arbitrary real square matrix with constant matrix elements, then $[Z_1(s)]$ given by

$$[Z_1(s)] = [A]_t[Z(s)][A] \qquad \textbf{13.1.15}$$

is also a $PR$ matrix.

*Proof*

Constructing the associate impedance functions (Eq. 13.1.2) for $[Z(s)]$ and $[Z_1(s)]$, we get

$$Z(s) = [N]_t[Z(s)][N] \quad [N] = [real]$$

and
$$Z_1(s) = [N_1]_t[A]_t[Z(s)][A][N_1] \quad [N_1] = [real]$$

13.1.16

Now $Z(s)$ is prf for all $[N]$ (by Theorem 13.1.1) including the values $[N] = [A][N_1]$. Then $Z_1(s)$ is also prf for all $[N_1]$, and $[Z_1(s)]$ is a $PR$ matrix.

*Proof completed*

In Section 13.5, it will be shown that $[Z_1(s)]$ can be represented by means of a physical network—called the congruence transformer—terminated in $[Z(s)]$ in an $n$-port sense.

It is important to note that

$$Z(s) = \sum \sum z_{pq} n_p n_q = [N]_t[Z(s)][N]$$

13.1.2

and therefore

$$\text{Re } Z(s) = \sum \sum r_{pq} n_p n_q = [N]_t \text{ Re } [Z(s)][N] \quad (r_{pq} = \text{Re } z_{pq})$$

$$\geq 0 \quad \text{Re } s = 0$$

$$> 0 \quad \text{Re } s > 0$$

13.1.17

It follows that

$$\text{Re } Z_1(s) = [N_1]_t[A]_t \text{ Re } [Z(s)][A][N_1]$$

$$\geq 0 \quad \text{Re } s = 0$$

$$> 0 \quad \text{Re } s > 0$$

13.1.18

## SOME MATHEMATICAL PROPERTIES OF POSITIVE REAL MATRICES 13.2

The primary purpose of this chapter is to show that a network that is described by means of a positive real matrix may be realized by means of $RLCT$ networks. Attention is called to the fact that a synthesis procedure that employs the "chop-chop" technique must, sooner or later, employ a process which amounts essentially to that of removing a zero (see Chapter 5). This procedure necessitates the inversion of the matrix. In this connection one may ask, is the inverse of a positive real matrix also positive real? In Section 2.1 it was shown that the reciprocal of a positive real function is also a positive real function. Can we extend this idea to matrices? The answer is yes. The proof of this statement will be given in Theorem 13.2.1. However, Lemma 13.2.1 will be proved first.

In Theorem 13.1.1 in the previous section it was shown that if $[Z(s)]$ is a positive real matrix, then the associated impedance function $Z(s)$ as given below is prf:

$$Z(s) = \sum\sum z_{pq}n_p n_q \qquad \text{13.2.1}$$
$$\text{(the } n\text{'s are } real)$$

It is possible to extend this result to include complex values of $n$ as follows:

### Lemma 13.2.1

If $[Z(s)]$ is a symmetric positive real matrix, then $Z(s)$ as given below is prf:

$$Z(s) = \sum\sum z_{pq}n_p \bar{n}_q \equiv [N]_t[Z(s)][\bar{N}] \qquad \text{13.2.2}$$

Here the $n$'s may be complex, and $[N]$ is a column matrix.

### Proof

Since a sum of positive real functions is *prf*, the following function is also prf:

$$Z(s) = \sum\sum z_{pq}a_p a_q + \sum\sum z_{pq}b_p b_q \qquad \text{13.2.3}$$

However, this is precisely the value one would obtain by expanding the following

$$Z(s) = \sum\sum z_{pq}(a_p + jb_p)(a_q - jb_q) \qquad \text{13.2.4}$$

where $z_{pq} = z_{qp}$. This expression may be put in the form of Eq. 13.2.2 by setting $n = a + jb$.

*Proof completed*

### Theorem 13.2.1

If $[Z(s)]$ is a nonsingular positive real matrix, then $[Z(s)]^{-1}$ is also a positive real matrix.

### Proof *

The theorem will be proved by examining the specific case when

---

* This proof is along the lines of the proof given by Duffin, R. J., "Elementary Operations Which Generate Network Functions," *Proceedings of the American Math Society*, Vol. 6, No. 3, pp. 335–339.

$[Z(s)]$ is a $2 \times 2$ $PR$ matrix and by recognizing that the procedure is entirely general. We shall write Eq. 13.2.2 in the matrix form:

$$Z(s) = [N]_t[Z(s)][\bar{N}] = [n_1 \quad n_2]\begin{bmatrix} z_{11} & z_{12} \\ z_{12} & z_{22} \end{bmatrix}\begin{bmatrix} \bar{n}_1 \\ \bar{n}_2 \end{bmatrix} \qquad \textbf{13.2.5}$$

Essentially, the problem at hand is to show that $Y(s)$ is prf if $Z(s)$ is prf, where $Y(s)$ is given by

$$Y(s) = [N']_t[Z(s)]^{-1}[\bar{N}'] \qquad \textbf{13.2.6}$$

and where the $N''$s are arbitrary and may be complex. Introduce the new matrix $[C]$ which is given by

$$[C] = [Z(s)]^{-1}[\bar{N}'] = \begin{bmatrix} \dfrac{z_{22}\bar{n}'_1 - z_{12}\bar{n}'_2}{|Z(s)|} \\[2ex] \dfrac{-z_{12}\bar{n}'_1 + z_{11}\bar{n}'_2}{|Z(s)|} \end{bmatrix} = \begin{bmatrix} c_1 \\ c_2 \end{bmatrix} \qquad \textbf{13.2.7}$$

Therefore, Eq. 13.2.6 becomes

$$Y(s) = [N']_t[C] \qquad \textbf{13.2.8}$$

From Eq. 13.2.7

$$[\bar{N}'] = [Z(s)][C] \qquad \textbf{13.2.9}$$

from which it follows that $[\bar{N}']_t = [C]_t[Z(s)]$ [note that $[Z(s)]_t = [Z(s)]$ by symmetry], and hence Eq. 13.2.8 becomes

$$\bar{Y}(s) = [C]_t[Z(s)][\bar{C}] = [c_1 \quad c_2]\begin{bmatrix} z_{11} & z_{12} \\ z_{12} & z_{22} \end{bmatrix}\begin{bmatrix} \bar{c}_1 \\ \bar{c}_2 \end{bmatrix} \qquad \textbf{13.2.10}$$

Note that $Z(s)$ in Eq. 13.2.2 is prf for all values of $[N]$ inclusive of the value $[N] = [C]$. Furthermore, since $\mathrm{Re}\ \overline{Y(s)} = \mathrm{Re}\ Y(s)$, then it follows from Eq. 13.2.10 that for any arbitrary point $s$ on the $j$ axis $\mathrm{Re}\ Y(s) \geq 0$ and, that for $s$ in the $r.h.p$ $\mathrm{Re}\ Y(s) > 0$. Hence $Y(s)$ is prf if $Z(s)$ is prf, and thus $[Z(s)]^{-1}$ is $PR$ if $[Z(s)]$ is $PR$.

*Proof completed*

## Alternate Proof

Consider

$$2\ \mathrm{Re}\ [Z(s)]^{-1} = [Z(s)]^{-1} + [\overline{Z(s)}]^{-1}$$

$$= [Z(s)]^{-1}([Z(s)] + [\overline{Z(s)}])[\overline{Z(s)}]^{-1} \qquad \textbf{13.2.11}$$

$$= [Z(s)]^{-1}\ 2(\mathrm{Re}\ [Z(s)])[\overline{Z(s)}]^{-1}$$

Computing the real part of the respective associate impedance functions gives

$$\text{Re } Z(s) = [N]_t(\text{Re } [Z(s)])[\overline{N}]$$

and                                                                  **13.2.12**

$$\text{Re } Y(s) = [N']_t(\text{Re } [Z(s)]^{-1})[\overline{N}']$$

$$= [N']_t[Z(s)]^{-1}(\text{Re } [Z(s)])[\overline{Z(s)}]^{-1}[\overline{N}'] \quad (\text{by 13.2.11}) \quad \textbf{13.2.13}$$

Thus, given a point $s$ in the right half plane, since $[Z(s)]$ is $PR$, Re $Z(s)$ in Eq. 13.2.12 is positive for all values of $[N]$ including the values $[N] = [Z(s)]^{-1}[N']$. Hence Re $Y$ is positive (in the r.h. plane) in Eq. 13.2.13 which gives the proof.

## 13.3. THE DEGREE OF A *PR* MATRIX

In the study of driving point impedance functions, the term degree was used to denote the highest of the degrees of the numerator and the denominator. In $n$-port analysis, the term is generalized. The term was defined by B. McMillan* and, independently, by B. D. H. Tellegen.† The three theorems which follow are important in our work. The proofs of the first two theorems are weaker than McMillan's, since simplifying assumptions are employed. For more comprehensive proofs the reader is referred to Appendix A. Several additional theorems important for degree computation are also proved there.

### Definition 13.3.1

The degree of a $PR$ matrix $[Z(s)]$ [denoted $\delta[Z(s)]$] is the maximum degree of the numerator polynomial of the determinant $|[Z(s)] + [A]|$ for any constant matrix $[A]$. Accordingly

$$\delta[Z(s)] = \underset{[A]}{\text{max}} \text{ deg num.}|[Z(s)] + [A]| \qquad \textbf{13.3.1}$$

If a particular $[A]$ achieves this maximum degree, then $[A]$ is said to uncover the degree of $[Z(s)]$. It is clear from the definition that $\delta[Z(s)] = \delta([Z(s)] + [A_1]) = \delta([Z(s)] + [A_2])$. Furthermore, if $[B]$ is a constant nonsingular matrix, $\delta[B] [Z(s)] = \delta[Z(s)]$.

---

* McMillan, B., "Introduction to Formal Realizability Theory," *The Bell System Technical Journal*, Vol. 31, pp. 217–299 and pp. 541–600 (1952).

† Tellegen, B. D. H., "Synthesis of 2$n$-Poles by Networks Containing the Minimum Number of Elements," *Journal of Mathematics and Physics*, Vol. 32, pp. 1–18 (1953).

## Example 13.3.1

Obtain the degree of the matrix $[Z(s)]$ given by

$$[Z(s)] = \begin{bmatrix} \dfrac{2s+1}{s+2} & \dfrac{s}{s+2} \\[2ex] \dfrac{s}{s+2} & \dfrac{s+3}{s+2} \end{bmatrix} \qquad 13.3.2$$

### Solution

Let all the elements of $[A]$ be the constant $a$. The combined matrix is as follows:

$$[Z(s)] + [A] = \begin{bmatrix} \dfrac{s(2+a)+1+2a}{s+2} & \dfrac{s(1+a)+2a}{s+2} \\[2ex] \dfrac{s(1+a)+2a}{s+2} & \dfrac{s(1+a)+3+2a}{s+2} \end{bmatrix} \qquad 13.3.3$$

Hence

$$\text{det.} \left( [Z(s)] + [A] \right) = \frac{s^2(1+a) + s(2a^2 + 8a + 7) + 3 + 8a}{(s+2)^2} \qquad 13.3.4$$

Thus, according to the definition above, the degree of $[Z(s)]$ is the maximum degree of the numerator of Eq. 13.3.4. Accordingly, $\delta[Z(s)] = 2$. Note that the degree of the numerator of Eq. 13.3.4 is smaller than 2 (and hence different from its maximum value) only for the very special case: $a = -1$.

From the foregoing example it is observed that the matrix $[A]$ is quite arbitrary. Moreover, in what follows, we shall further restrict $[A]$ to be nonsingular. Now we are in a position to prove two of McMillan's theorems concerning the degree of $PR$ matrices. These proofs are weaker than McMillan's since simplifying assumptions are employed at this stage for clarity. (For more comprehensive proofs, the reader is referred to Appendix A.)

## Theorem 13.3.1

The degree of $[Z(s)]$ equals the degree of $[Z(s)]^{-1}$.

### Proof

Consider the auxiliary matrix $[F]$:

$$[F] = [Z(s)]^{-1} + [A]^{-1} = [Z(s)]^{-1}([A] + [Z(s)])[A]^{-1} \qquad 13.3.5$$

The determinant of this matrix is given by

$$|Z[(s)]^{-1} + [A]^{-1}| = \frac{|[Z(s)] + [A]|}{|Z(s)||A|} \qquad 13.3.6$$

Let $|[Z(s)] + [A]| = p_1/q_1$ and $|Z(s)| = p_0/q_0$ and suppose that $[A]$ is selected to uncover the degree of $[Z(s)]$. Clearly, $q_1$ contains all the zeros of $q_0$. Hence

$$\delta \text{ num.}|[Z(s)]^{-1} + [A]^{-1}| = \delta \text{ num.}|[Z(s)] + [A]| - r$$
$$\leq \delta \text{ num.}|[Z(s)] + [A]| = \delta[Z(s)]$$

13.3.7

Here $r$ denotes the degree of a possible common factor of $p_1$ and $p_0$. Now, assuming that it is possible to select $[A]$ such that $[A]^{-1}$ also uncovers the degree of $[Z(s)]^{-1} + [A]^{-1}$, then

$$\delta[Z(s)]^{-1} = \delta([Z(s)]^{-1} + [A]^{-1}) \leq \delta([Z(s)] + [A]) = \delta[Z(s)] \quad \textbf{13.3.8}$$

But the above must also be true for $[Y(s)]$, and therefore $\delta[Y(s)]^{-1} \leq \delta[Y(s)]$. These two conditions may be satisfied simultaneously only with the equal sign.

*Proof completed*

**Theorem 13.3.2**

If $[Z_1(s)]$ and $[Z_2(s)]$ are matrices whose denominators share no common factors, then the degree of the sum is the sum of the degrees. Specifically, it is required to prove that $\delta([Z_1] + [Z_2]) = \delta[Z_1] + \delta[Z_2]$.

*Proof*

Consider the auxiliary matrix $[F]$:

$$[F] = ([Z_1(s)] + [A_1])^{-1} + ([Z_2(s)] + [A_2])^{-1}$$
$$= ([Z_1(s)] + [A_1])^{-1}([Z_1(s)] + [A_1] + [Z_2(s)] + [A_2])([Z_2(s)] + [A_2])^{-1}$$

13.3.9

The determinant of this matrix is as follows:

$$|F| = \frac{|[Z_1(s)] + [A_1] + [Z_2(s)] + [A_2]|}{|[Z_1(s)] + [A_1]|\,|[Z_2(s)] + [A_2]|} \qquad \textbf{13.3.10}$$

Furthermore, because the denominators of $[Z_1(s)]$ and $[Z_2(s)]$ share no common factors, the denominator polynomial of $|Z_1(s)|\,|Z_2(s)|$ is the same as that of $|[Z_1(s)] + [Z_2(s)]|$ and it follows that the numerator of $|F|$ (save for some common factors) is given by

$$\text{num. } |F| = \text{num. } |[Z_1(s)] + [A_1] + [Z_2(s)] + [A_2]| \qquad \textbf{13.3.11}$$

Similarly

$$\text{num. } |F|^{-1} = \text{num. } |[Z_1(s)] + [A_1]|\,|[Z_2(s)] + [A_2]|$$
$$= \text{num. } |[Z_1(s)] + [A_1]| \times \text{num. } |[Z_2(s)] + [A_2]|$$

13.3.12

Selecting $[A_1] + [A_2]$ to uncover the degree of $[Z_1(s)] + [Z_2(s)]$, we get

$$\delta[F] = \delta([Z_1(s)] + [Z_2(s)]) - r \qquad \text{(by 13.3.11)} \qquad \textbf{13.3.13}$$

Here $r$ denotes the degree of a possible common factor of the numerator and the denominator of 13.3.10. Now, assuming that $[A_1]$ and $[A_2]$ may be further selected to uncover the degrees of $[Z_1(s)] + [A_1]$ and $[Z_2(s)] + [A_2]$, we get

$$\delta[F]^{-1} = \delta[Z_1(s)] + \delta[Z_2(s)] - r \qquad \text{(by 13.3.12)} \qquad \textbf{13.3.14}$$

But by Theorem 13.3.1, $\delta[F] = \delta[F]^{-1}$. Hence $\delta([Z_1] + [Z_2]) = \delta[Z_1] + \delta[Z_2]$.

*Proof completed*

## Example 13.3.2

Determine the degree of

$$[Z(s)] = \begin{bmatrix} \dfrac{2s + 5}{s + 2} & -\dfrac{s + 1}{s + 2} \\[2ex] -\dfrac{s + 1}{s + 2} & \dfrac{s + 3}{s + 2} \end{bmatrix} \qquad \textbf{13.3.15}$$

### Solution

Let $[A]$ be given by

$$[A] = \begin{bmatrix} a_{11} & a_{12} \\ a_{12} & a_{22} \end{bmatrix} \qquad \textbf{13.3.16}$$

Now $|[Z(s)] + [A]|$ is evaluated to give

$$|[Z(s)] + [A]| = \frac{(s + 7) + a_{11}(s + 3) + a_{22}(2s + 5)}{(s + 2)} +$$

$$\frac{- 2a_{12}(s + 1) + (a_{11}a_{22} - a_{12}{}^2)(s + 2)}{(s + 2)} \qquad \textbf{13.3.17}$$

Thus $\delta[Z(s)] = 1$. Note that the degree of the whole matrix is the same as that of each of its minors. Can the degree of the matrix be smaller than that of an individual matrix minor? The answer is no.

## Theorem 13.3.3

The degree of a matrix minor cannot exceed the degree of the whole (from R. J. Duffin). The proof of this theorem will be given in Appendix A (corollary A.3).

**Corollary 13.3.1**

If the degree of a matrix is zero, then each matrix member is a constant.

*Proof*

By Theorem 13.3.3, the degree of each matrix member is zero and hence it is a constant.

*Proof completed*

## 13.4. THE n-PORT TRANSFORMER

The $n$-port transformer is composed of $n$ two-port transformers with all their primaries connected in parallel, or, perhaps, of $n$ separate windings on the same core, as illustrated in Fig. 13.2. The equations of the ideal system which neglects the resistances of the windings may be written directly as follows:

$$E_1 = sL_{11}I_1 + sL_{12}I_2 + \cdots sL_{1n}I_n$$
$$E_2 = sL_{12}I_1 + sL_{22}I_2 + \cdots sL_{2n}I_n$$
$$\cdot \quad \cdot \quad \cdot \quad \cdot \quad \cdot \quad \cdots \cdot \quad \cdot$$
$$E_n = sL_{1n}I_1 + sL_{2n}I_n + \cdots sL_{nn}I_n$$

13.4.1

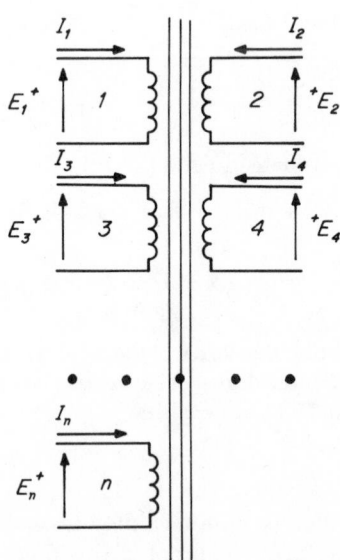

**Fig. 13.2. An n-port transformer**

In case of perfect coupling, the mutual inductance is related to the winding inductances by

$$L_{pq} = \sqrt{L_{pp}L_{qq}} \qquad\qquad \text{13.4.2}$$

It is convenient to write $L_{pp} = n_p^2 L$, where $n_p$ is the number of turns of the $p^{\text{th}}$ winding. Observe therefore that Eq. 13.4.2 becomes

$$L_{pq} = Ln_p n_q \qquad\qquad \text{13.4.3}$$

Now it is noted that in the case of a 3-port transformer Eq. 13.4.1 may be written in the explicit form as

$$
\begin{aligned}
E_1 &= sL(n_1^2 I_1 + n_1 n_2 I_2 + n_1 n_3 I_3) \\
E_2 &= sL(n_1 n_2 I_1 + n_2^2 I_2 + n_2 n_3 I_3) \qquad\qquad \text{13.4.4} \\
E_3 &= sL(n_1 n_3 I_1 + n_2 n_3 I_2 + n_3^2 I_3)
\end{aligned}
$$

This set of equations may be written in the matrix notation

$$[E] = sL[N][I]$$

where each matrix is directly defined to yield Eq. 13.4.4. Thus

$$
[E] = \begin{bmatrix} E_1 \\ E_2 \\ E_3 \end{bmatrix} \quad
[N] = \begin{bmatrix} n_1^2 & n_1 n_2 & n_1 n_3 \\ n_1 n_2 & n_2^2 & n_2 n_3 \\ n_1 n_3 & n_2 n_3 & n_3^2 \end{bmatrix} \quad
[I] = \begin{bmatrix} I_1 \\ I_2 \\ I_3 \end{bmatrix} \qquad \text{13.4.5}
$$

Attention is called to the fact that matrix $[N]$ is of rank 1. That is, the determinant $|N|$ and all its minors vanish except for the minors composed of a single element. This degeneracy of the matrix $[N]$ manifests itself also in the fact that

$$E_1 = \frac{n_1 E_2}{n_2} = \frac{n_1 E_3}{n_3} \qquad\qquad \text{13.4.6}$$

as can be verified by direct division.

The fact that the rank of the impedance matrix of the perfectly coupled transformer is unity does not change when one (or more) of the ports is shunted by an impedance. This fact may be demonstrated directly by Eq. 13.4.6, where it is shown that the voltage ratio is constant, irrespective of the currents. Hence, the impedance matrix is of rank 1 irrespective of the loading.

Suppose now that only one of the ports is loaded (say, the $n^{\text{th}}$ port). We may write the equations of the system shown in Fig. 13.3:

$$
\begin{aligned}
E_1 &= sL\big(n_1^2 I_1 + n_1 n_2 I_2 + \cdots n_1 n_n (I_n - E_n/\zeta)\big) \\
E_2 &= sL\big(n_1 n_2 I_1 + n_2^2 I_2 + \cdots n_2 n_n (I_n - E_n/\zeta)\big) \\
&\quad\cdot\qquad\cdot\qquad\cdot\qquad\cdot\qquad\cdot\qquad\cdot\qquad\cdot\qquad\cdot \\
&\qquad\qquad\qquad\qquad\qquad\qquad\qquad\qquad \text{13.4.7} \\
&\quad\cdot\qquad\cdot\qquad\cdot\qquad\cdot\qquad\cdot\qquad\cdot\qquad\cdot\qquad\cdot \\
E_n &= sL\big(n_1 n_n I_1 + n_2 n_n I_2 + \cdots n_n^2 (I_n - E_n/\zeta)\big)
\end{aligned}
$$

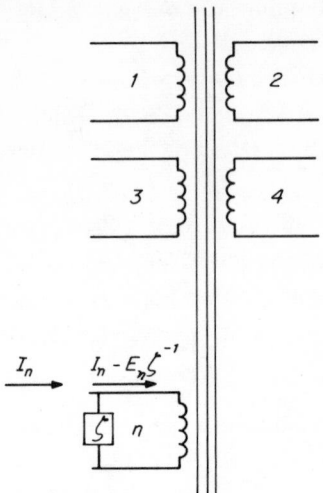

**Fig. 13.3. An n-port transformer with an impedance shunting the $n^{th}$ port**

Suppose that the last equation of Eq. 13.4.7 is rearranged. This gives

$$E_n = \frac{\zeta sL}{\zeta + sLn_n{}^2}(n_1 n_n I_1 + n_2 n_n I_2 + \cdots n_n{}^2 I_n) \qquad 13.4.$$

and therefore

$$(I_n - E_n/\zeta) = \frac{-sL}{\zeta + sLn_n{}^2}\left(n_1 n_n I_1 + n_2 n_n I_2 + \cdots - \frac{\zeta}{sL} I_n\right) \qquad 13.4.$$

This term is now substituted in the extreme right member of each equation in 13.4.7. Therefore

$$[E] = \frac{sL\zeta}{\zeta + sLn_n{}^2}[N][I] \qquad 13.4.1$$

Observe that if $\zeta = \dfrac{1}{Cs}$, then

$$[E] = \frac{(1/n_n{}^2 C)s}{s^2 + 1/n_n{}^2 LC}[N][I] \qquad 13.4.1$$

From this it follows that each member of $Z(s)$ is composed of a factor of the type $s/(s^2 + \omega_0{}^2)$. Hence the network of Fig. 13.3 is usually called a Foster network. Clearly when $L$ increases and approaches infinity (the case of an ideal transformer), Eq. 13.4.10 reduces to

$$[E] = \frac{\zeta}{n_n{}^2}[N][I] \qquad 13.4.1$$

Thus the loading, $\zeta$, manifests itself as a multiplying factor of each of the members of the matrix $[N]$.

As might be anticipated from the known results from the study of the 2-port ideal transformer (Section 6.2), the currents are related to each other. Recall, first, that in the 2-port ideal transformer

$$\frac{-I_1}{I_2} = \frac{E_2}{E_1} = \frac{n_2}{n_1} \qquad \text{13.4.13}$$

We shall utilize the first of Eqs. 13.4.4 to derive the corresponding constraint governing the relation between the currents in the $n$-port ideal transformer. Thus, in the general case

$$\frac{E_1}{sLn_1} = n_1I_1 + n_2I_2 + \cdots + n_nI_n \qquad \text{13.4.14}$$

which reduces to the following when $L$ approaches infinity:

$$n_1I_1 + n_2I_2 + \cdots + n_nI_n = \sum n_pI_p = 0 \qquad \text{13.4.15}$$

## THE CONGRUENCE TRANSFORMER 13.5

Attention is now directed to Corollary 13.1.2 which states that if $Z(s)]$ is a $PR$ matrix where $[A]$ is a real matrix, then $[A]_t[Z(s)][A]$ is also a $PR$ matrix. We now wish to show that this transformation possesses a physical representation. The $n$-port element generating these functions from $[Z(s)]$ is here called a congruence transformer.*

Consider the 4-port network illustrated in Fig. 13.4. Actually the procedure to be adopted is perfectly general and would apply to the $n$-port case also. The transformer illustrated is also called a 1 by 3 transformer. From Eq. 13.4.15 we have

$$\sum n_pI_p = 0 \qquad \begin{matrix} \text{13.4.15} \\ \text{13.5.1} \end{matrix}$$

if due account is taken of the reference directions for current, and therefore

$$I_1 = A_{11}I'_1 + A_{12}I'_2 + A_{13}I'_3 \qquad \text{13.5.2}$$

Now let us digress for a moment and note that if

$$[E] = [Z][I] \qquad \text{13.5.3}$$

---

* Bayard calls this element a translator. However, this may imply that the transformation $[A]_t[Z][A]$ represents a geometrical translation, but this is not the case. We selected the name "congruence transformer" to denote the "congruence transformation."

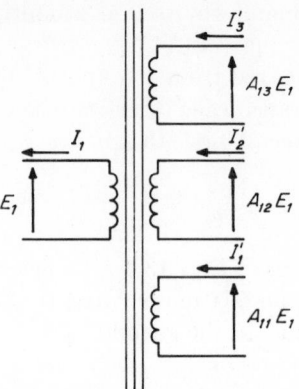

**Fig. 13.4. A 1 by 3 (or 4)-port ideal transformer. $A_{ij}$ is the turn ratio between the $j^{th}$ term on the right and the first (on the left). The i stands for the $i^{th}$ element (here only one such element)**

then

$$[A]_t[E] = [A]_t[Z][I] \qquad\qquad 13.5.4$$

Now define the quantity $[E']$ and $[I']$ by the relations

$$[E'] = [A]_t[E]$$

and

$$[I] = [A][I'] \qquad\qquad 13.5.$$

If these are combined with Eq. 13.5.4, it follows that

$$[E'] = [A]_t[Z][A][I'] \qquad\qquad 13.5.6$$

which may be written as

$$[E'] = [Z'][I']$$

where

$$[Z'] = [A]_t[Z][A] \qquad\qquad 13.5.7$$

Attention is called to the fact that in Eq. 13.5.5 $[E']$ is given in term of $[E]$, whereas $[I]$ is given in terms of $[I']$.

Refer now to the interconnected system of 1 by 3 transformer illustrated in Fig. 13.5. Observe that for this system

$$\begin{bmatrix} E'_1 \\ E'_2 \\ E'_3 \end{bmatrix} = \begin{bmatrix} A_{11} & A_{21} & A_{31} \\ A_{12} & A_{22} & A_{32} \\ A_{13} & A_{23} & A_{33} \end{bmatrix} \begin{bmatrix} E_1 \\ E_2 \\ E_3 \end{bmatrix} \qquad\qquad 13.5.$$

which is

$$[E'] = [A]_t[E] \qquad\qquad 13.5.$$

ere

$$[A] = \begin{bmatrix} A_{11} & A_{12} & A_{13} \\ A_{21} & A_{22} & A_{23} \\ A_{31} & A_{32} & A_{33} \end{bmatrix} \qquad 13.5.10$$

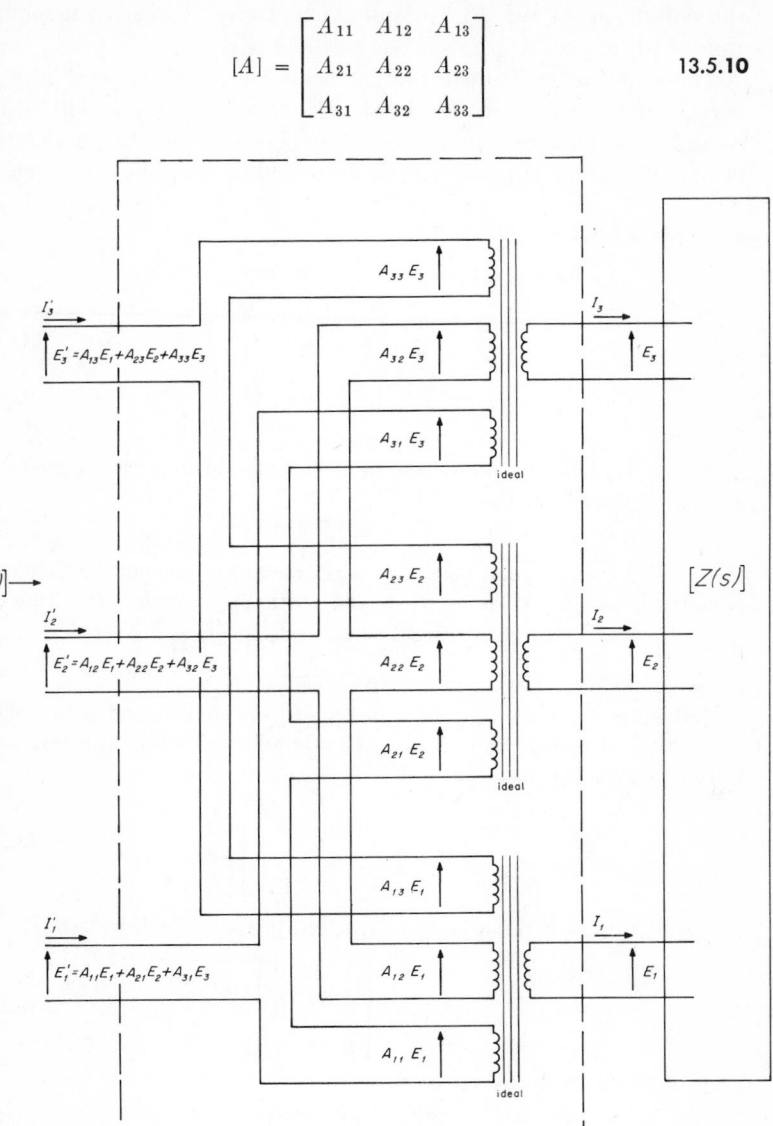

**Fig. 13.5. A 3-port congruence transformer (inside the broken line)**

imilarly it follows from Eq. 13.5.2 that

$$[I] = [A][I'] \qquad 13.5.11$$

Consequently the voltages and currents in the system above satisfy the definitions of Eq. 13.5.5, and this network represents a realization of $[Z'(s)] = [A]_t[Z(s)][A]$ in terms of $[Z(s)]$.

The congruence transformer is very useful in the synthesis of one-element-kind networks. In the following example it will be observed that the synthesis procedure depends on the diagonalization of matrices. This subject will be discussed in the following section.

### Example 13.5.1

Realize the following 3 by 3 inductance matrix:

$$[Z(s)] = s \begin{bmatrix} 7 & 0 & 2 \\ 0 & 3 & -1 \\ 2 & -1 & 1 \end{bmatrix} \qquad \text{13.5.1}$$

### Solution

The matrix will first be written in a diagonalized form by means of the congruence transformation

$$[Z'] = [B]_t[Z][B] \qquad \text{13.5.1}$$

where $[B]$ is a nonsingular matrix whose elements are constant. It follows by premultiplying both sides by $[B]_t^{-1}$ and postmultiplying by $[B]^{-1}$ that

$$[Z(s)] = [B]_t^{-1}[Z'][B]^{-1} \equiv [A]_t[Z'][A], \qquad \text{13.5.1}$$

where by definition $[A]_t \equiv [B]_t^{-1}$; $[A] \equiv [B]^{-1}$.

Methods of determination of the matrix $[B]$ will be discussed in the following section. Although there is no unique method, the following matrix is satisfactory for our purposes:

$$[B] = \begin{bmatrix} 1 & -1 & -3 \\ 0 & 1 & 1 \\ 0 & 0 & 1 \end{bmatrix} \qquad \text{13.5.1}$$

Hence, carrying out the operations specified in Eq. 13.5.14, we get

$$[Z'] = s \begin{bmatrix} 1 & 0 & 0 \\ 0 & 2 & 0 \\ 0 & 0 & 1 \end{bmatrix} \qquad \text{13.5.1}$$

Thus $[Z(s)]$ can be expressed as

$$[Z(s)] = [A]_t[Z'][A] \qquad \text{13.5.1}$$

yielding

$$[Z(s)] = \begin{bmatrix} 1 & 1 & 2 \\ 0 & 1 & -1 \\ 0 & 0 & 1 \end{bmatrix} s \begin{bmatrix} 1 & 0 & 0 \\ 0 & 2 & 0 \\ 0 & 0 & 1 \end{bmatrix} \begin{bmatrix} 1 & 0 & 0 \\ 1 & 1 & 0 \\ 2 & -1 & 1 \end{bmatrix} \qquad \text{13.5.1}$$

The final network then has the form shown in Fig. 13.6:

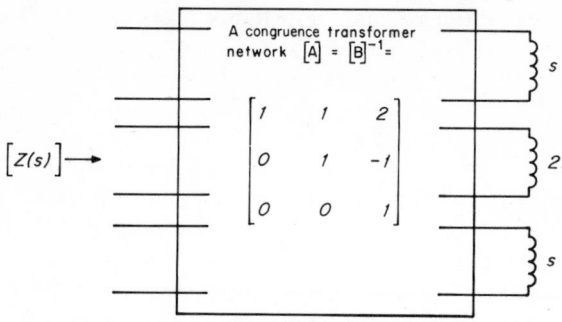

**Fig. 13.6. A congruence transformer rezlization of $[Z(s)]$ in Example 13.5.1**

The congruence transformer is also useful in the synthesis of singular $PR$ matrices, i.e., those for which det. $[Z(s)] \equiv 0$. For example, the following $PR$ matrix is singular for all values of $s$:

$$[Z(s)] = \begin{bmatrix} 2s + 2 & -s - 3 & 6s + 2 \\ -s - 3 & s + 6 & -2s \\ 6s + 2 & -2s & 20s + 8 \end{bmatrix} \qquad \textbf{13.5.18}$$

In this connection, we note the following:

### Theorem 13.5.1

If $[Z(s)]$ is a singular $n$ by $n$ $PR$ matrix of rank $r$, then there exists a matrix $[A]$ which is real, constant, and nonsingular, such that $[Z'(s)] = [A]_t [Z(s)][A]$ is effectively an $r$ by $r$ $PR$ matrix.

The word "effectively" is inserted to show that $[Z'(s)]$ is indeed an $n$ by $n$ matrix but that $n - r$ rows and $n - r$ columns, intersecting on the principal diagonal, are identically zero.

The theorem means that any singular $PR$ impedance matrix can be realized by means of a congruent transformer terminated in a $PR$ impedance matrix of reduced order.

### Proof*

Let $s$ be any positive number, say $s = 1$. Now $Z(1)$ is a *real* symmetric matrix. By a standard diagonalization theorem† there exists a matrix $[A]$ which is *real*, constant, and nonsingular such that $[Z'(s)] = [A]_t [Z(s)][A]$ is diagonal at the point $s = 1$. Because det.

---

\* This proof is along the lines given by R. J. Duffin—reference cited on page 246.
† See, for example, Theorem 13.6.1 in the following section.

$[Z(s)] \equiv 0$, some diagonal element of $[Z'(1)]$ must vanish. Withou loss of generality, assume that $z'(1)_{nn} = 0$.

Now construct the associate impedance function $Z'(s)$ (Eq. 13.1.2)

$$Z'(s) = [N]_t [Z'(s)][N] = \sum z'_{pq} n_p n_q \qquad \text{13.5.1}$$

where $[N]$ is a real column matrix.

Because $Z'(s)$ is prf, $Z'(1)$ must be positive for all values of th $n's$, but $z'_{nn}(1)$ is zero; hence all the $z'_{nq}(1)$ must be zero. Otherwis Re $z_{nn}(1)$ Re $z_{qq}(1)$ $-$ (Re $z_{nq}(1))^2$ is not positive. Furthermore $z'_{nn}(s)$ is prf. It must be identically zero, since zero is the onl positive real function which has a zero in the r.h.s. plane. Again using the associate impedance function argument, the $z'_{nq}(s)$ term must be zero.

This process now may be continued to show that if $[Z(s)]$ is of rank $r$ ther would result only $r$ nonzero terms in $[Z'(1)]$, and hence the final matrix woul be an $r$ by $r$ matrix effectively.

*Proof complete*

### Example 13.5.2

Realize the matrix impedance function given in Eq. 13.5.18.

*Solution*

By a diagonalization procedure given in the following section, we have

$$[Z'(s)] = \begin{bmatrix} 1 & 0 & 0 \\ 1 & 1 & 0 \\ -4 & -2 & 1 \end{bmatrix} \begin{bmatrix} 2s + 2 & -s - 3 & 6s + 2 \\ -s - 3 & s + 6 & -2s \\ 6s + 2 & -2s & 20s + 8 \end{bmatrix} \begin{bmatrix} 1 & 1 & -4 \\ 0 & 1 & -2 \\ 0 & 0 & 1 \end{bmatrix}$$

$$= \begin{bmatrix} 2s + 2 & s - 1 & 0 \\ s - 1 & s + 2 & 0 \\ 0 & 0 & 0 \end{bmatrix} \qquad \text{13.5.2}$$

Note that $[Z'(1)]$ is the diagonalized matrix. The final network is given i Fig. 13.7.

## 13.6. REMARKS ON DIAGONALIZATION OF MATRICES

Diagonalization of matrices is of considerable importance in mos $n$-port synthesis procedures. Two methods that are especially usefu because of their simplicity are discussed in this section. It i attempted here to be convincing rather than rigorous, since th

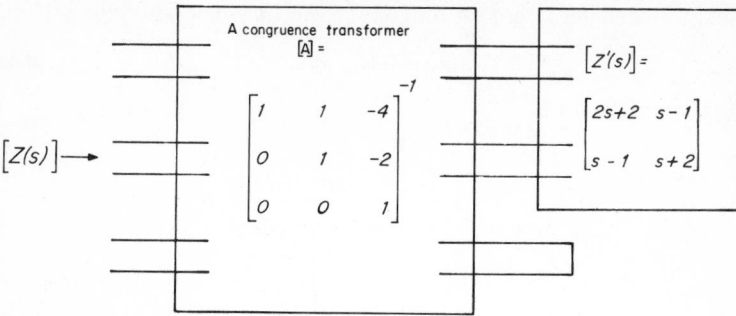

**Fig. 13.7. A realization of Z(s) in Example 13.5.2**

mathematical details are readily available in many texts.* We first consider a theorem that will be useful later.

## Theorem 13.6.1

If $[Z(\sigma)]$ ($\sigma$ is a positive constant) is a real symmetric matrix, there exists a matrix $[A]$ which is *real*, constant, and nonsingular such that

$$[G(\sigma)] = [A]_t[Z(\sigma)][A] \qquad 13.6.1$$

is a diagonal matrix.

## Proof

It is first noted that the matrix $[A]$ is not unique. To prove the theorem, it is only necessary to find one $[A]$ for each $[Z(\sigma)]$. In what follows we shall use a scheme for determining $[A]$ which is related to the Lagrange-Gauss method of completing the squares of quadratic forms discussed in Section 13.2. The proof will progress by first demonstrating a process for determining $[A]$ for a 2 by 2 and 3 by 3 matrix and then by demonstrating the relation between the method and the Lagrange-Gauss method of completing the square. The main feature of the process is that the matrix $[A]$ is further restricted to be triangular.

(1) *Proof for a 2 by 2 matrix:*

Let $\alpha_{pq} = z_{pq}(\sigma)$ and $[A] = \begin{bmatrix} 1 & a \\ 0 & 1 \end{bmatrix}$ then

$$
[G(\sigma)] = [A]_t[Z(\sigma)][A] = \begin{bmatrix} 1 & 0 \\ a & 1 \end{bmatrix}\begin{bmatrix} \alpha_{11} & \alpha_{12} \\ \alpha_{12} & \alpha_{22} \end{bmatrix}\begin{bmatrix} 1 & a \\ 0 & 1 \end{bmatrix}
$$

$$
= \begin{bmatrix} \alpha_{11} & a\alpha_{11} + \alpha_{12} \\ a\alpha_{11} + \alpha_{12} & a^2\alpha_{11} + 2a\alpha_{12} + \alpha_{22} \end{bmatrix}
$$

---

* See, for example, Mirsky, L., "An Introduction to Linear Algebra," Oxford University Press, Oxford, England, 1961.

Thus, to force $[G(\sigma)]$ into a diagonal form, it is necessary to set

$$a\alpha_{11} + \alpha_{12} = 0 \qquad \text{13.6.2}$$

which requires that

$$a = -\frac{\alpha_{12}}{\alpha_{11}} \qquad \text{13.6.3}$$

Thus for a 2 by 2 matrix, it is possible to select

$$[A] = \begin{bmatrix} 1 & -\dfrac{\alpha_{12}}{\alpha_{11}} \\ 0 & 1 \end{bmatrix} \qquad \text{13.6.4}$$

which is nonsingular and real as required. This completes the proof of (1).

Calculating $[G(\sigma)]$ for the value of a in Eq. 13.6.3, we get

$$[G(\sigma)] = \begin{bmatrix} \alpha_{11} & 0 \\ 0 & \dfrac{\alpha_{11}\alpha_{22} - \alpha_{12}{}^2}{\alpha_{11}} \end{bmatrix} \qquad \text{13.6.5}$$

Note that $[A]$ in Eq. 13.6.4 is triangular. This is a characteristic feature of the present method as will be seen for the diagonalization of the 3 by 3 matrix.

(2). *Proof for a 3 by 3 matrix*:

Let $[A]$ be given by

$$[A] = \begin{bmatrix} 1 & a & b \\ 0 & 1 & c \\ 0 & 0 & 1 \end{bmatrix} \qquad \text{13.6.6}$$

Construct $[G(\sigma)]$ to satisfy

$$[G(\sigma)] = [A]_t[Z(\sigma)][A]$$

now

$$[G(\sigma)] = \begin{bmatrix} 1 & 0 & 0 \\ a & 1 & 0 \\ b & c & 1 \end{bmatrix} \begin{bmatrix} \alpha_{11} & \alpha_{12} & \alpha_{13} \\ \alpha_{12} & \alpha_{22} & \alpha_{23} \\ \alpha_{13} & \alpha_{23} & \alpha_{33} \end{bmatrix} \begin{bmatrix} 1 & a & b \\ 0 & 1 & c \\ 0 & 0 & 1 \end{bmatrix} \qquad \text{13.6.7}$$

Again, to put $[G(\sigma)]$ into a diagonal form, let

$$a\alpha_{11} + \alpha_{12} = 0 \qquad \text{13.6.8a}$$

$$b\alpha_{11} + c\alpha_{12} + \alpha_{13} = 0 \qquad \text{13.6.8b}$$

$$ab\alpha_{11} + (b + ac)\alpha_{12} + a\alpha_{13} + \alpha_{23} + c\alpha_{22} = 0 \qquad \text{13.6.8c}$$

Solving these equations for $a$, $b$, and $c$, we get

$$a = -\frac{\alpha_{12}}{\alpha_{11}} \qquad \textbf{13.6.9a}$$

$$b = \frac{\alpha_{12}\alpha_{23} - \alpha_{13}\alpha_{22}}{\alpha_{11}\alpha_{22} - \alpha_{12}{}^2} \equiv \frac{\Delta_{13}}{\Delta_{33}} \qquad \textbf{13.6.9b}$$

$$c = \frac{\alpha_{12}\alpha_{13} - \alpha_{11}\alpha_{23}}{\alpha_{11}\alpha_{22} - \alpha_{12}{}^2} \equiv \frac{\Delta_{23}}{\Delta_{33}} \qquad \textbf{13.6.9c}$$

where the $\Delta$'s are the respective cofactors of $|Z(\sigma)|$. This completes the proof of (2).

With these values of $a$, $b$, and $c$, $\mathrm{G}(\sigma)$ in Eq. 13.6.7 becomes

$$[G(\sigma)] = \begin{bmatrix} \alpha_{11} & & \\ & \dfrac{\Delta_{33}}{\alpha_{11}} & \\ & & \dfrac{|Z(\sigma)|}{\Delta_{33}} \end{bmatrix}; \qquad \textbf{13.6.10}$$

$$|Z(\sigma)| = \text{det. } [Z(\sigma)]$$

This process of constructing a diagonal matrix can be continued to show that any $n$ by $n$ matrix may be diagonalized. However, the process is related to the Lagrange-Gauss method of completing the square. To show this, construct the associate impedance function of $[Z(\sigma)]$ (Eq. 13.1.2)

$$Z(\sigma) = [N]_t[Z(\sigma)][N]$$

where $[N]$ is a column matrix ($= \textit{real}$).

For a 3 by 3 matrix, this expansion becomes

$$Z(\sigma) = n_1{}^2\alpha_{11} + n_2{}^2\alpha_{22} + n_3{}^2\alpha_{33} + 2n_1n_2\alpha_{12} + 2n_2n_3\alpha_{23} + 2n_1n_3\alpha_{13} \qquad \textbf{13.6.11}$$

Recall from Corollary 13.1.1 that the strategy of completing the squares was the following:

Form squares such that the first square will contain all the $n$'s; the second square will contain all the $n$'s but one; the third all the $n$'s but two, and so on. For example, Eq. 13.6.11 will become

$$Z(\sigma) = g_{11}(n_1 + a'n_2 + b'n_3)^2 + g_{22}(n_2 + c'n_3)^2 + g_{33}n_3{}^2 \qquad \textbf{13.6.12}$$

But this can also be written as

$$Z(\sigma) = [N']_t[G(\sigma)][N'] \qquad \textbf{13.6.13a}$$

where

$$[N'] = [B][N] \equiv \begin{bmatrix} 1 & a' & b' \\ & 1 & c' \\ & & 1 \end{bmatrix} \begin{bmatrix} n_1 \\ n_2 \\ n_3 \end{bmatrix} \qquad \textbf{13.6.13b}$$

and

$$[G(\sigma)] = \begin{bmatrix} g_{11} & & \\ & g_{22} & \\ & & g_{33} \end{bmatrix}$$ 13.6.13c

Thus identification of corresponding terms in Eqs. 13.6.13 and 13.6.7 reveals that $[B] = [A]^{-1}$. Furthermore, by the nature of the expansion, $[B]$ must be triangular and nonsingular; hence $[A]$ is triangular and nonsingular. This completes the proof of Theorem 13.6.1.

Note that Eqs. 13.6.12 and 13.6.13 make it possible to find $[A]$ and $[G]$ directly from the Lagrange-Gauss method of completing the squares.* Also it is important to observe that there are other non-singular real matrices useful for synthesis purposes.† For example, in the 2 by 2 case $[A]$ may be selected as follows:

$$[G(\sigma)] = [A]_t[Z(\sigma)][A]$$ 13.6.14

where $[A] = \begin{bmatrix} 1 & a \\ b & 1 \end{bmatrix}$ $\quad a \neq b^{-1}$

Expanding $[G(\sigma)]$ above, we get

$$[G(\sigma)] = \begin{bmatrix} \alpha_{11} + 2b\alpha_{12} + b^2\alpha_{22} & b(a\alpha_{12} + \alpha_{22}) + a\alpha_{11} + \alpha_{12} \\ b(a\alpha_{12} + \alpha_{22}) + a\alpha_{11} + \alpha_{12} & a^2\alpha_{11} + 2a\alpha_{12} + \alpha_{22} \end{bmatrix}$$ 13.6.15

Hence if $b$ is selected as

$$b = -\frac{a\alpha_{11} + \alpha_{12}}{a\alpha_{12} + \alpha_{22}}$$ 13.6.16

$[G(\sigma)]$ is diagonalized as follows:

$$[G(\sigma)] = \frac{a^2\alpha_{11} + 2a\alpha_{12} + \alpha_{22}}{(a\alpha_{12} + \alpha_{22})^2} \begin{bmatrix} \alpha_{11}\alpha_{22} - \alpha_{12}^2 & \\ & (a\alpha_{12} + \alpha_{22})^2 \end{bmatrix}$$ 13.6.17

The advantage of this scheme is that $a$ is arbitrary and can be used to some advantage. Note that with the choice of $b$ given in Eq 13.6.16 $[A]$ becomes

$$[A] = \begin{bmatrix} 1 & a \\ -\dfrac{a\alpha_{11} + \alpha_{12}}{a\alpha_{12} + \alpha_{22}} & 1 \end{bmatrix}$$ 13.6.18

---

* Bayard, M., "Synthesis of n-Terminal Pair Networks," Proc. Symposium on Modern Network Synthesis, Polytechnic Institute of Brooklyn, p. 69, Eq. (7) 1952.

† Joseph, R. D., "Rank and Degree Reduction in Reciprocal n-Port Network Synthesis", M.S. Thesis, Case Institute of Technology, June, 1962.

## MATRIX DIAGONALIZATION SYNTHESIS—ONE-ELEMENT-KIND 13.7

Perhaps the primary reason for the wide use of diagonalization of matrices in $n$-port synthesis is the fact that congruence transformation of $PR$ matrices generates $PR$ matrices (Corollary 13.2.2). Thus if the transformation generates a diagonal matrix, each member of the matrix is prf (Corollary 13.2.1). But an $n$ by $n$ diagonal matrix can be decomposed into $n$ parts, each of which has only one entry on the principal diagonal. This is the basis for the following theorem.

### Theorem 13.7.1—Oono's Theorem

Any $n$ by $n$ $PR$ matrix (of rank $r$) can be decomposed into a sum of $r$ $PR$ matrices of rank 1.

### Proof

The proof will be given in two parts. In the first part only one-element-kind networks will be considered. In the second part (Section 13.9) the proof will be completed also for all $PR$ minimum reactive matrices.

For one-element-kind networks we shall use a congruence transformation to diagonalize the matrix. Without loss of generality, assume that $[Z(s)]$ is a *resistive matrix*, since to convert the matrix to an inductance or capacitance matrix all that is necessary is to multiply the final expansion by $s$ or $1/s$ respectively (see the following example). Now let us write $[Z]$ in the form

$$[Z] = [A]_t^{-1}[A]_t[Z][A][A]^{-1} = [A]_t^{-1}[G][A]^{-1} \qquad \textbf{13.7.1}$$

where $[G]$ is a diagonal matrix. $[A]$ is a real nonsingular $n$ by $n$ matrix. The fact that $[A]$ can be found was shown in the previous section. Let, for example, $n$ equal 3. Then

$$[Z(\alpha)] = [A]_t^{-1}\begin{bmatrix} g_{11} & & \\ & g_{22} & \\ & & g_{33} \end{bmatrix}[A]^{-1} \qquad \textbf{13.7.2}$$

This is now written as the sum of three matrix products:

$$[Z(\alpha)] = [A]_t^{-1}\begin{bmatrix} g_{11} & & \\ & 0 & \\ & & 0 \end{bmatrix}[A]^{-1} + [A]_t^{-1}\begin{bmatrix} 0 & & \\ & g_{22} & \\ & & 0 \end{bmatrix}[A]^{-1}$$

$$\qquad\qquad\qquad + [A]_t^{-1}\begin{bmatrix} 0 & & \\ & 0 & \\ & & g_{33} \end{bmatrix}[A]^{-1} \qquad \textbf{13.7.3}$$

Each of the three matrices above is $PR$ of rank 1, since its corresponding diagonal form is $PR$ and it has only one element. Similarly, if $[Z(s)]$ is an $n$ by $n$ matrix, $n$ parts similar to those above would be formed. However, if it is of rank $r$, there will be only $r$ diagonal terms and only $r$ matrices will result.

*Proof completed*

### Example 13.7.1

Realize the inductance matrix

$$[Z(s)] = s \begin{bmatrix} 7 & 0 & 2 \\ 0 & 3 & -1 \\ 2 & -1 & 1 \end{bmatrix} \qquad 13.7.4$$

This example was realized in Section 13.5 by means of a congruence transformer.

### Solution

From Section 13.5 we have

$$[(Z(s)] = \begin{bmatrix} 1 & 1 & 2 \\ 0 & 1 & -1 \\ 0 & 0 & 1 \end{bmatrix} s \begin{bmatrix} 1 & & \\ & 2 & \\ & & 1 \end{bmatrix} \begin{bmatrix} 1 & 0 & 0 \\ 1 & 1 & 0 \\ 2 & -1 & 1 \end{bmatrix} \qquad 13.7.5$$

which is now decomposed into the following matrices:

$$[Z(s)] = \begin{bmatrix} 1 & 1 & 2 \\ 0 & 1 & -1 \\ 0 & 0 & 1 \end{bmatrix} s \begin{bmatrix} 1 & & \\ & 0 & \\ & & 0 \end{bmatrix} \begin{bmatrix} 1 & 0 & 0 \\ 1 & 1 & 0 \\ 2 & -1 & 1 \end{bmatrix}$$

$$+ \begin{bmatrix} 1 & 1 & 2 \\ 0 & 1 & -1 \\ 0 & 0 & 1 \end{bmatrix} s \begin{bmatrix} 0 & & \\ & 2 & \\ & & 0 \end{bmatrix} \begin{bmatrix} 1 & 0 & 0 \\ 1 & 1 & 0 \\ 2 & -1 & 1 \end{bmatrix} \qquad 13.7.6$$

$$+ \begin{bmatrix} 1 & 1 & 2 \\ 0 & 1 & -1 \\ 0 & 0 & 1 \end{bmatrix} s \begin{bmatrix} 0 & & \\ & 0 & \\ & & 1 \end{bmatrix} \begin{bmatrix} 1 & 0 & 0 \\ 1 & 1 & 0 \\ 2 & -1 & 1 \end{bmatrix}$$

$$\equiv s \begin{bmatrix} 1 & 0 & 0 \\ 0 & 0 & 0 \\ 0 & 0 & 0 \end{bmatrix} + s \begin{bmatrix} 2 & 2 & 0 \\ 2 & 2 & 0 \\ 0 & 0 & 0 \end{bmatrix} + s \begin{bmatrix} 4 & -2 & 2 \\ -2 & 1 & -1 \\ 2 & -1 & 1 \end{bmatrix} \qquad 13.7.6$$

The first two matrices are highly degenerate and may be realized each by single inductor. The third matrix can be realized by means of a perfectl

:oupled 3-port transformer (Section 13.4). The final network is given in
Fig. 13.8.

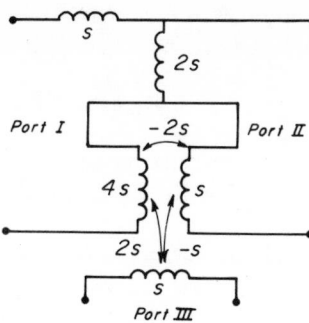

**Fig. 13.8. A realization of Z(s) in Example 13.7.1**

## SYNTHESIS OF TWO-ELEMENT-KIND $n$-PORT 13.8

Synthesis of two-element kind driving point impedance functions
1-port) can be readily extended to $n$-port. Most of the characteristic
wo-element 1-port kind properties are also true for the $n$-port.

### emma 13.8.1

If $[Z(s)]$ is a $PR$ matrix, all $j$ axis poles are simple with real
:sidues.

### oof

Let $j\omega_0$ denote the location of a $j$ axis pole. Construct the associate
1pedance function, and let $s = j\omega_0 + \rho e^{i\theta}$. The fact that $s$
pproaches the pole means that all the terms containing the higher-
der poles will predominate. Hence

$$Z(s) \doteq \sum \frac{k_{pq}n_p n_q}{(s - j\omega_0)^{t_{pq}}} \doteq \frac{1}{\rho^{t_{pq}}} \sum (e^{-j\theta\, t_{pq}}) k_{pq}n_p n_q \qquad \textbf{13.8.1}$$

et all the $n$'s be zero except $n_p$ and $n_q$. The fact that $z_{pp}$ and $z_{qq}$ are
·f means that they may not have higher-order poles. The only term
ft is

$$Z(s) \doteq \frac{1}{\rho^{t_{pq}}} n_p n_q k_{pq} e^{-j\theta\, t_{pq}} \qquad \textbf{13.8.2}$$

1d therefore

$$\operatorname{Re} Z(s) \doteq \frac{1}{\rho^{t_{pq}}} n_p n_q \operatorname{Re} (k_{pq} e^{-j\theta\, t_{pq}}) \qquad \textbf{13.8.3}$$

But since the $n$'s may be negative, we may find a set of numbers $n_p$ and $n_q$ such that the above will be negative and still be in the r.h.s. plane. Thus this term does not exist and the poles must be simple.

Again, let all the $n$'s be zero except $n_p$ and $n_q$. The fact that the poles are simple means that $z_{pp}$ and $z_{qq}$ are present. $Z(s)$ becomes

$$Z(s) = \frac{1}{\rho} (k_{pp}n_p^2 + 2k_{pq}n_pn_q + k_{qq}n_q^2)e^{-j\theta} \qquad 13.8.4$$

The fact that $z_{pp}$ and $z_{qq}$ are prf means that $k_{pp}$ and $k_{qq}$ are real (Theorem 2.2.1). Calculating Re $Z(s)$, we get

$$\text{Re } Z(s) = \frac{1}{\rho} (k_{pp}n_p^2 + 2 \text{ Re } k_{pq}n_pn_q + k_{qq}n_q^2) \cos \theta$$

$$13.8.5$$

$$+ \frac{1}{\rho} \text{ Im } k_{pq}n_pn_q \sin \theta$$

Thus if we let $\theta = \frac{\pi}{2}$, Re $Z(s) = \frac{1}{\rho} \text{ Im } k_{pq}n_pn_q$. Again a proper selection of $n_p$ and $n_q$ will make this negative unless Im $k_{pq} = 0$.

*Proof complete*

## Theorem 13.8.1

If $[Z(s)]$ is a $PR$ matrix, all $j$ axis poles are simple and the matrix of the residues $[K]$ is a resistive matrix. The removal of a $j$ axis pole and its conjugate generates a $PR$ matrix.

The proof will be given in two parts. In the first part it will be shown that the residue matrices are resistive matrices, and in the second part that the generated matrix is also $PR$ if $[Z(s)]$ is $PR$.

### *Proof: Part 1*

By the above lemma, the poles are simple. If the $j$ axis pole is located at $j\omega_0$ and $s$ approaches the pole from the r.h.s plane, $s = j\omega_0 + \epsilon$ ($\epsilon > 0$). When $\epsilon \to 0$, the terms containing the pole will predominate, and $[Z(s)]$ will essentially reduce to

$$[Z(j\omega_0 + \epsilon)] = \frac{1}{\epsilon} [K] \qquad 13.8$$

where the $[K]$ matrix is the residue matrix. By the above lemma, the residue matrix is a real matrix; hence the corresponding associated impedance function becomes

$$Z(j\omega_0 + \epsilon) = \frac{1}{\epsilon} [N]_t[K][N] \qquad 13.8$$

$$[N] = \text{a } real \text{ column matrix.}$$

$Z(j\omega_0 + \epsilon) > 0$ because all the quantities involved are *real*. Eq. 13.8.7 is identical with the requirement that a resistive matrix is *PR*. Hence the residue matrix at a $j$ axis pole of a *PR* matrix is a *PR* resistive matrix.

*Proof completed*

This theorem is the generalization of the residue condition of Section 6.6. Correspondingly, if $[Z(s)]$ is nonreciprocal, the terms that are off the principal diagonal are permitted to have imaginary values such that $k_{pq} = \bar{k}_{qp}$. The $[K]$ matrix then is said to be Hermitian.

## Proof: Part 2

To show that the matrix generated by removing a $j$ axis pole is itself a *PR* matrix, note that

$$[Z_1(j\omega)] = [Z(j\omega)] - \frac{1}{j(\omega - \omega_0)} [K] - \frac{1}{j(\omega + \omega_0)} [K] \qquad \textbf{13.8.8}$$

where $[Z_1(j\omega)]$ is the remainder matrix (the conjugate pole is also removed to insure that $[Z_1(\sigma)] = [\text{real}]; \sigma > 0$). Thus

$$\text{Re } [Z_1(j\omega)] = \text{Re } [Z(j\omega)] \qquad \textbf{13.8.9}$$

and in terms of the associated impedance functions $\text{Re } Z_1(j\omega) = \text{Re } Z(j\omega) \geq 0$. However, removing a $j$ axis pole does not introduce poles in the *r.h.s* plane. Hence by the minimum real-part theorem $\text{Re } Z_1(s) > 0$ for $\text{Re } s > 0$, and it follows that $[Z_1(s)]$ is *PR*.

*Proof completed*

All the poles of the associate impedance function of a lossless network must lie on the $j$ axis. It follows that all poles of an immittance matrix must lie on the $j$ axis. Expanding each matrix element in a partial fraction expansion and grouping together elements corresponding to each pole gives

$$[Z(s)] = s[K_\infty] + \frac{1}{s} [K_0] + \sum \frac{2s}{s^2 + \omega_p^2} [K_p] \qquad \textbf{13.8.10}$$

where the $[K]$'s are residue matrices. As explained by the above theorem, they can be realized as resistive *PR* matrices. Thus $[Z(s)]$ may be realized by realizing the $[K]$ matrices by any one-element-kind synthesis procedure and then multiplying through by the corresponding function of $s$.

Eq. 13.8.10 is the Foster $n$-port canonic form for lossless networks. The corresponding Cauer $n$-port canonic form would be obtained by performing a matrix continued fraction expansion. The process would lead to ladder $n$-port networks. These will be discussed in Section 13.10 (see Fig. 13.9).

By virtue of the similarity between any two-element kind network, it follows that equations similar to Eq. 13.8.10 may be found for $RC$ and $RL$ functions as well. In fact the corresponding partial fraction expansion for $RC$ and $RL$ may be found from Eq. 13.8.10 by performing a simple change in variables (also see Section 11.2):

$$[Z(x)]_{RC} = \left.\frac{[Z(s)]_{LC}}{s}\right|_{s^2=x} \qquad \text{13.8.11a}$$

and

$$[Z(x)]_{RL} = \left. s[Z(s)]_{LC}\right|_{s^2=x} \qquad \text{13.8.11b}$$

Thus if we wish, for example, to realize an $RC$ $n$-port, we may do so by first realizing the corresponding $LC$ function given in Eq. 13.8.11. Once the network is obtained, the corresponding $RC$ network is found by multiplying each element by $\dfrac{1}{s}$ and setting $s^2 = x$. $x$ will be the new frequency variable. Now it is possible to prove statement 12.3.7 of the preceding chapter (page 229).

> *If $[Z(s)]$ represents an immittance matrix of a two-element-kind network $(RC, RL)$ then all its poles are simple and lie on the negative real axis.*     **12.3.7**

The proof of this statement can be obtained by noting that Eq. 13.8.10 as modified by Eq. 13.8.11 has only simple negative real axis poles. A similar expansion for an *admittance* function will also yield only negative real axis poles.

*Proof completed*

## 13.9. MATRIX DIAGONALIZATION SYNTHESIS—MINIMUM REACTANCE

In the last section it was shown that if $[Z(s)]$ has a $j$ axis pole it may be removed, thereby generating a $PR$ matrix. Once all the $j$ axis poles have been removed, the remainder is called a minimum reactive matrix.

### Theorem 13.9.1—Oono's Theorem

Any $n$ by $n$ minimum reactive $PR$ matrix whose even-part matrix is of rank $r$ can be split into a sum of $r$ $PR$ matrices. The even part of each of these matrices is of rank 1.

*Proof*

This theorem is the second part of Theorem 13.7.1. To prove this theorem diagonalization of matrices will be used again. However, in the congruence transformation the matrix $[A]$ will no longer be constant. We will permit it to be frequency dependent. The fundamental approach will be that of decomposing the even part into rational $PR$ matrices. The diagonalization techniques described in Section 13.6 yield rational matrices and hence are satisfactory.

Let $j\omega$ be any point along the $j$ axis. Then Re $[Z(j\omega)]$ ($\equiv [r]$) is a real symmetric matrix. By the diagonalization techniques described in Section 13.6 there is a matrix $[A(j\omega)]$ which is real and nonsingular such that

$$\text{Re } [G(j\omega)] = [A(j\omega)]_t[r][A(j\omega)] \quad {}_{[r]=\text{Re}[Z(j\omega)]} \qquad \textbf{13.9.1}$$

is a diagonal matrix. For example, in a 2 by 2 $PR$ matrix we have, following a similar process in Section 13.6 (see Eqs. 13.6.4 and 5)

$$[A] = \begin{bmatrix} 1 & -\dfrac{r_{12}}{r_{11}} \\ 0 & 1 \end{bmatrix}, \text{Re } [G] = \begin{bmatrix} r_{11} & 0 \\ 0 & \dfrac{|r|}{r_{11}} \end{bmatrix} \qquad \textbf{13.9.2}$$

Here $|r| = |\text{Re }[Z(j\omega)]|$ and $r_{pq} = \text{Re } z_{pq}(j\omega)$.

It is important to note that Eqs. 13.9.1 and 13.9.2 are valid for all points on the $j$ axis. Furthermore, because of the congruence transformation utilized, each member of the diagonal matrix Re $[G]$ is positive on the $j$ axis. Hence, if $[r]$ is reconstructed by using the inverse congruence transformation on each member of the diagonal matrix, we shall obtain $r$ ($=$ rank) matrices. Each of these matrices is $PR$ in the sense that if we construct its associate impedance function $Z(s)$, we have Re $Z(s) \geq 0$ on the $j$ axis. Thus (for a 2 by 2)

$$\text{Re } [Z(j\omega)] \equiv [r] = \begin{bmatrix} 1 & 0 \\ -\dfrac{r_{12}}{r_{11}} & 1 \end{bmatrix}^{-1} \begin{bmatrix} r_{11} & 0 \\ 0 & \dfrac{|r|}{r_{11}} \end{bmatrix} \begin{bmatrix} 1 & -\dfrac{r_{12}}{r_{11}} \\ 0 & 1 \end{bmatrix}^{-1} \qquad \textbf{13.9.3}$$

which is now expanded to give

$$[r] = \begin{bmatrix} 1 & 0 \\ \dfrac{r_{12}}{r_{11}} & 1 \end{bmatrix} \begin{bmatrix} r_{11} & 0 \\ 0 & 0 \end{bmatrix} \begin{bmatrix} 1 & \dfrac{r_{12}}{r_{11}} \\ 0 & 1 \end{bmatrix} + \begin{bmatrix} 1 & 0 \\ \dfrac{r_{12}}{r_{11}} & 1 \end{bmatrix} \begin{bmatrix} 0 & 0 \\ 0 & \dfrac{|r|}{r_{11}} \end{bmatrix} \begin{bmatrix} 1 & \dfrac{r_{12}}{r_{11}} \\ 0 & 1 \end{bmatrix} \qquad \textbf{13.9.4}$$

Evaluating the matrix products, we get

$$[r] = \begin{bmatrix} r_{11} & r_{12} \\ r_{12} & \dfrac{r_{12}{}^2}{r_{11}} \end{bmatrix} + \begin{bmatrix} 0 & 0 \\ 0 & \dfrac{|r|}{r_{11}} \end{bmatrix} \qquad \textbf{13.9.5}$$

A similar development which is based on Eqs. 13.6.9 and 13.6.10 for a 3 by 3 $PR$ matrix yields

$$[r] = \begin{bmatrix} 1 & 0 & 0 \\ -\dfrac{r_{12}}{r_{11}} & 1 & 0 \\ \dfrac{\Delta_{13}}{\Delta_{33}} & \dfrac{\Delta_{23}}{\Delta_{33}} & 1 \end{bmatrix}^{-1} \begin{bmatrix} r_{11} & 0 & 0 \\ 0 & \dfrac{\Delta_{33}}{r_{11}} & 0 \\ 0 & 0 & \dfrac{|r|}{\Delta_{33}} \end{bmatrix} \begin{bmatrix} 1 & -\dfrac{r_{12}}{r_{11}} & \dfrac{\Delta_{13}}{\Delta_{33}} \\ 0 & 1 & \dfrac{\Delta_{23}}{\Delta_{33}} \\ 0 & 0 & 1 \end{bmatrix}^{-1} \qquad 13.9.6$$

where the $\Delta$'s are the respective cofactors, now expanded as follows:

$$[r] = \begin{bmatrix} 1 & 0 & 0 \\ \dfrac{r_{12}}{r_{11}} & 1 & 0 \\ \dfrac{r_{13}}{r_{11}} & -\dfrac{\Delta_{23}}{\Delta_{33}} & 1 \end{bmatrix} \begin{bmatrix} r_{11} & 0 & 0 \\ 0 & 0 & 0 \\ 0 & 0 & 0 \end{bmatrix} \begin{bmatrix} 1 & \dfrac{r_{12}}{r_{11}} & \dfrac{r_{13}}{r_{11}} \\ 0 & 1 & -\dfrac{\Delta_{23}}{\Delta_{33}} \\ 0 & 0 & 1 \end{bmatrix} +$$

$$\begin{bmatrix} 1 & 0 & 0 \\ \dfrac{r_{12}}{r_{11}} & 1 & 0 \\ \dfrac{r_{13}}{r_{11}} & -\dfrac{\Delta_{23}}{\Delta_{33}} & 1 \end{bmatrix} \begin{bmatrix} 0 & 0 & 0 \\ 0 & \dfrac{\Delta_{33}}{r_{11}} & 0 \\ 0 & 0 & 0 \end{bmatrix} \begin{bmatrix} 1 & \dfrac{r_{12}}{r_{11}} & \dfrac{r_{13}}{r_{11}} \\ 0 & 1 & -\dfrac{\Delta_{23}}{\Delta_{33}} \\ 0 & 0 & 1 \end{bmatrix} + \qquad 13.9.7$$

$$\begin{bmatrix} 1 & 0 & 0 \\ \dfrac{r_{12}}{r_{11}} & 1 & 0 \\ \dfrac{r_{13}}{r_{11}} & -\dfrac{\Delta_{23}}{\Delta_{33}} & 1 \end{bmatrix} \begin{bmatrix} 0 & 0 & 0 \\ 0 & 0 & 0 \\ 0 & 0 & \dfrac{|r|}{\Delta_{33}} \end{bmatrix} \begin{bmatrix} 1 & \dfrac{r_{12}}{r_{11}} & \dfrac{r_{13}}{r_{11}} \\ 0 & 1 & -\dfrac{\Delta_{23}}{\Delta_{33}} \\ 0 & 0 & 1 \end{bmatrix}$$

Evaluating each of the products, we get

$$[r] = \begin{bmatrix} r_{11} & r_{12} & r_{13} \\ r_{12} & \dfrac{r_{12}^2}{r_{11}} & \dfrac{r_{12}r_{13}}{r_{11}} \\ r_{13} & \dfrac{r_{12}r_{13}}{r_{11}} & \dfrac{r_{13}^2}{r_{11}} \end{bmatrix} + \begin{bmatrix} 0 & 0 & 0 \\ 0 & \dfrac{\Delta_{33}}{r_{11}} & -\dfrac{\Delta_{23}}{r_{11}} \\ 0 & -\dfrac{\Delta_{23}}{r_{11}} & \dfrac{\Delta_{23}^2}{\Delta_{33}r_{11}} \end{bmatrix} + \begin{bmatrix} 0 & 0 & 0 \\ 0 & 0 & 0 \\ 0 & 0 & \dfrac{|r|}{\Delta_{33}} \end{bmatrix} \qquad 13.9.8$$

It follows that this process may be continued to obtain an expansion for any $n$ by $n$ $PR$ matrix. However, these expansions are in terms of Re $[Z(s)]$ on the $j$ axis. The expansions will become more useful if they are carried out in terms of the *even part* (Ev $[Z(s)]$), since on the $j$ axis the results would be the same.

In the general expansion for an $n$ by $n$ Ev $[Z(s)]$ matrix parallel to that in Eq. 13.9.8, each term is designated by "regular reduced matrix" (Leroy).* The adjective "regular" shall be omitted henceforth. It follows that because of the nature of the expansion, each term is of rank 1. If Ev $[Z(s)]$ is of rank $r$, $r$ terms will be present. Let these matrices be denoted by $[R_i^0(s)]$; then

$$\text{Ev}\,[Z(s)] = \sum_{i=1}^{r} [R_i^0(s)] \qquad\qquad 13.9.9$$

Each principal diagonal element of these functions is positive along the $j$ axis. Hence its poles must possess quadrantal symmetry (Theorem 7.2.1). Furthermore, the fact that the $[R_i^0]$'s are of rank 1 means that every off diagonal matrix element may be obtained as the square root of two diagonal elements. It follows that their poles are given precisely in terms of those of the corresponding diagonal elements, and hence these poles possess quadrantal symmetry as well.

Let $[R_i]$ be the matrix obtained by reconstructing the function from the even part of each element of $[R_i^0]$ such that all the r.h.s plane poles of each element are discarded (see Section 7.2). Because $[Z(s)]$ has no $j$ axis poles, the $[R_i]$'s may not have them either, and therefore

$$[Z(s)] = \sum_{i=1}^{r} [R_i(s)] \qquad\qquad 13.9.10$$

Constructing the associate impedance function of $[R_i(s)]$, we have

$$\text{Re}\,R_i(s) = [N]_t\,\text{Re}\,[R_i(s)][N] = [N]_t[R_i^0(s)][N] \geq 0 \quad \text{on}\,j\,\text{axis} \quad 13.9.11$$

because of the nature of the expansion used to obtain the $[R_i^0]$'s. Furthermore, the $[R]$'s are analytic in the r.h.s plane since the r.h.s plane poles were discarded. Then, applying the minimum real-part theorem (Theorem 2.5.2), we get

$$\text{Re}\,R_i(s) > 0 \qquad \text{in the}\,r.h.s\,\text{plane}$$

which means that $R_i(s)$ is prf and $[R_i(s)]$ is a $PR$ matrix. This completes the proof of Theorem 13.9.1.

---

* On the other hand, the term "reduced matrix" was used by Gewertz for 2 port.

The matrix expansion discussed above is widely used in $RLCT$ $n$-port synthesis. It was discovered by Gewertz (for a 2 by 2 only). The extension to $n$ port was done by Oono and Bayard independently (Oono first).

In conclusion, we would like to point out the reduced matrices that would be obtained by using the second diagonalization technique discussed in Section 13.6. Accordingly, we have

$$\text{Re}\,[Z(j\omega)] = \frac{a^2 r_{11} + 2ar_{12} + r_{22}}{(ar_{12} + r_{22})^2} \times$$

$$\begin{bmatrix} 1 & -\dfrac{ar_{11} + r_{12}}{ar_{12} + r_{22}} \\ a & 1 \end{bmatrix}^{-1} \begin{bmatrix} r_{11}r_{22} - r_{122} & 0 \\ 0 & (ar_{12} + r_{22})^2 \end{bmatrix} \begin{bmatrix} 1 & a \\ -\dfrac{ar_{11} + r_{12}}{ar_{12} + r_{22}} & 1 \end{bmatrix}^{-1}$$

**13.9.12**

which is decomposed as follows:

$$\text{Re}\,[Z(j\omega)] = \frac{1}{a^2 r_{11} + 2ar_{12} + r_{22}} \times$$

$$\left\{ \begin{bmatrix} 1 & \dfrac{ar_{11} + r_{12}}{ar_{12} + r_{22}} \\ -a & 1 \end{bmatrix} \begin{bmatrix} r_{11}r_{22} - r_{12}^2 & 0 \\ 0 & 0 \end{bmatrix} \begin{bmatrix} 1 & -a \\ \dfrac{ar_{11} + r_{12}}{ar_{12} + r_{22}} & 1 \end{bmatrix} + \right.$$

$$\left. \begin{bmatrix} 1 & \dfrac{ar_{11} + r_{12}}{ar_{12} + r_{22}} \\ -a & 1 \end{bmatrix} \begin{bmatrix} 0 & 0 \\ 0 & (ar_{12} + r_{22})^2 \end{bmatrix} \begin{bmatrix} 1 & -a \\ \dfrac{ar_{11} + r_{12}}{ar_{12} + r_{22}} & 1 \end{bmatrix} \right\}$$

**13.9.13**

Evaluating each of the matrix products, we get

$$\text{Re}\,[Z(j\omega)] = \frac{r_{11}r_{22} - r_{12}^2}{a^2 r_{11} + 2ar_{12} + r_{22}} \begin{bmatrix} 1 & -a \\ -a & a^2 \end{bmatrix} +$$

$$\frac{1}{a^2 r_{11} + 2ar_{12} + r_{22}} \begin{bmatrix} (ar_{11} + r_{12})^2 & (ar_{12} + r_{22})(ar_{11} + r_{12}) \\ (ar_{12} + r_{22})(ar_{11} + r_{12}) & (ar_{12} + r_{22})^2 \end{bmatrix}$$

**13.9.14**

All these quantities are now generalized into even parts; that is, $\text{Re}\,z_{pq} = r_{pq} \rightarrow \text{Ev}\,z_{pq}$. Thus again each of the matrices above is in the form of Eq. 13.9.8. Note that the $a$ is arbitrary and may be used to some advantage. For example, if $[Z(s)]$ is minimum resistive at $j\omega_0$, that is, $r_{11}(\omega_0)r_{22}(\omega_0) - r_{12}^2(\omega_0) = 0$, we may select $a = -\,r_{12}(\omega_0)/r_{11}(\omega_0)$. Furthermore, since $a^2 r_{11} + 2ar_{12} + r_{22}$ may be written as $\dfrac{1}{r_{11}}\,(ar_{11} + r_{12})^2 + (r_{11}r_{22} - r_{12}^2)/r_{11}$, it follows that a choice of $a$ as above will force the cancellation of the factor $(s^2 + \omega_0^2)^2$ from each of the matrix terms.

## Example 13.9.1

Obtain the reduced matrices for $[Z(s)]$ by the two methods discussed above, where $[Z(s)]$ is given by

$$[Z(s)] = \begin{bmatrix} \dfrac{2s^2 + 4s + 5}{2s^2 + s + 1} & \dfrac{s^2 + 2s + 2}{2s^2 + s + 1} \\[2ex] \dfrac{s^2 + 2s + 2}{2s^2 + s + 1} & \dfrac{s^2 + s + 1}{2s^2 + s + 1} \end{bmatrix} \qquad \textbf{13.9.15}$$

## Solution

Ev $[Z(s)]$ is given by

$$[r] = \begin{bmatrix} \dfrac{4s^4 + 8s^2 + 5}{4s^4 + 3s^2 + 1} & \dfrac{2s^4 + 3s^2 + 2}{4s^4 + 3s^2 + 1} \\[2ex] \dfrac{2s^4 + 3s^2 + 2}{4s^4 + 3s^2 + 1} & \dfrac{2s^4 + 2s^2 + 1}{4s^4 + 3s^2 + 1} \end{bmatrix} \qquad \textbf{13.9.16}$$

and a preliminary check shows that

$$|r| = \frac{(s^2 + 1)^2(2s^2 + 1)^2}{(4s^4 + 3s^2 + 1)^2} \qquad \textbf{13.9.17}$$

Thus $|r|$ is zero at $s = \pm j$ and at $s = \pm j\dfrac{\sqrt{2}}{2}$. In accordance with the argument advanced above it may be advantageous to utilize the decomposition shown in Eq. 13.9.14. This will be done, but first we shall use the scheme of Eq. 13.9.5. Accordingly, we have

$$[r] = \begin{bmatrix} \dfrac{4s^4 + 8s^2 + 5}{4s^4 + 3s^2 + 1} & \dfrac{2s^4 + 3s^2 + 2}{4s^4 + 3s^2 + 1} \\[2ex] \dfrac{2s^4 + 3s^2 + 2}{4s^4 + 3s^2 + 1} & \dfrac{(2s^4 + 3s^2 + 2)^2}{(4s^4 + 8s^2 + 5)(4s^4 + 3s^2 + 1)} \end{bmatrix}$$

$$\qquad \textbf{13.9.18}$$

$$+ \begin{bmatrix} 0 & 0 \\[2ex] 0 & \dfrac{(s^2 + 1)^2(2s^2 + 1)^2}{(4s^4 + 3s^2 + 1)(4s^4 + 8s^2 + 5)} \end{bmatrix} \equiv [R_1^0] + [R_2^0]$$

If decomposition 13.9.14 is used, let $a = -\,r_{12}(\omega_0)/r_{11}(\omega_0) = -1(\omega_0 = 1)$. Thus

$$a^2 r_{11} + 2a r_{12} + r_{22} = r_{11} - 2r_{12} + r_{22} = \frac{2(s^2 + 1)^2}{4s^4 + 3s^2 + 1} \qquad \textbf{13.9.19}$$

Note that this term has the factor $(s^2 + 1)^2$ in its numerator. This factor is a factor of $|r|$ in Eq. 13.9.17. Constructing the rest of the terms of Eq. 13.9.14, we get

$$[r] = \begin{bmatrix} \dfrac{(2s^2 + 3)^2}{2(4s^4 + 3s^2 + 1)} & \dfrac{2s^2 + 3}{2(4s^4 + 3s^2 + 1)} \\ \dfrac{2s^2 + 3}{2(4s^4 + 3s^2 + 1)} & \dfrac{1}{2(4s^4 + 3s^2 + 1)} \end{bmatrix} \qquad \text{13.9.20}$$

$$+ \frac{(2s^2 + 1)^2}{2(4s^4 + 3s^2 + 1)} \begin{bmatrix} 1 & 1 \\ 1 & 1 \end{bmatrix} \equiv [R'_1{}^0] + [R'_2{}^0]$$

To appreciate the difference between the two decompositions, recall that the term "degree" (Section 13.2) was defined as the maximum degree of the numerator polynomial of the determinant $[Z(s)] + [A]$ for any constant matrix $[A]$. Accordingly, the degree of $[R_1{}^0]$ is 8 and that of $[R_2{}^0]$ is 8, whereas the degree of $[R'_1{}^0]$ is 4 and that of $[R'_2{}^0]$ is also 4.

## 13.10. THE GEWERTZ*-OONO† NETWORKS

The reduced matrices of the previous section (see Eq. 13.9.8) were discovered by Gewertz for 2 port. The results were extended to $n$ port by Oono and independently by Bayard.† Oono's procedure, independent of Gewertz, will be discussed in Chapter 15. Oono has devised another method which reduces to the Gewertz method for 2 port. The method realized each of the reduced matrices separately, and bears a strong similarity to the Miyata 1-port synthesis handled in Chapter 9. Thus, each of the reduced matrices is inverted repeatedly. After each inversion, a pole is removed at the origin and another one at infinity.

Synthesis by inversion of matrices as applied to the reduced matrices reduces to the realization by means of Stieljes continued fraction expansion in the 1-port case. The resulting network structure would be a ladder. Hence the corresponding $n$-port network shall be called a "ladder" network (Fig. 13.9).

In spite of the similarity to the one-port case, extreme caution must be exercised when the connections are made. Isolation transformers may be necessary lest the connections change the circuit values (see Section 10.4).

---

* Gewertz, C., "Synthesis of a Finite, Four-terminal Network from Its Prescribed Driving Point Functions and Transfer Function," *J. of Math. and Phys.* Vol. 12 (1932).

† Bayard, M., "Synthesis of $n$-Terminal Pair Networks," Proc. Symposium on Modern Network Synthesis, Polytechnic Institute of Brooklyn, 1952.

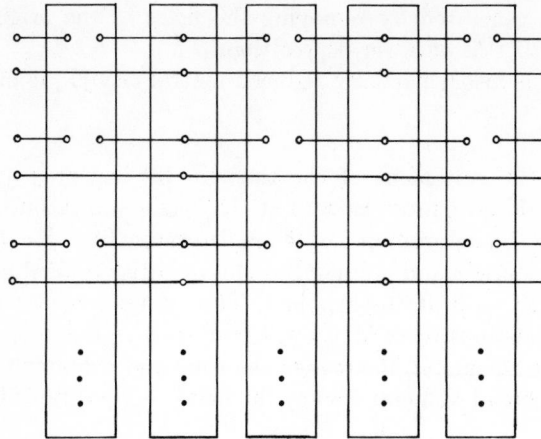

*Fig. 13.9. A "ladder" n-port network*

The process of repeated matrix inversions continues until the degree of the final matrix is reduced to zero. Hence the terminal impedance is resistive.

In the latter part of the section it will also be shown that partially reduced matrices may be synthesized in the same way. These matrices are similar to the reduced matrices in the sense that their *even-part* matrix is identically singular though not necessarily of rank 1.

The procedure is based on the following theorems

### Theorem 13.10.1

If det. $[Z(s)] \neq 0$, then the rank of Ev $[Z(s)]$ is the same as the rank of Ev $[Z(s)]^{-1}$.

*Proof*

$$2\text{Ev } [Z(s)] = [Z(s)] + [Z(-s)] = [Z(s)]([Y(s)] + [Y(-s)])[Z(-s)]$$
$$= [Z(s)] \,(2\text{Ev } [Y(s)])[Z(-s)] \qquad ([Y] = [Z]^{-1}) \qquad \text{13.10.1}$$

and since $[Z(s)]$ is not identically singular, it follows that the rank of Ev $[Y(s)]$ equals the rank of Ev $[Z(s)]$.

*Proof completed*

### Theorem 13.10.2*

Given a nonsingular $n$ by $n$ $PR$ matrix $[Z]$ without $j$ axis poles and such that Ev $[Z]$ is of rank $r$ $(r < n)$, then

(1). $[Z]^{-1}$ has poles at the origin and infinity whose residue matrices are of rank $n - r$.

---

* The proof is not the same as in Bayard's original paper.

(2). $[Y']$ generated by removing the poles at the origin and at infinity of $[Z]^{-1}$ is of lower degree than $[Z]$.

(3). $[Y']$ is also a partially reduced matrix (Ev $[Y]$ is of rank $r$).

*Proof*

(1). By the statement of the theorem $[Z]$ has no $j$ axis poles. Hence its odd part must be zero at the origin and at infinity. This means that the determinant of $[Z]$ is determined by $|$Ev $[Z]|$ at the points of the origin and infinity. But this quantity is identically zero; then det. $[Z] = 0$ at these points. Thus if we consider the point $s = 0$, diagonalization of $[Z(0)]$ will produce $n - r$ zero elements on the principal diagonal. Rearrange the rows and columns so that all the zero diagonal elements occupy the first $n - r$ positions $(|C| \neq 0)$.

$$[Z^1(0)] = [C]_t[Z(0)][C] = \begin{bmatrix} 0 & & & & & \\ & \cdot & & & & \\ & & 0 & & & \\ & & & \text{Ev } z_{(n-r+1)(n-r+1)}^{1}(0) & & \\ & & & & \cdot & \\ & & & & & \cdot \\ & & & & & \text{Ev } z_{nn}^{1}(0) \end{bmatrix}$$

**13.10.2**

Let $s = \epsilon \, (\epsilon \to 0^+)$ and apply the same congruence transformation to $[Z(s)]$. Ignoring higher-order terms in $\epsilon$ would give $z_{pq}^{1}(\epsilon) = $ Ev $z_{pq}^{1}(0) + \epsilon a_{pq}(0)$ where $\epsilon a_{pq}(0) = $ Od $z_{pq}^{1}(\epsilon)$. Hence

$$[Z^1(\epsilon)] = [C]_t[Z(\epsilon)][C] = [C]_t[Z(0)][C] + \epsilon \begin{bmatrix} [A_{11}(0)] & \vdots & [A_{12}(0)] \\ \hdashline [A_{21}(0)] & \vdots & [A_{22}(0)] \end{bmatrix}$$

**13.10.3**

Hence $\epsilon \, [A_{11}(0)]$ denotes

$$\epsilon[A_{11}(0)] \equiv \epsilon \begin{bmatrix} a_{11}(0) & \cdots & a_{1(n-r)}(0) \\ \cdot & & \cdot \\ \cdot & & \cdot \\ \cdot & & \cdot \\ a_{n-r,1}(0) & \cdots & a_{(n-r)(n-r)}(0) \end{bmatrix}$$

**13.10.4**

$$= \begin{bmatrix} z_{11}^{1}(\epsilon) & \cdots & z_{1(n-r)}^{1}(\epsilon) \\ \cdot & & \cdot \\ \cdot & & \cdot \\ z_{(n-r)1}^{1}(\epsilon) & \cdots & z_{(n-r)(n-r)}^{1}(\epsilon) \end{bmatrix}$$

Without any loss in generality it is assumed that the matrix $[C]$ in Eq. 13.10.3 also diagonalized the submatrix $[A_{11}(0)]$, since otherwise we may apply the nonsingular congruence transformation $[F]_t[Z^1(\epsilon)][F]$

$$[F] = \begin{bmatrix} [D] & \vdots & [0] \\ \cdots & \cdots & \cdots \\ [0] & \vdots & [I] \end{bmatrix} \quad ([I] \text{ is an } r \text{ by } r \text{ unit matrix})$$

to do the diagonalization. Note that this transformation does not change the nature of Eq. 13.10.2.

Clearly the diagonal matrix $[A_{11}(0)]$ may not be singular. This may be shown by assuming that it is singular and therefore one of its elements, say $a_{11}(0)$, is zero. But this term is obtained from $z_{11}{}^1(s)/s$ as $s$ approaches zero (see Eq. 13.10.4). However, $z_{11}{}^1(s)$ is prf and cannot have a higher order zero at the origin unless it is zero. If this term is zero, the real part condition $(\mathrm{Re}\ z_{11}{}^1(\epsilon)\ \mathrm{Re}\ z_{pp}{}^1(\epsilon) - (\mathrm{Re}\ z_{1p}{}^2(\epsilon))^2 > 0$ for $\epsilon > 0)$ requires that all the terms $z_{1p}{}^2(s)$ are zero. Then $[Z^1]$ and, therefore, $[Z]$ are identically singular which is not true. Thus $[A_{11}(0)]$ is not singular and $[A_{11}(0)]^{-1}$ exists.

Evaluating $[Z^1(\epsilon)]^{-1}$ from Eq. 13.10.3 gives

$$[Z^1(\epsilon)]^{-1} = \frac{1}{\epsilon} \begin{bmatrix} [A_{11}(0)]^{-1} & \vdots & [0] \\ \cdots & \cdots & \cdots \\ [0] & \vdots & [0] \end{bmatrix} \qquad \textbf{13.10.5}$$

which means that $[Z^1(s)]^{-1}$ has a pole at the origin and that

$$\begin{bmatrix} [A_{11}(0)]^{-1} & \vdots & [0] \\ \cdots & \cdots & \cdots \\ [0] & \vdots & [0] \end{bmatrix}$$

is the residue matrix. But $[Z(s)]^{-1} = [C][Z^1(s)]^{-1}[C]_t$. Hence it has a pole at the origin whose residue matrix is of rank $n - r$ (the rank of $[A_{11}(0)]^{-1}$). A similar proof also shows that $[Z(s)]^{-1}$ has a pole at infinity whose residue matrix is of rank $n - r$. This completes the proof of (1).

(2). Express $[Z]^{-1}$ as follows:

$$[Z]^{-1} = [Y'] + \frac{[K_0]}{s} + s[K_\infty] \qquad \textbf{13.10.6}$$

According to Theorems 13.3.1 and 13.3.2, we have

$$\text{degree } [Z] = \text{degree } [Z]^{-1} = \text{degree } [Y'] + \text{degree } \frac{[K_0]}{s} + \text{degree } s[K_\infty]$$

$$\textbf{13.10.7}$$

since each of the last two terms is at least unity the degree of $[Y']$

is at least 2 less than the degree of $[Z]$. This completes the proof of (2).

(3). We note that the rank of Ev $[Z]$ is the same as that of Ev $[Z]^{-1}$ (Theorem 13.10.1); furthermore, from Eq. 13.10.6 we see that Ev $[Z]^{-1}$ = Ev $[Y']$. Then the respective rank is also equal. This completes the proof of (3) and the theorem.

The two theorems discussed above show that the Gewertz-Oono synthesis procedure leads to physical networks. Each of the reduced matrices of the last section fits the categories of the theorems. Thus, repeated inversions of these matrices and removal of the ensuing poles at the origin and at infinity produce a converging sequence.

We pause to make the following observation:

Section 13.5 shows how to dispose of a singular matrix. Two-element-kind networks were handled in Section 13.8, and consequently (Theorem 13.8.1) it was shown how to remove $j$ axis poles. Sections 13.9 and 13.10 show how to split any $PR$ matrices without $j$ axis poles into a sum of reduced matrices and how these may be realized. It follows that since all $PR$ matrices which are nonsingular (identically) and have no $j$ axis poles may be realized through the reduced matrices, the general $n$-port existence theorem has been proved.

**Example 13.10.1**

Realize the impedance matrix

$$[Z(s)] = \begin{bmatrix} \dfrac{s+2}{s+1} & \dfrac{s+1}{s+2} \\[2mm] \dfrac{s+1}{s+2} & \dfrac{s+4}{s+3} \end{bmatrix} \tag{13.10.8}$$

Using the results of Section 13.9, we have

$$\text{Ev } [Z(s)] = \begin{bmatrix} r_{11} & r_{12} \\[1mm] r_{12} & \dfrac{r_{12}^2}{r_{11}} \end{bmatrix} + \begin{bmatrix} 0 & 0 \\[1mm] 0 & \dfrac{r_{11}r_{22} - r_{12}^2}{r_{11}} \end{bmatrix} \tag{13.10.9}$$

or more specifically

$$\text{Ev } [Z(s)] = \begin{bmatrix} \dfrac{s^2-2}{s^2-1} & \dfrac{s^2-2}{s^2-4} \\[2mm] \dfrac{s^2-2}{s^2-4} & \dfrac{s^4-3s^2+2}{s^4-8s^2+16} \end{bmatrix} + \begin{bmatrix} 0 & 0 \\[1mm] 0 & \dfrac{24s^4-135s^2+238}{(9-s^2)(s^4-8s^2+16)} \end{bmatrix}$$

$$= [R_1^0] + [R_2^0] \tag{13.10.10}$$

$[R_2{}^0]$ has only one nonzero element. It may be realized from its even part by any of the methods of Chapter 7 or 9 (specifically see Section 7.6). Hence the realization of this term will not be discussed here. The first term $[R_1{}^0]$ may also be synthesized directly from its even part by Oono's method which will be discussed in Chapter 15. Following the Gewertz-Oono method, however we must evaluate $[R_1]$ from its even part $([R_1{}^0])$. Recall that for $[R_1]$ to be realizable it must have only the *l.h.s* plane poles of $[R_1{}^0]$. Furthermore, note that $z'_{11}$ and $z'_{12}$ of $[R_1]$ are the same as those of $[Z(s)]$, since the respective even part was not tampered with. Thus, essentially, we have only to evaluate $z'_{22}$ from

$$\text{Ev } z'_{22} = \frac{s^4 - 3s^2 + 2}{s^4 - 8s^2 + 16} \qquad \textbf{13.10.11}$$

We shall start from its denominator. Selecting *r.h.s* plane poles can be done as follows:

$$m_2{}^2 - n_2{}^2 = s^4 - 8s^2 + 16 = (s^2 - 4)^2 = (s + 2)^2(s - 2)^2$$

$$= \underbrace{(s^2 + 4s + 4)}_{m_2 + n_2} \times \underbrace{(s^2 - 4s + 4)}_{m_2 - n_2}$$

Now assume that $z'_{22}$ is given by

$$z'_{22} = \frac{s^2 + as + b}{s^2 + 4s + 4} \qquad \textbf{13.10.12}$$

Computing the corresponding even part and comparing it with Eq. 13.10.11, we get

$$\text{Ev } z'_{22} = \frac{(s^2 + b)(s^2 + 4) - 4as^2}{s^4 - 8s^2 + 16} = \frac{s^4 - 3s^2 + 2}{s^4 - 8s^2 + 16} \qquad \textbf{13.10.13}$$

Hence $b = \dfrac{1}{2}$, $a = \dfrac{15}{8}$, and $[R_1]$ is as follows:

$$[R_1] = \begin{bmatrix} \dfrac{s + 2}{s + 1} & \dfrac{s + 1}{s + 2} \\[3mm] \dfrac{s + 1}{s + 2} & \dfrac{s^2 + \dfrac{15}{8} s + \dfrac{1}{2}}{s^2 + 4s + 4} \end{bmatrix} \qquad \textbf{13.10.14}$$

According to the Gewertz-Oono procedure, now $[R]^{-1}$ is obtained. $[R]^{-1}$ must have a pole at the origin and another at infinity. Thus

$$[R]^{-1} = \begin{bmatrix} \dfrac{8s^3 + 23s^2 + 19s + 4}{s(7s + 10)} & -\dfrac{8(s^3 + 4s^2 + 5s + 2)}{s(7s + 10)} \\[4mm] -\dfrac{8(s^3 + 4s^2 + 5s + 2)}{s(7s + 10)} & \dfrac{8(s^3 + 6s^2 + 12s + 8)}{s(7s + 10)} \end{bmatrix} \qquad \textbf{13.10.15}$$

Separating the poles at the origin and infinity, we get

$$[R]^{-1} = \frac{8}{7}s\begin{bmatrix} 1 & -1 \\ -1 & 1 \end{bmatrix} + \frac{2}{5s}\begin{bmatrix} 1 & -4 \\ -4 & 16 \end{bmatrix} + \frac{81}{35}\frac{5s+7}{7s+10}\begin{bmatrix} 1 & -\dfrac{16}{9} \\ -\dfrac{16}{9} & \dfrac{256}{81} \end{bmatrix}$$

$$[a] \qquad\qquad [b] \qquad\qquad\qquad [c]$$

**13.10.16**

Associating a network with each of these matrices, we get Figs. 13.10a-c.

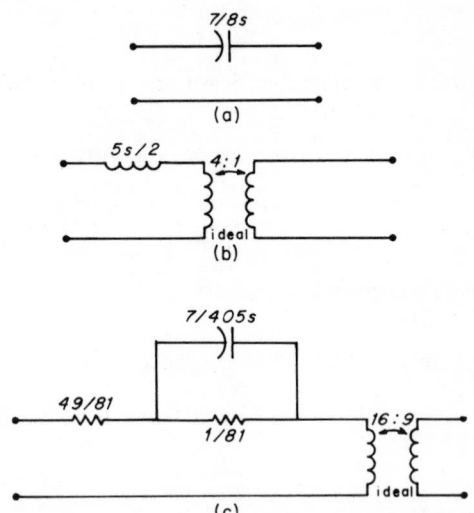

**Fig. 13.10. A realization of the matrices [a], [b], and [c] in Eq. 13.10.16**

The final network is obtained by connecting the three networks (Fig. 13.11) in parallel.

The basic philosophy of the Gewertz-Oono method is that of performing an *even*-part split such that each resulting member has an *even part* of rank 1. However, the split need not be that extreme. The two basic theorems of these sections are general and cover *PR* matrices which are also partially reduced; namely only $|\text{Ev }[Z]| = 0$. Recall that the reduced matrices were formed by splitting the diagonal of the diagonalized even-part matrix into $r$ parts, each of which contains only one diagonal member. Similarly, we may split this diagonal into two parts; the resulting matrices will be necessarily singular.

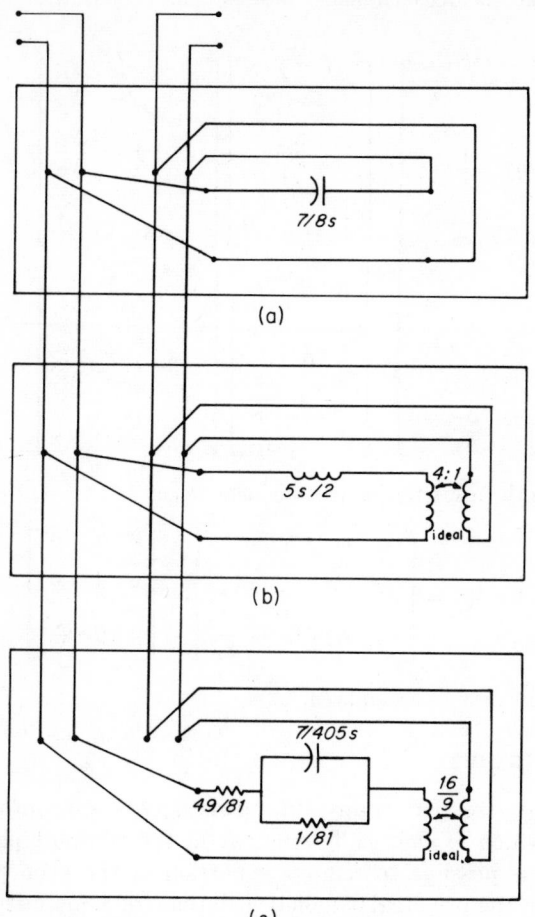

(a)

(b)

(c)

*Fig. 13.11. A realization of [R] in Eq. 13.10.16*

## Example 13.10.2

Split the even part of a 3 by 3 $PR$ matrix into two singular matrices.

### Solution

Rewriting Eq. 13.9.6, we get

$$
[r] = \begin{bmatrix} 1 & & \\ -\dfrac{r_{12}}{r_{11}} & 1 & \\ \dfrac{\Delta_{13}}{\Delta_{33}} & \dfrac{\Delta_{23}}{\Delta_{33}} & 1 \end{bmatrix}^{-1} \begin{bmatrix} r_{11} & & \\ & \dfrac{\Delta_{33}}{r_{11}} & \\ & & \dfrac{|r|}{\Delta_{33}} \end{bmatrix} \begin{bmatrix} 1 & -\dfrac{r_{12}}{r_{11}} & \dfrac{\Delta_{13}}{\Delta_{33}} \\ & 1 & \dfrac{\Delta_{23}}{\Delta_{33}} \\ & & 1 \end{bmatrix}^{-1}
$$

13.9.6
13.10.17

Now we split the diagonal matrix into two parts resulting in the following expansion:

$$[r] = \begin{bmatrix} 1 & & \\ -\dfrac{r_{12}}{r_{11}} & 1 & \\ \dfrac{\Delta_{13}}{\Delta_{33}} & \dfrac{\Delta_{23}}{\Delta_{33}} & 1 \end{bmatrix}^{-1} \begin{bmatrix} r_{11} & & \\ & \dfrac{\Delta_{33}}{r_{11}} & \\ & & 0 \end{bmatrix} \begin{bmatrix} 1 & -\dfrac{r_{12}}{r_{11}} & \dfrac{\Delta_{13}}{\Delta_{33}} \\ & 1 & \dfrac{\Delta_{23}}{\Delta_{33}} \\ & & 1 \end{bmatrix}^{-1} +$$

$$\begin{bmatrix} 1 & & \\ -\dfrac{r_{12}}{r_{11}} & 1 & \\ \dfrac{\Delta_{13}}{\Delta_{33}} & \dfrac{\Delta_{23}}{\Delta_{33}} & 1 \end{bmatrix}^{-1} \begin{bmatrix} 0 & & \\ & 0 & \\ & & \dfrac{|r|}{\Delta_{33}} \end{bmatrix} \begin{bmatrix} 1 & -\dfrac{r_{12}}{r_{11}} & \dfrac{\Delta_{13}}{\Delta_{33}} \\ & 1 & \dfrac{\Delta_{23}}{\Delta_{33}} \\ & & 1 \end{bmatrix}^{-1} \qquad \text{13.10.18}$$

Performing the respective matrix products we get

$$[r] = \begin{bmatrix} r_{11} & r_{12} & r_{13} \\ r_{12} & r_{22} & r_{23} \\ r_{13} & r_{23} & r_{33} - \dfrac{|r|}{\Delta_{33}} \end{bmatrix} + \begin{bmatrix} 0 & 0 & 0 \\ 0 & 0 & 0 \\ 0 & 0 & \dfrac{|r|}{\Delta_{33}} \end{bmatrix} \qquad \text{13.10.19}$$

These results may be generalized.

**Theorem 13.10.3**

(1). The even part of any $PR$ matrix may be split into two parts, each of which is identically singular in the complex plane.

(2). It is possible to remove a portion of the even part of one member of the principal diagonal such that the remainder is singular in the complex plane.

The first part is a mere statement of the fact that the diagonalized even-part matrix may be split in two; whereas the second part is a result of the fact that diagonalization by triangular matrices (discussed in Section 13.9) makes it possible to identify a matrix with only one element with one member of the diagonalized matrix (see the second matrix on the right of Eq. 13.10.19).

*Proof completed*

Synthesis by partially reduced matrices offers some distinct computational advantages. We note from Eq. 13.10.19 that only one member of the original even-part matrix is tampered with. Hence, in general, only one element has to be evaluated from its even part. For example, the complete form of Eq. 13.10.19 will be as follows:

$$[Z] = \begin{bmatrix} z_{11} & z_{12} & z_{13} \\ z_{12} & z_{22} & z_{23} \\ z_{13} & z_{23} & z_{33} - \mathrm{Ev}^{-1} \dfrac{|r|}{\Delta_{33}} \end{bmatrix} + \begin{bmatrix} 0 & 0 & 0 \\ 0 & 0 & 0 \\ 0 & 0 & \mathrm{Ev}^{-1} \dfrac{|r|}{\Delta_{33}} \end{bmatrix} \qquad 13.10.\mathbf{20}$$

where $\mathrm{Ev}^{-1} \dfrac{|r|}{\Delta_{33}}$ reads: "the positive real function whose even part is $\dfrac{|r|}{\Delta_{33}}$."

The first element on the right of Eq. 13.10.20 is a partially reduced matrix. Each inversion of this matrix will yield a removable pole at the origin and at infinity. Removing these poles will yield a reduced matrix of reduced degree.

## PROBLEMS

13.1. Show that if $[Z(s)]$ is $PR$ and $[A]$ is an $n$ by $n$ complex constant matrix, and if $[Z_1] = [A]_t[Z][\bar{A}]$, then

$$Z_1(s) = [N]_t[Z_1][\bar{N}] \qquad [N] = \text{column matrix}$$

is prf.

13.2. Use the results of the first problem and the fact that Ev $[Y] = [Z(s)]^{-1}$ (Ev $[Z])[Z(-s)]^{-1}$ to show that if $[Z]$ is $PR$ the real part of the associate admittance

$$\mathrm{Re}\ Y = [N]_t\ \mathrm{Re}\ [Y][\bar{N}]$$

is positive on the $j$ axis.

13.3. Show that if $[Z]$ has no poles at infinity and is given by $\lfloor P \rfloor / q \left( \dfrac{p_{ij}}{q} \text{ has no common factor} \right)$, then the degree of $[Z]$ is certainly smaller than the degree of $q^n$ if det. $[P]$ has common factors with $q$.

13.4. Find the degree of the following matrices:

(a). $\qquad \begin{bmatrix} \dfrac{s+3}{s+1} & \dfrac{s+2}{s+1} \\ \dfrac{s+2}{s+1} & \dfrac{2s+3}{s+1} \end{bmatrix} \qquad$ Answer $\delta = 2$

(b). $\qquad \begin{bmatrix} \dfrac{2s+3}{s+1} & \dfrac{s+2}{s+1} \\ \dfrac{s+2}{s+1} & \dfrac{3s+4}{s+1} \end{bmatrix} \qquad$ Answer $\delta = 1$

(c). 
$$\begin{bmatrix} \dfrac{s^2 + s + 2}{s^2 + s + 1} & \dfrac{2s^2 + 2s + 3}{s^2 + s + 1} \\[2ex] \dfrac{2s^2 + s + 3}{s^2 + s + 1} & \dfrac{3s^2 + 2s + 4}{s^2 + s + 1} \end{bmatrix}$$
Answer
$\delta = 2$

(d). 
$$\begin{bmatrix} \dfrac{s^2 + s + 3}{s^2 + s + 1} & \dfrac{2s^2 + 2s + 3}{s^2 + s + 1} \\[2ex] \dfrac{2s^2 + 2s + 3}{s^2 + s + 1} & \dfrac{3s^2 + s + 4}{s^2 + s + 1} \end{bmatrix}$$
Answer
$\delta = 4$

13.5. Realize the following impedance matrices by means of congruence transformers:

(a). 
$$[Z] = \begin{bmatrix} 8 & 1 & 2 \\ 1 & 4 & -1 \\ 2 & -1 & 1 \end{bmatrix}$$

(b). 
$$[Z] = s \begin{bmatrix} 11 & -2 & 4 \\ -2 & 4 & -2 \\ 4 & -2 & 2 \end{bmatrix}$$

(c). 
$$[Z] = \frac{1}{s} \begin{bmatrix} 5 & -2 & 2 \\ -2 & 1 & -1 \\ 2 & -1 & 1 \end{bmatrix}$$

13.6. Construct a congruence transformer for a 4 by 4 impedance matrix

13.7. Synthesize the following function by means of one congruence transformer:

$$[Z(s)] = \begin{bmatrix} s + 1 & 2s & 5s - 1 \\ 2s & 5s + 2 & 13s + 6 \\ 5s - 1 & 13s + 6 & 34s + 19 \end{bmatrix}$$

Hint: $[Z(s)]$ is singular.

13.8. If det. Re $[Z(j\omega)]$ is zero at $s = j\omega_0$, show that it is possible to select $[N]$ in

$$Z = [N]_t [Z][N]$$

$[N]$ = real column matrix

such that Re $Z(j\omega_0) = 0$.

13.9. Realize the impedance functions of Problem 13.5 by means of the techniques of diagonalization of matrices.

13.10. Synthesize the following impedance matrix:

$$[Z(s)] = \begin{bmatrix} \dfrac{s(10s^2 + 19)}{(s^2 + 1)(s^2 + 2)} & -\dfrac{s(3s^2 + 7)}{(s^2 + 1)(s^2 + 2)} & \dfrac{4s}{s^2 + 1} \\[3mm] -\dfrac{s(3s^2 + 7)}{(s^2 + 1)(s^2 + 2)} & \dfrac{s(3s^2 + 5)}{(s^2 + 1)(s^2 + 2)} & -\dfrac{2s}{s^2 + 1} \\[3mm] \dfrac{4s}{s^2 + 1} & -\dfrac{2s}{s^2 + 1} & \dfrac{2s}{s^2 + 1} \end{bmatrix}$$

13.11. (1). Obtain the reduced matrices of the following impedance matrix

$$[Z(s)] = \begin{bmatrix} \dfrac{6s^2 + 4s + 4}{s^2 + s + 2} & \dfrac{2s^2 - s + 1}{s^2 + s + 2} \\[3mm] \dfrac{2s^2 - s + 1}{s^2 + s + 2} & \dfrac{6s^2 + 6s + 2}{s^2 + s + 2} \end{bmatrix}$$

by the two methods mentioned in Section 13.9. (2). Discuss the degree of each of the resulting matrices. (3). Realize $[Z(s)]$ by means of realizing the two reduced matrices of the second method.

Hint: det. Ev $[Z(j)] = 0$.

13.12. If $[Z(s)]$ is $PR$ and det. Ev $[Z(s)]$ is not zero on the $j$ axis, show that it is possible to make it zero by removing a finite amount of resistance from any one of the ports.

Hint: You may find Theorem 13.10.3 (part 2) useful.

13.13. Show that the degree of the inductance matrix $s[K]$ is the same as its rank.

Hint: Use congruence transformation.

## FURTHER READING

A RELATED BOOK

13.1. Cauer, W., "Synthesis of Linear Communication Networks," Chap. 4, McGraw-Hill Book Co., Inc., New York, 1958.

ONE-ELEMENT-KIND NETWORK PAPERS

13.2. Braun, D. P., and Tokad, Y., "On the Synthesis of $R$ Networks," *IRE Trans. on Circuit Theory*, Vol. CT-8, pp. 31–39, March (1961).

13.3. Biorci, G., and Civalleri, P. P., "On the Synthesis of Resistive $n$-Port Networks," *IRE Trans. on Circuit Theory*, Vol. CT-8, pp. 22–28, March (1961).

13.4. Biorci, G., and Civalleri, P. P., "Conditions for the Realizability of a Conductance Matrix," *IRE Trans. on Circuit Theory*, Vol. CT-9, pp. 312–317, Sept. (1961).

13.5. Cederbaum, I., "Paramount Matrices and Synthesis of Resistive $n$-Ports," *IRE Trans. on Circuit Theory*, Vol. CT-8, pp. 28–31, March (1961).

13.6. Cederbaum, I., "Topological Considerations in the Realization of Resistive n-Port Networks," *IRE Trans. on Circuit Theory*, Vol. CT-9, pp. 324–329, Sept. (1961).

13.7. Guillemin, E. A., "On the Realization of an $n^{th}$-Order $G$ Matrix," *IRE Trans. on Circuit Theory*, Vol. CT-9, pp. 318–323, Sept. (1961).

RELATED PAPERS

13.8. Belevitch, V., "On the Brune Process for n-Ports," *IRE Trans. on Circuit Theory*, Vol. CT-7, pp. 280–296, Sept. (1960).

13.9. Leroy, R., "Sur la Synthese des Reseaux Passifs a $n$ Paires de Bornes," *Cables and Transmission*, Vol. 4, pp. 234–247 (1950).

13.10. McMillan, B., "Introduction to Formal Realizability Theory," *The Bell System Technical Journal*, Vol. 31, pp. 217–299 and 541–600 (1950).

13.11. Oono, Y., "Synthesis of a Finite 2n-Terminal Network by a Group of Networks Each of Which Contains Only One Ohmic Resistance," *Journal of Math. and Phys.*, Vol. 29, pp. 13–26 (1950).

13.12. Oono, Y, "Synthesis of a Finite 2n-Terminal Network as the Extension of Brune's Theory of Two Terminal Network Synthesis," *J. of Inst. Elec. Comm. Engrs. of Japan*, Vol. 31, pp. 163–181, Aug. (1948) (in Japanese).

13.13. Tellegen, B. D. H., "Synthesis of 2n-Poles by Networks Containing the Minimum Number of Elements," *J. of Math and Phys.*, Vol. 32, pp. 1–18 (1953).

# Synthesis Through Matrix—Richards' Transformation*

# CHAPTER 14

## INTRODUCTION 14.1

The ideas of Chapters 5 and 8 are extended to $n$-port synthesis. In Chapter 5 we saw that any driving point impedance function can be realized in terms of a 2-port lossless section (denoted as a buffer) that terminates in a 1-port network having a built in arbitrary constant. In Chapter 8 it was demonstrated that the same can be done with two arbitrary constants. However, in the corresponding $n$-port development the buffer becomes a $2n$-port lossless section. The realization of $[Z(s)]$ in terms of a $2n$-port buffer terminated in an $n$-port network is denoted as "cascade synthesis." Noncascade types of synthesis are also presented, although they require a substantial increase in the number of elements.

In Section 14.2 a mathematical expansion is developed for $[Z(s)]$ in terms of two other functions with a built in arbitrary constant $k$; this constant may be utilized directly for synthesis purposes if det. Ev $[Z(s)]$ has a real axis zero. Moreover, in Section 14.3 it is shown that this expansion has a cascade physical representation. A parallel development with two arbitrary constants is carried out in Section 14.4. Furthermore, the terminal impedance matrix $[\zeta]$

---

* The material in this chapter is based on work by E. K. Boyce, R. J. Duffin H. J. Nain, and D. Hazony. An important part of this material is being prepared for publication as a joint paper, "Synthesis of $n$-Port Networks by a Matrix Richards' Theorem." The abstract of the paper is presented in the Notices of the American Mathematical Society, Vol. 9, No. 4, issue No. 62, p. 290, Aug., 1962. See also Report No. 35, U.S.A.F. Cambridge Research Center Contract No. AF 19(604)–3997.

may be reduced in degree if the constants are selected as roots of det. Ev $[Z(s)]$.

A direct extension of the Bott-Duffin synthesis is developed in Section 14.6. The situation is similar to the 1-port problem in a sense that special tailoring of the impedance function is required *a priori*.

## 14.2. EXTENDING THE BOTT-DUFFIN SYNTHESIS TO *n*-PORT

Recall that it was shown in Chapter 5 that any driving point impedance function may be expressed as a sum of two other driving point impedance functions which were defined in terms of an arbitrary constant $k$ $(k > 0)$, namely

$$Z(s) = k\,\frac{kZ(s) - sZ(k)}{k^2 - s^2} + s\,\frac{kZ(k) - sZ(s)}{k^2 - s^2}$$

5.3.2<br>14.2.1

This process may be readily extended to *n*-port synthesis by replacing the $Z$'s with $PR$ matrices. The development begins with the expression

$$[Z(s)] = k\,\frac{k[Z(s)] - s[Z(k)]}{k^2 - s^2} + s\,\frac{k[Z(k)] - s[Z(s)]}{k^2 - s^2}$$

14.2.2

$$\equiv [Z_1(s)] + [Z_2(s)]$$

For our subsequent needs, we consider the following theorem.

### Theorem 14.2.1

If $[Z(s)]$ is a $PR$ symmetric matrix, then $[Z_1(s)]$ and $[Z_2(s)]$ as defined in Eq. 14.2.2 are also $PR$ matrices for all positive $k$.

### Proof

Construct the associate impedance functions for the even parts of $[Z_1(s)]$ and $[Z_2(s)]$:

$$\text{Ev } Z_1(s) \equiv [N]_t \text{ Ev } [Z_1(s)][N] = \frac{k^2}{k^2 - s^2}\,[N]_t \text{ Ev } [Z(s)][N]$$

14.2.3

$$\text{Ev } Z_2(s) \equiv [N]_t \text{ Ev } [Z_2(s)][N] = \frac{-s^2}{k^2 - s^2}\,[N]_t \text{ Ev } [Z(s)][N]$$

where $[N]$ = real column matrix. On the $j$ axis, these driving point impedance functions are, within a positive multiplier, the same as the associate impedance function for $[Z(s)]$. Hence

$$\text{Re } Z_1(s) \geq 0$$
$$\text{Re } Z_2(s) \geq 0$$

14.2.4

on the $j$ axis if $\text{Re } Z(s) \geq 0$ (that is, if $[Z(s)]$ is $PR$). Now it is observed that both $k[Z(s)] - s[Z(k)]$ and $k[Z(k)] - s[Z(s)]$ may not have any $r.h.s$ plane poles. Hence the only possible $r.h.s$ plane pole of $[Z_1(s)]$ or $[Z_2(s)]$ is at $k = s$, but this pole cancels with a built-in zero of the respective numerator. Thus $[Z_1(s)]$ and $[Z_2(s)]$ are analytic in the $r.h.s$ plane. Furthermore, these matrices have $j$ axis poles only if $[Z(s)]$ has them, which means that all $j$ axis poles of the respective associate impedance functions ($Z_1(s)$ and $Z_2(s)$) are simple with positive residues. Therefore we may apply the minimum real-part theorem to show that Eqs. 14.2.4 extend into the $r.h.s$ plane as follows:

$$\text{Re } Z_1(s) > 0 \qquad \text{Re } s > 0$$

and                                                                                          14.2.5

$$\text{Re } Z_2(s) > 0 \qquad \text{Re } s > 0$$

This means that the associate impedance functions of $[Z_1(s)]$ and $[Z_2(s)]$ are prf, and therefore the respective matrices are $PR$.

*Proof completed*

Now assume that $[Z(s)]$ is not identically singular. We may proceed by paralleling the development for 1 port. Note that $[Z_1(s)]$ goes to zero for $s$ approaching infinity (at least) like $\frac{k}{s}[Z(k)]$. This means that we may remove this zero. The term "at least" is inserted to show that this may not be the whole zero if $[Z(s)]$ itself has a pole at the infinity.* Let $[\zeta]^{-1}$ denote

$$[\zeta]^{-1} = [Z_1(s)]^{-1} - \frac{s}{k}[Z(k)]^{-1} \qquad 14.2.6$$

which is $PR$ since it is formed by removal of a pole on the $j$ axis. $[\zeta]^{-1}$ may also be written as follows:

$$[\zeta]^{-1} = [Z_1(s)]^{-1}\big([Z(k)] - \frac{s}{k}[Z_1(s)]\big)[Z(k)]^{-1}$$

$$= \frac{k}{s}[Z_1(s)]^{-1}[Z_2(s)][Z(k)]^{-1} \qquad 14.2.7$$

which may be put into a more recognizable form

$$[\zeta]^{-1} = \big(k[Z(s)] - s[Z(k)]\big)^{-1}\big(k[Z(k)] - s[Z(s)]\big)[Z(k)]^{-1} \qquad 14.2.8$$

which reduces to Richards' theorem [within a multiplying constant $Z(k)$] for the 1-port case.

---

* To avoid this difficulty we shall assume that $[Z(s)]$ does not have a pole at infinity, since these are easy to identify and remove. Furthermore, a possible pole at the origin is also removed.

Similarly, we may define the matrix $[\eta]$ given by

$$[\eta] = [Z_2(s)]^{-1} - \frac{k}{s}[Z(k)]^{-1}$$

$$= [Z_2(s)]^{-1}\left([Z(k)] - \frac{k}{s}[Z_2(s)]\right)[Z(k)]^{-1}$$

14.2.9

which simplifies into

$$[\eta] = \frac{s}{k}[Z_2(s)]^{-1}[Z_1(s)][Z(k)]^{-1} = \frac{s}{k}\left([Z_1(s)]^{-1}[Z_2(s)]\right)^{-1}[Z(k)]^{-1}$$

$$= [Z(k)]^{-1}[\zeta][Z(k)]^{-1} \qquad \text{(by 14.2.7)}$$

14.2.10

Thus, if $[Z(s)]$ is assumed reciprocal, $[\zeta]$ and $[\eta]$ are obtained from each other by a congruence transformation. $[Z(s)]$ in Eq. 14.2.2 may be expressed as follows:

$$[Z(s)] = [Z_1(s)] + [Z_2(s)]$$

$$= \left([\zeta]^{-1} + \frac{s}{k}[Z(k)]^{-1}\right)^{-1} + \left([\eta] + \frac{k}{s}[Z(k)]^{-1}\right)^{-1}$$

$$= \left([\zeta]^{-1} + \frac{s}{k}[Z(k)]^{-1}\right)^{-1} + \left([Z(k)]^{-1}[\zeta][Z(k)]^{-1} + \frac{k}{s}[Z(k)]^{-1}\right)^{-1}$$

14.2.11

Corresponding to this decomposition we now construct the Bott-Duffin network for an $n$-port (Fig. 14.1).

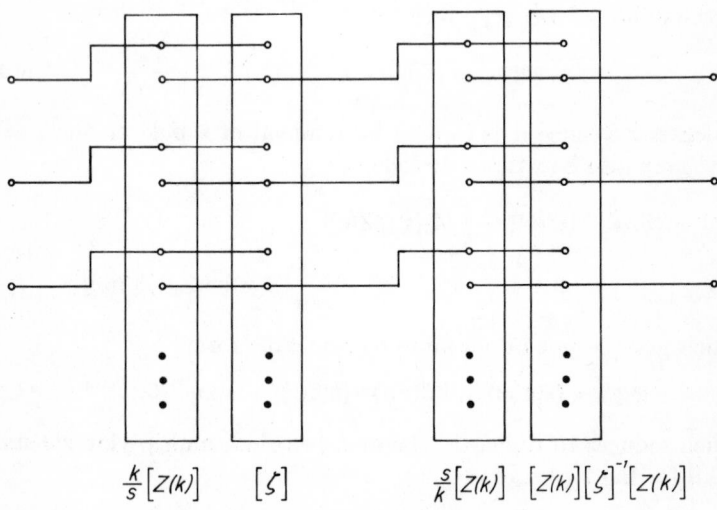

Fig. 14.1. The Bott-Duffin n-port network

We pause now to make the following observations:

## Lemma 14.2.1

If $[Z(k)]$ is nonsingular, the degrees of $[\zeta]$ and of $[\eta]$ are equal to or smaller than the degree of $[Z(s)]$.

### Proof

In order to determine the degree of $[\zeta]$, we shall use Eq. 14.2.6. It will suffice to prove the Lemma for $[\zeta]$ alone, since the degree of $[\zeta]$ equals that of $[\eta]$ by Eq. 14.2.10. Utilizing McMillan's Theorems (Theorems 13.3.1 and 13.3.2), we have

$$\delta[\zeta] = \delta[\zeta]^{-1} = \delta\left( [Z_1(s)]^{-1} - \frac{s}{k} [Z(k)]^{-1} \right) = \delta[Z_1(s)] - n \qquad \textbf{14.2.12}$$

Here the degree of $s[Z(k)]^{-1}$ is $n$ since det. $s[Z(k)]^{-1} = s^n |Z(k)|^{-1}$. Note that each entry of $[Z_1(s)]$ (Eq. 14.2.2) has the factor $(s - k)$ cancelling the same factor in the denominator. Furthermore, each entry of $[Z_1(s)]$ has the pole $(s + k)$ in addition to all the poles of $[Z(s)]$. Then

$$\delta[Z_1(s)] \leqslant n + \delta[Z(s)] \qquad \textbf{14.2.13}$$

The inequality stems from the fact that det. $(k[Z(s)] - s[Z(k)])$ may also have factors in common with $(s + k)$. Putting the value of $\delta[Z_1(s)]$ from Eq. 14.2.13 in Eq. 14.2.12 gives the proof.

Thus we have succeeded in expressing $[Z(s)]$ in terms of two other $PR$ matrices of equal degree and with a built-in arbitrary constant $k$. Can this constant be utilized to some advantage? The answer is yes.

A Bott-Duffin-like synthesis procedure for $n$ port will be developed in Section 14.6. Here we shall attempt to use the constant $k$ to reduce the degree of $[\zeta]$.

It is noted from Eq. 14.2.6 (also see Lemma 14.2.1) that the degree of $[\zeta]$ is governed by the degree of $[Z_1(s)]$. Hence it will be attempted to utilize $k$ to reduce the degree of $[Z_1(s)]$. This will be achieved if we can generate new common factors in the numerator and denominator of

$$\det. [Z_1(s)] = k^n \det. \frac{k[Z(s)] - s[Z(k)]}{k^2 - s^2} \qquad \textbf{14.2.14}$$

The word "new" denotes the fact that some common factors might be present for any arbitrary $k$. One such factor is, for example, $(s - k)$. It may be that a new common factor $(s + k_0)$ will be generated for $k = k_0$, but then the numerator of Eq. 14.2.14 must be zero for $s = -k_0$. Thus

$$k_0{}^n \text{ det. } k_0[Z(s)] - s[Z(k_0)]|_{s=-k_0} = k_0{}^n \text{ det. } k_0[Z(-k_0)] + k_0[Z(k_0)]$$

$$= 2^n k_0{}^{2n} \text{ det. Ev } [Z(k_0)] = 0 \quad \textbf{14.2.15}$$

Thus if $k$ is to reduce the degree of $[\zeta]$, it should be selected from the roots of det. Ev $[Z(s)]$. Clearly if num. det. Ev $[Z(s)]$ has the zero $(s - k_0)^r$, and if $r \leq n$, then the degree of $[\zeta]$ will be $r$ less than the degree of $[Z(s)]$. Note that Eq. 14.2.15 reduces to Ev $Z(k_0) = 0$ in the 1-port case. If, however, det. Ev $[Z(s)]$ has only complex roots, it is then necessary to generate $[\zeta]$ with two arbitrary constants $a$ and $b$ which may be complex conjugates. This will be done in Section 14.4. In the following section a cascade representation is developed for the Bott-Duffin $n$-port network.

## 14.3. COMMENTS ON CASCADE SYNTHESIS

In 1-port synthesis problems, the term cascade implied a 2-port buffer network terminated in a driving point impedance. Similarly, the term "cascade" in $n$ port implies a $2n$-port buffer network terminated in an $n$-port network as in Fig. 14.2.

The equations of the $2n$-port network are as follows:

$$
\begin{bmatrix} E_1 \\ \cdot \\ \cdot \\ \cdot \\ E_n \\ \hline E_{n+1} \\ \cdot \\ \cdot \\ \cdot \\ E_{2n} \end{bmatrix}
=
\left[ \begin{array}{ccc|ccc}
z_{11} & \cdots & z_{1n} & z_{1(n+1)} & \cdots & z_{1(2n)} \\
\cdot & \cdot & \cdot & \cdot & \cdot & \cdot \\
\cdot & \cdot & \cdot & \cdot & \cdot & \cdot \\
\cdot & \cdot & \cdot & \cdot & \cdot & \cdot \\
z_{n1} & \cdots & z_{nn} & z_{n(n+1)} & \cdots & z_{n(2n)} \\
\hline
z_{(n+1)(1)} & \cdots & z_{(n+1)(n)} & z_{(n+1)(n+1)} & \cdots & z_{(n+1)(2n)} \\
\cdot & \cdot & \cdot & \cdot & \cdot & \cdot \\
\cdot & \cdot & \cdot & \cdot & \cdot & \cdot \\
\cdot & \cdot & \cdot & \cdot & \cdot & \cdot \\
z_{(2n)(1)} & \cdots & z_{(2n)(n)} & z_{(2n)(n+1)} & \cdots & z_{(2n)(2n)}
\end{array} \right]
\begin{bmatrix} I_1 \\ \cdot \\ \cdot \\ \cdot \\ I_n \\ \hline I_{n+1} \\ \cdot \\ \cdot \\ \cdot \\ I_{2n} \end{bmatrix}
\quad \textbf{14.3.1}
$$

It is convenient to partition the matrices of Eq. 14.3.1 in accordance with the broken lines and thus define the following quantities:

$$[E_1] = [Z_{11}][I_1] + [Z_{12}][I_2]$$

$$[E_2] = [Z_{21}][I_1] + [Z_{22}][I_2] \quad \textbf{14.3.2}$$

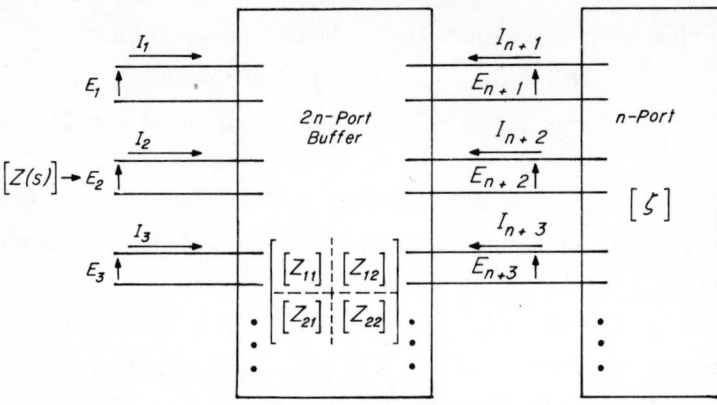

**Fig. 14.2. A cascade n-port network**

where

$$
[E_1] = \begin{bmatrix} E_1 \\ \cdot \\ \cdot \\ \cdot \\ E_n \end{bmatrix}, \quad [E_2] = \begin{bmatrix} E_{n+1} \\ \cdot \\ \cdot \\ \cdot \\ E_{2n} \end{bmatrix}, \quad [I_1] = \begin{bmatrix} I_1 \\ \cdot \\ \cdot \\ \cdot \\ I_n \end{bmatrix}, \quad [I_2] = \begin{bmatrix} I_{n+1} \\ \cdot \\ \cdot \\ \cdot \\ I_{2n} \end{bmatrix}
$$

and

$$
[Z_{11}] = \begin{bmatrix} z_{11} & \cdots & z_{1n} \\ \cdot & \cdot & \cdot \\ \cdot & \cdot & \cdot \\ z_{n1} & \cdots & z_{nn} \end{bmatrix}, \quad [Z_{12}] = \begin{bmatrix} z_{1(n+1)} & \cdots & z_{1(2n)} \\ \cdot & \cdot & \cdot \\ \cdot & \cdot & \cdot \\ z_{n(n+1)} & \cdots & z_{n(2n)} \end{bmatrix}
$$

$$
[Z_{21}] = \begin{bmatrix} z_{(n+1)1} & \cdots & z_{(n+1)n} \\ \cdot & \cdot & \cdot \\ \cdot & \cdot & \cdot \\ z_{(2n)1} & \cdots & z_{(2n)n} \end{bmatrix}, \quad [Z_{22}] = \begin{bmatrix} z_{(n+1)(n+1)} & \cdots & z_{(n+1)2n} \\ \cdot & \cdot & \cdot \\ \cdot & \cdot & \cdot \\ z_{2n(n+1)} & \cdots & z_{(2n)(2n)} \end{bmatrix}
$$

In accordance with these definitions and allowing for the polarity of the currents into the $n$ port $[\zeta]$, we may write:

$$
[E_2] = -[\zeta][I_2] \qquad\qquad \textbf{14.3.3}
$$

Substitution of this value into the second of Eqs. 14.3.2 yields

$$
[E_2] = -[\zeta][I_2] = [Z_{21}][I_1] + [Z_{22}][I_2] \qquad\qquad \textbf{14.3.4}
$$

This may be solved for $[I_2]$ to give

$$
[I_2] = -([\zeta] + [Z_{22}])^{-1}[Z_{21}][I_1] \qquad\qquad \textbf{14.3.5}
$$

Use this result to eliminate $[I_2]$ in the first of Eqs. 14.3.2:

$$[E_1] = ([Z_{11}] - [Z_{12}]([\zeta] + [Z_{22}])^{-1}[Z_{21}])[I_1]$$

Identifying terms of this equation with the terms of Fig. 14.2, we see that

$$[Z] = [Z_{11}] - [Z_{12}]([\zeta] + [Z_{22}])^{-1}[Z_{21}] \qquad \textbf{14.3.6}$$

By matrix manipulation this expression can be put into the following form:

$$[Z] = [Z_{12}]([\zeta] + [Z_{22}])^{-1}([\zeta] + [Z_{22}] - [Z_{21}][Z_{11}]^{-1}[Z_{12}])[Z_{12}]^{-1}[Z_{11}] \qquad \textbf{14.3.7}$$

This equation will be used now to find the $n$-port cascade equivalence of the Bott-Duffin network. Recall that the Bott-Duffin 1-port network can be put into networks of the following cascade forms. (See Example 6.3.1.)

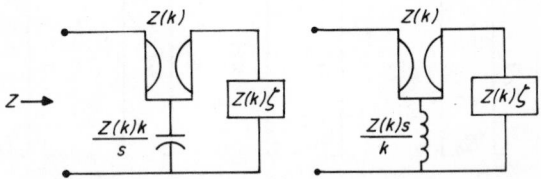

**Fig. 14.3. Two equivalent networks of the Bott-Duffin 1-port network**

To find the corresponding $n$-port networks we first have to obtain a solution for $[Z(s)]$ from Eq. 14.2.6 in a form comparable to that in Eq. 14.3.7.

$$[\zeta]^{-1} = -\left(\frac{s}{k}[Z(k)]^{-1} - [Z_1(s)]^{-1}\right)$$

$$= -[Z(k)]^{-1}\left(\frac{s}{k}[Z_1(s)] - [Z(k)]\right)[Z_1(s)]^{-1} \qquad \begin{matrix} \textbf{14.2.6} \\ \textbf{14.3.8} \end{matrix}$$

$$= \frac{k}{s}[Z(k)]^{-1}[Z_2(s)][Z_1(s)]^{-1}$$

Hence $[\zeta]$ is given by

$$[\zeta] = (k[Z(s)] - s[Z(k)]) \times (k[Z(k)] - s[Z(s)])^{-1}[Z(k)] \qquad \textbf{14.3.9}$$

Solving for $[Z(s)]$, we get

$$[Z(s)] = \frac{k}{s}[Z(k)]\left([\zeta] + \frac{k}{s}[Z(k)]\right)^{-1}\left([\zeta] + \frac{s}{k}[Z(k)]\right) \qquad \textbf{14.3.10}$$

This expression also may be written in the following form:

$$[Z(s)] = \left(\frac{k+s}{s}\right)[Z(k)]\left([\zeta] + \frac{k}{s}[Z(k)]\right)^{-1} \times$$

$$\left([\zeta] + \frac{k}{s}[Z(k)] - \frac{k-s}{s}[Z(k)]\frac{s}{k}[Z(k)]^{-1} \times \frac{k+s}{s}[Z(k)]\right) \times$$

$$\left(\frac{s}{s+k}\right)[Z(k)]^{-1}\frac{k}{s}[Z(k)] \quad \textbf{14.3.11}$$

It is identical with Eq. 14.3.7 if we set

$$[Z_{11}] = [Z_{22}] = \frac{k}{s}[Z(k)]; \ [Z_{12}] = \frac{k+s}{s}[Z(k)]$$

$$\textbf{14.3.12}$$

$$\text{and } [Z_{21}] = \frac{k-s}{s}[Z(k)]$$

Thus the final impedance matrix of the $2n$-port buffer associated with the synthesis may be decomposed into two parts as follows (*Case A*):

$$\begin{matrix}[Z]\\2n\text{-port}\end{matrix} = \frac{k}{s}\begin{bmatrix}[Z(k)] & \vdots & [Z(k)]\\ \hdashline [Z(k)] & \vdots & [Z(k)]\end{bmatrix} + \begin{bmatrix}[0] & \vdots & [Z(k)]\\ \hdashline -[Z(k)] & \vdots & [0]\end{bmatrix} \quad \textbf{14.3.13}$$

Thus the $2n$-port buffer is a lossless device. The first matrix on the right of Eq. 14.3.13 represents a capacitive network, whereas the second represents a gyrator network. It may be recognized that the method of determination of the buffer is a Darlingtonlike process of *Case A*. To arrive at *Case B*, rewrite Eq. 14.3.10 once more. (Recall that $[\eta] = [Z(k)]^{-1}[\zeta][Z(k)]^{-1}$):

$$[Z(s)] = \frac{s}{k}[Z(k)]\left([\eta]^{-1} + \frac{s}{k}[Z(k)]\right)^{-1}\left([\eta]^{-1} + \frac{k}{s}[Z(k)]\right) \quad \textbf{14.3.14}$$

Now cast this expression into the form of Eq. 14.3.11:

$$[Z(s)] = \frac{s+k}{k}[Z(k)]\left([\eta]^{-1} + \frac{s}{k}[Z(k)]\right)^{-1} \times$$

$$\left([\eta]^{-1} + \frac{s}{k}[Z(k)] - \frac{s-k}{k}[Z(k)]\frac{k}{s}[Z(k)]^{-1}\right. \quad \textbf{14.3.15}$$

$$\left.\times \frac{s+k}{k}[Z(k)]\right)\frac{k}{s+k}[Z(k)]^{-1}\frac{s}{k}[Z(k)]$$

By comparing this expression with Eq. 14.3.7 we conclude that

$$[Z_{11}] = [Z_{22}] = \frac{s}{k}[Z(k)]; \ \ [Z_{12}] = \frac{s+k}{k}[Z(k)];$$

$$\textbf{14.3.16}$$

$$[Z_{21}] = \frac{s-k}{k}[Z(k)] \text{ and the termination is } [\eta]^{-1}.$$

The resulting $2n$-port matrix can also be decomposed as follows (*Case B*):

$$\begin{matrix}[Z]\\2n\text{ port}\end{matrix} = \frac{s}{k}\begin{bmatrix}[Z(k)] & [Z(k)]\\ \hdashline [Z(k)] & [Z(k)]\end{bmatrix} + \begin{bmatrix}[0] & [Z(k)]\\ \hdashline -[Z(k)] & [0]\end{bmatrix} \qquad \text{14.3.17}$$

It is noted that the first matrix is an inductive matrix, whereas the second is a gyrator matrix. The corresponding networks are given in Fig. 14.4.

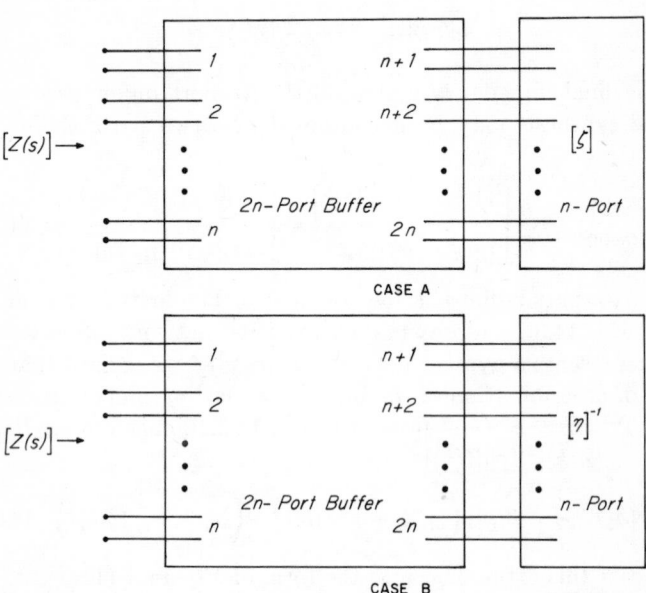

Fig. 14.4. Two equivalent networks of the Bott-Duffin n-port network

The buffer networks are made up of two one-element-kind networks. The reciprocal matrices may be realized by diagonalization of matrices (Section 13.7). However there is a great deal of symmetry involved which permits considerable simplification. For example, the $n$-port network in Fig. 14.5 is modified readily into a $2n$ port which has the required impedance matrix for the one-element-kind matrix of Fig. 14.4.

Similarly the nonreciprocal matrix may have a fairly simplified configuration of gyrators. In Fig. 14.6 a realization of the 2 by 2 matrix is shown.

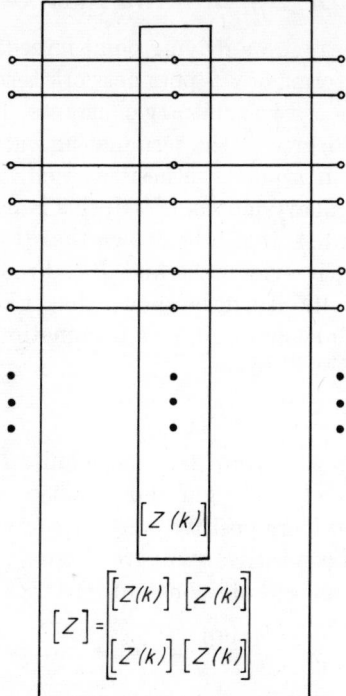

**Fig. 14.5.  A 2n-port network element**

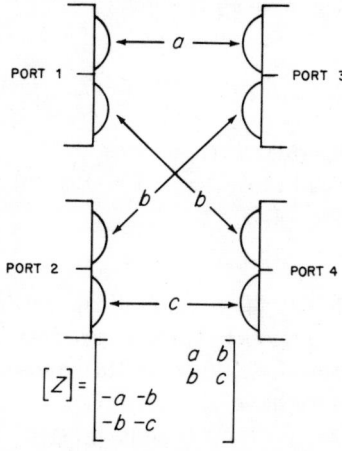

**Fig. 14.6.  A nonreciprocal network corresponding to the nonreciprocal matrix appearing in Eqs. 14.3.13 and 14.3.17**

## 14.4. CASCADE SYNTHESIS OF $[Z(s)]$ WITH TWO ARBITRARY CONSTANTS

Recall that in Chapter 8 a driving point impedance function $Z(s)$ was represented in terms of a 2-port network terminated in $\zeta$, with $\zeta$ expressed in terms of two arbitrary constants. These were utilized later to reduce the degree of the terminating impedance. The same approach is useful in $n$-port synthesis as well. We shall begin by introducing the auxilliary matrix $[F(s)]$; this is parallel to the function $F(s)$ of Section 8.4. It will be shown that $[F(s)]$ is a symmetric $PR$ matrix if $[Z(s)]$ is symmetric and $PR$. From this function $[\zeta]$ will be defined. Finally, it will be shown that it is possible to determine a lossless buffer such that upon a termination with $[\zeta]$ a cascade realization for $[Z(s)]$ will result.

**Theorem 14.4.1**

Given: (I). $[Z(s)]$ is a symmetric nonsingular $PR$ matrix without poles at the origin and infinity.

(II). $a$ and $b$ are positive constants or complex conjugates with a positive real part (Re $a \geq 0$ and Re $b \geq 0$)

(III). $[A]$ and $[B]$ are constant matrices given by

$$[A] = \frac{a[Z(b)] - b[Z(a)]}{a^2 - b^2} \text{ and } [B] = \frac{a[Z(a)] - b[Z(b)]}{a^2 - b^2}$$

Then: Part (1). $[A]$, $[B]$ and $[F(s)]$ given by

$$[F(s)] = \frac{s}{s^4 - s^2(a^2 + b^2) + a^2 b^2} (ab[A] + s^2[B] - s[Z(s)]) \quad \text{14.4.1}$$

and $[\zeta]$ given by

$$[\zeta] \equiv [F(s)]^{-1} - \frac{ab}{s}[A]^{-1} - s[B]^{-1} \quad \text{14.4.2}$$

are symmetric nonsingular $PR$ matrices.

Part (2). The special case $a = -b = j\omega_0$ and det. Ev $[Z(s)] =$ is taken up in Section 14.5.

*Proof of Part (1)*

By setting $a = \bar{b} = x + jy$ and $[Z(a)] = \overline{[Z(b)]} = [U] + j[V]$ we can see that the matrices $[A]$ and $[B]$ are real. They are also finite since $a - b$ is a factor of $a[Z(b)] - b[Z(a)]$ and of $a[Z(a)] - b[Z(b)]$ Hence on the $j$ axis we have

$$\text{Re } [F(j\omega)] = \frac{\omega^2 \text{ Re } [Z(j\omega)]}{\omega^4 + \omega^2(a^2 + b^2) + a^2 b^2}$$

Constructing $F(s)$ the associate impedance function for $[F(s)]$ on the $j$ axis, it is noted that

$$\text{Re } F(j\omega) = [N]_t \text{ Re } [F(j\omega)][N]$$

$$= \frac{\omega^2}{\omega^4 + \omega^2(a^2 + b^2) + a^2b^2} [N]_t \text{ Re } [Z(j\omega)][N] \quad \textbf{14.4.3}$$

where $[N]$ is a real column matrix. But the associate impedance function for $[Z(s)]$ is $Z(s)$. Thus

$$\text{Re } Z(j\omega) = [N]_t \text{ Re } [Z(j\omega)][N]$$

It follows that $\text{Re } F(j\omega) \geq 0$ if $\text{Re } Z(j\omega) \geq 0$. Also, note that $[F(s)]$ is so chosen that its only two $r.h.s$ plane poles are cancelled by two of its zeros. Thus it is analytic in the $r.h.s$ plane. Hence, to complete the proof of the theorem, we have to show that all $j$ axis poles of $F(s)$ are simple and have positive residues. This is done by showing that $F(s)$ has poles on the $j$ axis only if $Z(s)$ has them. Thus these poles must be simple, and it follows that the respective residues are positive. Now we may apply the minimum real-part theorem to show that $\text{Re } F(s) > 0$ throughout the $r.h.s$ plane if $\text{Re } F(j\omega) \geq 0$. Then $F(s)$ is prf and therefore $[F(s)]$ is $PR$.

Now we shall show that $[F(s)]$, $[A]$, and $[B]$ are not singular. Suppose that $[F(s)]$ is singular, then we may find a real, nonsingular, constant matrix $[C]$ such that at least one member on the principal diagonal of $[F'(s)] = [C]_t[F(s)][C]$ is zero (Theorem 13.5.1 p. 259). Let this member be

$$f'_{pp} = \left(\frac{ab}{s} a'_{pp} + sb'_{pp} - z'_{pp}\right)/(s^2 - a^2 - b^2 + a^2b^2/s^2) \quad \textbf{14.4.4}$$

But $[Z(s)]$ is not singular and therefore $z'_{pp}$ may not be zero. Then $f'_{pp}$ may be zero only if $\frac{ab}{s} a'_{pp} + sb'_{pp} = z'_{pp}$. This is excluded by postulate (I). Then $[F(s)]$ is not singular and therefore all the members of $[F(s)]^{-1}$ are finite. Observe that $ab[A]^{-1}$ and $[B]^{-1}$ are residue matrices at poles at the origin and infinity of $[F(s)]^{-1}$. Thus they are finite resistive $PR$ matrices.

It is noted that $[\zeta]$ is a $PR$ matrix since it is generated by the removal of $j$ axis poles of a $PR$ matrix (see Eq. 14.4.2).

To complete the proof of the theorem we still have to show that $[\zeta]$ is nonsingular. Since all the quantities involved are nonsingular we may express $[\zeta]$ as follows:

$$[\zeta] = [F(s)]^{-1}\left[\left(\frac{ab}{s}[A]^{-1} + s[B]^{-1}\right)^{-1} - [F(s)]\right]\left(\frac{ab}{s}[A]^{-1} + s[B]^{-1}\right)$$

the term inside the heavy brackets is in the form of $[F(s)]$ in Eq. 14.4.1. Hence following the arguments advanced above it is nonsingular. It follows that $[\zeta]$ is nonsingular. Note further that Eqs. 14.4.1 and 14.4.2 do not alter the symmetry of the matrices.

*Proof completed*

Substituting the value of $[F(s)]$ as given in Eq. 14.4.1 into Eq. 14.4.2 and bringing the terms of Eq. 14.4.2 into a common inverse matrix, we get

$$[\zeta] = (ab[A] + s^2[B] - s[Z(s)])^{-1}$$
$$\{(ab[A]^{-1} + s^2[B]^{-1})[Z(s)] - s(ab([A]^{-1}[B] \quad \text{14.4.5}$$
$$+ [B]^{-1}[A]) + (a^2 + b^2)[I])\}$$

where $[I]$ is the unit matrix.

It is important to note that $[\zeta]$ is of the same degree (or less) as $[Z(s)]$. This may be shown by noting that the apparent degree of $[F(s)]$ is that of $[Z(s)]$ plus $4n$ (assuming that $[Z(s)]$ is not identically singular). But two zeros of the numerator will cancel two of the poles (i.e., zeros at $a$ and $b$) which reduces the degree by $2n$. Furthermore, from Eq. 14.4.2 it is seen that $[\zeta]$ is at least $2n$ less in degree than $[F(s)]$. It then follows that $[\zeta]$ is of the same degree or less as $[Z(s)]$. (For more details on degree computation, see Lemma 14.2.1). Now we shall show that the degree of $[\zeta]$ will be at least 2 less than the degree of $[Z(s)]$ if det. Ev $[Z(a)] = $ det. Ev $[Z(b)] = 0$.

## Theorem 14.4.2

The degree of $[\zeta]$ is at least 1 less than that of $[Z(s)]$ if det. Ev $[Z(a)] = 0$. It is at least 2 less than that of $[Z(s)]$ if also det. Ev $[Z(b)] = 0$.

### Proof

The degree of $[\zeta]$ is $2n$ less than the degree of $[F(s)]$ (Eq. 14.4.2). In turn, the degree of $[F(s)]$ is determined by the degree of the numerator of det. Ev $[(s)]$ after common factors have been cancelled:

$$\text{det. } [F(s)] = \frac{s^n \text{ det. } (ab[A] + s^2[B] - s[Z(s)])}{(s^2 - a^2)^n(s^2 - b^2)^n} \quad \text{14.4.6}$$

Clearly the factor $(s - a)^n(s - b)^n$ is cancelled out. At least one additional factor $(s + a)$ will be cancelled if

$$\text{det. } ab[A] + s^2[B] - s[Z(s)])|_{s=-a} = 0 \quad \text{14.4.7}$$

Then

$$\text{det. } ab[A] + a^2[B] + a[Z(-a)] = 0 \quad \text{14.4.8}$$

Substituting values for $[A]$ and $[B]$ as given in Theorem 14.4.1, we get

$$\text{det. Ev } [Z(a)] = 0 \quad \text{14.4.9}$$

The same result is obtained when $s = -b$. This completes the proof of the theorem.

It is noted from Eqs. 14.4.6 and 14.4.8 that the degree of $[F(s)]$ will be reduced further if det. Ev $[Z(a)]$ has higher-order zeros at $s = -a$. This explains the phrase "at least" in the statement of the theorem. Clearly if it is desired to have $[\zeta]$ less in degree than $[Z(s)]$, $a$ and $b$ must be selected from the roots of det. Ev $[Z(s)] = 0$.

Now we wish to follow the pattern of the last section to show that $[Z(s)]$ may be realized in terms of a specified lossless buffer terminated in $[\zeta]$. Toward this end, Eq. 14.4.5 is solved for $[Z(s)]$ yielding

$$[Z(s)] = \left(\frac{ab}{s}[A]^{-1} + s[B]^{-1} + [\zeta]\right)^{-1}$$

$$\left\{[\zeta]\left(\frac{ab}{s}[A] + s[B]\right) + ab([A]^{-1}[B]\right. \qquad \textbf{14.4.10}$$

$$\left. + [B]^{-1}[A]) + (a^2 + b^2)[I]\right\}$$

This equation is to be compared with Eq. 14.3.7 describing the impedance matrix of a $2n$-port network terminated with an $n$-port network $[\zeta]$. We shall modify Eq. 14.3.7 as follows:

$$[Z(s)] = [Z_{12}]([\zeta] + [Z_{22}])^{-1}([\zeta][Z_{12}]^{-1}[Z_{11}]$$

$$+ [Z_{22}][Z_{12}]^{-1}[Z_{11}] - [Z_{21}]) \quad \textbf{14.4.11}$$

Comparing terms in Eqs. 14.4.10 and 14.4.11, we note that $[Z_{22}]$ must be given by

$$[Z_{22}] = \frac{ab}{s}[A]^{-1} + s[B]^{-1} \qquad \textbf{14.4.12}$$

Furthermore, Eq. 14.4.10 does not seem to have a matrix multiplier corresponding to $[Z_{12}]$ which is the first multiplier on the right of Eq. 14.4.11. This suggests that $[Z_{12}]$ must be a scalar times a unit matrix. We try

$$[Z_{12}] = \frac{(s + a)(s + b)}{s}[I] \qquad \textbf{14.4.13}$$

Inserting the values of $[Z_{22}]$ and $[Z_{12}]$ as given in Eqs. 14.4.12, 13 into their respective places in Eq. 14.4.11 and proceeding to compare the rest of the terms with the corresponding terms of Eq. 14.4.10, we get

$$[Z_{11}] = \frac{ab}{s}[A] + s[B] \qquad \textbf{14.4.14}$$

and

$$[Z_{21}] = \frac{(s - a)(s - b)}{s}[I] \qquad \textbf{14.4.15}$$

The information expressed in Eqs. 14.4.12 through 14.4.15 describes a $2n$-port network. Putting these matrices together we have

$$\begin{matrix} [Z] \\ 2n \text{ port} \end{matrix} = \begin{bmatrix} [Z_{11}] & \vdots & [Z_{12}] \\ \cdots & \vdots & \cdots \\ [Z_{21}] & \vdots & [Z_{22}] \end{bmatrix} = \frac{ab}{s} \begin{bmatrix} [A] & \vdots & [I] \\ \cdots & \vdots & \cdots \\ [I] & \vdots & [A]^{-1} \end{bmatrix} +$$

$$s \begin{bmatrix} [B] & \vdots & [I] \\ \cdots & \vdots & \cdots \\ [I] & \vdots & [B]^{-1} \end{bmatrix} + (a+b) \begin{bmatrix} [0] & \vdots & [I] \\ \cdots & \vdots & \cdots \\ -[I] & \vdots & [0] \end{bmatrix} \qquad \textbf{14.4.16}$$

Thus, upon realizing a network for the impedance matrix of Eq. 14.4.16, we would achieve one of the primary goals of this section, namely a $2n$-port buffer such that upon terminating with $[\zeta]$ a cascade realization for $[Z(s)]$ would result.

Starting with the nonreciprocal part of Eq. 14.4.16, note that it may be realized in terms of $n$ identical gyrators (Fig. 14.7). Perhaps it would be useful to define this element as the $2n$-port gyrator.

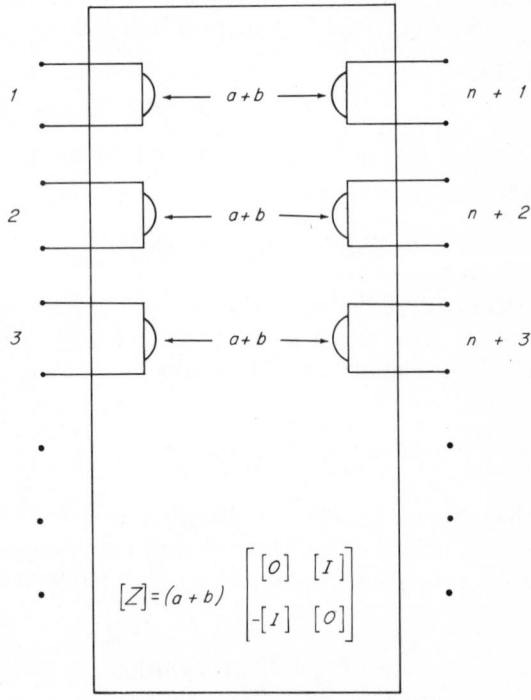

**Fig. 14.7.  A 2n-port gyrator**

Each of the reciprocal matrices of Eq. 14.4.16 represents a one-element kind network. It may be realized by any of the techniques of

the previous chapter (see Sections 13.5 or 13.7), although we have
not shown that each of these matrices is realizable. Because the two
reciprocal matrices are similar to each other, it will suffice to show
that the middle one (the inductance matrix) is realizable.

### Corollary 14.4.1

The inductance matrix (divided by $s$) (representing a residue
matrix at infinity) is $PR$ resistive.

### Proof

It must be shown that the matrix

$$[K_\infty] = \begin{bmatrix} [B] & [I] \\ [I] & [B]^{-1} \end{bmatrix} \qquad \textbf{14.4.17}$$

is $PR$ resistive.

Construct the associate impedance function of this matrix:

$$K_\infty = [N]_t[K_\infty][N] \qquad \textbf{14.4.18}$$

where $[N]$ = real column matrix. Thus it is necessary to show that
$K_\infty$ is a resistance for all values of $[N]$. Rewrite Eq. 14.4.18 as follows:

$$K_\infty = [N]_t \begin{bmatrix} [B] & [I] \\ [I] & [B]^{-1} \end{bmatrix} [N] \qquad \textbf{14.4.19a}$$

which is written in the form

$$K_\infty = [N]_t \begin{bmatrix} [I] & [0] \\ -[B]^{-1} & [I] \end{bmatrix}^{-1} \begin{bmatrix} [I] & [0] \\ -[B]^{-1} & [I] \end{bmatrix}$$

$$\times \begin{bmatrix} [B] & [I] \\ [I] & [B]^{-1} \end{bmatrix} \begin{bmatrix} [I] & -[B]^{-1} \\ [0] & [I] \end{bmatrix} \begin{bmatrix} [I] & -[B]^{-1} \\ [0] & [I] \end{bmatrix}^{-1} [N] \qquad \textbf{14.4.19b}$$

This becomes, by combining the middle group of three matrices

$$K_\infty = [N]_t \begin{bmatrix} [I] & [0] \\ [B]^{-1} & [I] \end{bmatrix} \begin{bmatrix} [B] & [0] \\ [0] & [0] \end{bmatrix} \begin{bmatrix} [I] & [B]^{-1} \\ [0] & [I] \end{bmatrix} [N] \qquad \textbf{14.4.19c}$$

which is written as

$$K_\infty = [N']_t \begin{bmatrix} [B] & [0] \\ [0] & [0] \end{bmatrix} [N'] \qquad \textbf{14.4.19d}$$

where $[N'] = \begin{bmatrix} [I] & [B]^{-1} \\ [0] & [I] \end{bmatrix} [N]$    = real column matrix.

It is seen that $K_\infty$ is also the associate impedance of the matrix

$$\begin{bmatrix} [B] & [0] \\ [0] & [0] \end{bmatrix} \qquad \textbf{14.4.20}$$

and since this matrix is resistive (by Theorem 14.4.1), $K_\infty$ is a resistance; then $[K_\infty] = PR$ resistive.

*Proof completed*

## Example 14.4.1

Realize the following 2 by 2 impedance matrix.

$$[Z(s)] = \begin{bmatrix} \dfrac{10s^2 + 14s + 13}{s^2 + s + 1} & \dfrac{4s^2 + 8s + 7}{s^2 + s + 1} \\[4mm] \dfrac{4s^2 + 8s + 7}{s^2 + s + 1} & \dfrac{2s^2 + 6s + 5}{s^2 + s + 1} \end{bmatrix} \qquad \textbf{14.4.21}$$

*Solution*

$[Z(s)]$ will be realized in terms of a 4-port lossless network terminated in a 2-port network. According to Theorem 14.4.2, the terminal impedance matrix will be 2 less in degree than $[Z(s)]$ if $a$ and $b$ of Eq. 14.4.2 are roots of det. Ev $[Z(s)] = 0$. Here

$$\text{det. Ev } [Z(s)] = \frac{4(s^4 + 4)}{s^4 + s^2 + 1} \qquad \textbf{14.4.22}$$

Hence $a = \bar{b} = 1 + j$. Computing $[A]$ and $[B]$ as given in Theorem 14.4.1, we get

$$[A] = \frac{1}{2}\begin{bmatrix} 13 & 7 \\ 7 & 5 \end{bmatrix}, \quad [B] = \frac{1}{2}\begin{bmatrix} 11 & 5 \\ 5 & 3 \end{bmatrix}$$

It is expedient to compute $[\zeta]$ from Eq. 14.4.2

$$[\zeta] = [F(s)]^{-1} - \frac{ab}{s}[A]^{-1} - s[B]^{-1} \qquad \textbf{14.4.2}$$

whereas $[F(s)]$ is defined in Eq. 14.4.1:

$$[F(s)] = s\frac{ab[A] + s^2[B] - s[Z(s)]}{s^4 - s^2(a^2 + b^2) + a^2b^2} \qquad \textbf{14.4.1}$$

Here $[F(s)]$ becomes

$$[F(s)] = \frac{s}{2(s^2 + 2s + 2)(s^2 + s + 1)} \qquad \textbf{14.4.23}$$

$$\times \begin{bmatrix} 11s^2 + 13s + 13 & 5s^2 + 7s + 7 \\ 5s^2 + 7s + 7 & 3s^2 + 5s + 5 \end{bmatrix}$$

Finally, an evaluation of $[\zeta]$ yields

$$[\zeta] = \frac{1}{4}\begin{bmatrix} 5 & -7 \\ -7 & 13 \end{bmatrix} \qquad \textbf{14.4.24}$$

The impedance matrix of the lossless 4-port network is given in Eq. 14.4.16. We proceed to decompose the inductive and capacitive parts by diagonalization of matrices (Section 13.7) as follows:

$$
\begin{aligned}
\frac{[Z(s)]}{\text{4-port}} = {} & \frac{1}{13s}\begin{bmatrix} 169 & 91 & 26 & 0 \\ 91 & 49 & 14 & 0 \\ 26 & 14 & 4 & 0 \\ 0 & 0 & 0 & 0 \end{bmatrix} + \frac{1}{26s}\begin{bmatrix} 0 & 0 & 0 & 0 \\ 0 & 16 & -28 & 52 \\ 0 & -28 & 49 & -91 \\ 0 & 52 & -91 & 169 \end{bmatrix} \\[2mm]
& + \frac{s}{22}\begin{bmatrix} 121 & 55 & 22 & 0 \\ 55 & 25 & 10 & 0 \\ 22 & 10 & 4 & 0 \\ 0 & 0 & 0 & 0 \end{bmatrix} + \frac{s}{11}\begin{bmatrix} 0 & 0 & 0 & 0 \\ 0 & 1 & -5 & 11 \\ 0 & -5 & 25 & -55 \\ 0 & 11 & -55 & 121 \end{bmatrix} \\[2mm]
& + 2\begin{bmatrix} 0 & 0 & 1 & 0 \\ 0 & 0 & 0 & 1 \\ -1 & 0 & 0 & 0 \\ 0 & -1 & 0 & 0 \end{bmatrix}
\end{aligned}
$$

14.4.25

The final network is given in Fig. 14.8.

## THE "BRUNE" n-PORT NETWORK 14.5

In the previous section it was shown that any $n$-port $PR$ impedance matrix $[Z(s)]$ may be realized in terms of a $2n$-port lossless network terminated in $[\mathfrak{z}]$ which is an $n$-port network of reduced degree. The impedance function of the associated $2n$-port network is given in Eq. 14.4.16:

$$
\begin{aligned}
\frac{[Z]}{\text{2n-port}} = {} & \frac{ab}{s}\left[\begin{array}{c|c} [A] & [I] \\ \hline [I] & [A]^{-1} \end{array}\right] + s\left[\begin{array}{c|c} [B] & [I] \\ \hline [I] & [B]^{-1} \end{array}\right] \\[2mm]
& + (a+b)\left[\begin{array}{c|c} [0] & [I] \\ \hline -[I] & [0] \end{array}\right]
\end{aligned}
$$

14.4.16
14.5.1

It is seen that the nonreciprocal term vanishes if $a = -b$. Furthermore, since the quantities above are realizable only if $a$ and $b$ are in the $r.h.p.$, it follows that if $a = -b$ then $a = j\omega_0$. However setting $a$ and $b$ to be imaginary leads to several difficulties. Specifically, the quantities $[A]$, $[B]$, and $[F(s)]$ as defined in the previous section become infinite. Nevertheless, the termination $[\mathfrak{z}]$ is completely defined in terms of the inverses of these matrices if det. Ev $[Z(j\omega_0)]$ $= 0$. Recall that this special case in 1-port (Section 8.5) was called the Brune network.

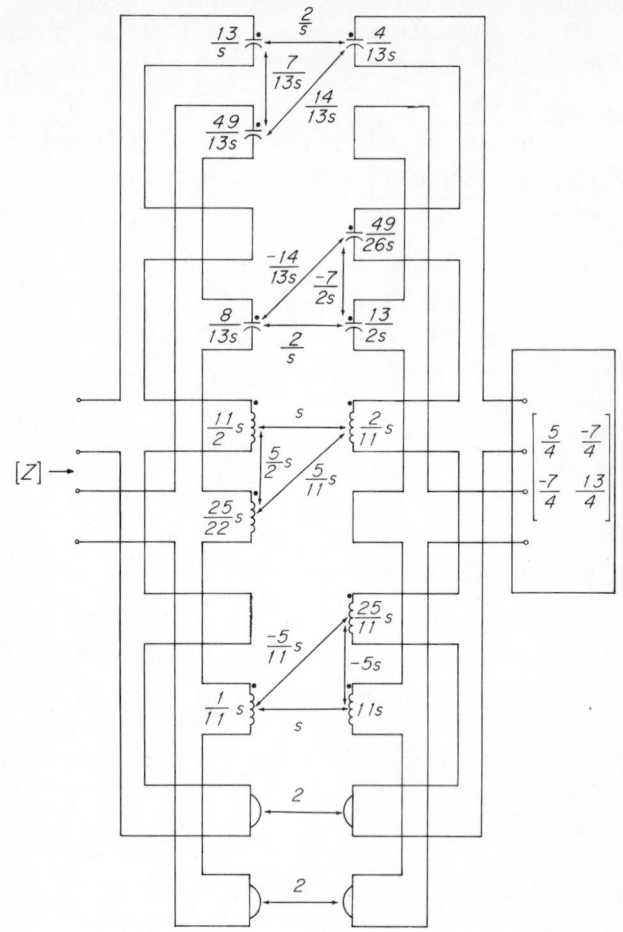

**Fig. 14.8. A realization of $[Z(s)]$ in Example 14.4.1**

### Theorem 14.5.1

[Theorem 14.4.1, Part (2)]

If (I). $[Z(s)]$ is a symmetric, nonsingular, $PR$ matrix without poles or zeros on the $j$ axis and det. Ev $[Z(j\omega_0)] = 0$

(II). $a = \bar{b} = j\omega_0$

(III). $[A]^{-1}$ and $[B]^{-1}$ are constant matrices given by

$$[A]^{-1} = (a^2 - b^2)(a[Z(b)] - b[Z(a)])^{-1}$$
$$[B]^{-1} = (a^2 - b^2)(a[Z(a)] - b[Z(b)])^{-1}$$

14.5.2

then $[F(s)]^{-1}$ defined as

$$[F(s)]^{-1} = \frac{s^4 - s^2(a^2 + b^2) + a^2b^2}{s} \cdot (ab[A] + s^2[B] - s[Z(s)])^{-1} \quad \textbf{14.5.3}$$

and $[\zeta]$ given by

$$= [F(s)]^{-1} - \frac{ab}{s}[A]^{-1} - s[B]^{-1} \qquad \textbf{14.5.4}$$

exist and are $PR$.

Note that $\dfrac{ab}{s}[A]^{-1}$ and $s[B]^{-1}$ are the poles at zero and infinity of $[F(s)]^{-1}$. Hence if $[F(s)]^{-1}$ exists and is $PR$, so is $[\zeta]$. Of course if $[A]$ and $[B]$ (not their inverses) exist, then $[F(s)]$ also exists (Theorem 14.4.1) and is $PR$.

The proof of Theorem 14.5.1 will be given in two parts. In Part 1 (see Appendix B for this proof) it will be shown that $[A]^{-1}$, $[B]^{-1}$, and $[F(s)]^{-1}$ exist. In Part 2 below, it will be shown that $[F(s)]^{-1}$ is $PR$ and hence $[\zeta]$ is $PR$.

### Proof that $[F(s)]^{-1}$ is PR: Part 2

By Theorem 14.4.1 $[F(s)]^{-1}$ is $PR$ if $a = j\omega_0 + \epsilon$, $b = -j\omega_0 + \epsilon(\epsilon > 0)$. Construct the associate impedance function $[N]_t[F(s)]^{-1}[N]$ ($[N]$ = real column matrix). Let $s = s_0$ in the $r.h.p.$ Then for all $\epsilon > 0$, Re $[N]_t[F(s_0)]^{-1}[N]$ is a rational function of $\epsilon$. Furthermore, since $[F(s_0)]^{-1}$ exists—Lemma B.4—as $\epsilon$ approaches zero, the function $[N]_t[F(s_0)]^{-1}[N]$ is a continuous function of $\epsilon$ in the neighborhood of $\epsilon = 0$ (i.e., it does not have a pole at $\epsilon = 0$). But a continuous function cannot change sign without going through a zero; then if $\epsilon = 0$, Re $[N]_t[F(s_0)]^{-1}[N]$ is nonnegative for any point $s_0$ in the $r.h.p.$ Then $[F(s)]^{-1}$ is $PR$.

*Proof completed*

The fact that $[A]$ blows up but $[A]^{-1}$ is finite leads to realization in terms of ideal transformers. For example, one may define the impedance matrix of a 2 by 2 ideal transformer as the inverse of a singular matrix. True ideal transformers are not practical because of the infinite (value) elements needed. Thus, perhaps, a satisfactory synthesis of the Brune problem would be through the addition of a series resistor to one or more of the ports such that det. Re $[Z(j\omega_0)] > 0$. Now the synthesis would yield finite elements. Reducing the value of each of the added resistors will increase the value of some of the elements of the network. However only the $2n$-port buffer would require ideal transformers per cycle.

## 14.6. BOTT-DUFFIN $n$-PORT SYNTHESIS CONTINUED

The Bott-Duffin $n$-port synthesis was introduced in Section 14.2. It was shown that any symmetric $PR$ matrix can be decomposed into two symmetric $PR$ matrices with a "built-in" arbitrary constant $k$. Recall that $k$ may be used for synthesis purposes if det. Ev $[Z(s)]$ has zeros on the real axis. This approach would lead to zero cancellation schemes. In this section, however, the Bott-Duffin original scheme of utilizing the $k$ to force a pole or a zero on the $j$ axis is extended. Recall further that in the one-port case it was necessary to tailor the impedance function by first stripping off all the $j$ axis poles and zeros and the minimum resistance. Correspondingly, here $[Z(s)]$ may have no poles and zeros on the $j$ axis in addition to the fact that it is a minimum resistance in the absolute sense. By this, we mean:

### Definition 14.6.1

$[Z(s)]$ is a minimum resistance function in the absolute sense if Re $[Z(s)]$ = $[0]$ for some point on the $j$ axis.

The words "absolute sense" emphasize the difference between this case and that of det. Ev $[Z(s)] = 0$ for some point on the $j$ axis. In the latter case, the function is said to be minimum resistive (in the usual sense). Of course, a function which is minimum resistive in the absolute sense is also minimum resistive in the usual sense.

In what follows, we shall show that if $[Z(s)]$ satisfies the requirements of absolute minimum resistance and of no poles or zeros at the origin or infinity, then it is possible to utilize $k$ to produce a pole or a zero on the $j$ axis. In the following section a procedure will be shown for tailoring $[Z(s)]$ into the form of a minimum resistance in the absolute sense. For the sake of convenience, several key formulas of Section 14.2 are reproduced now:

$$[Z(s)] = [Z_1(s)] + [Z_2(s)]$$

$$[Z_1(s)] = k \frac{k[Z(s)] - s[Z(k)]}{k^2 - s^2} \qquad \begin{matrix} 14.2.2 \\ 14.6.1 \end{matrix}$$

$$[Z_2(s)] = s \frac{k[Z(k)] - s[Z(s)]}{k^2 - s^2}$$

$$[\zeta]^{-1} = [Z_1(s)]^{-1} - \frac{s}{k}[Z(k)]^{-1} \qquad \begin{matrix} 14.2.6 \\ 14.6.2 \end{matrix}$$

$$[\eta] = [Z_2(s)]^{-1} - \frac{k}{s}[Z(k)]^{-1} \qquad \begin{matrix} 14.2.9 \\ 14.6.3 \end{matrix}$$

$$[\eta] = [Z(k)]^{-1}[\zeta][Z(k)]^{-1} \qquad \begin{matrix} 14.2.10 \\ 14.6.4 \end{matrix}$$

In proving the principal theorem of this section, the following lemma will be used.

## Lemma 14.6.1

If $[Z(s)]$ is $PR$ and has no poles or zeros at the origin and or at infinity, then $z_{pp}(k)$ (an element of the principal diagonal of $[Z(k)]$) is bounded from above and below, that is, $0 < z_{pp}(k) < \infty$ for $0 \leq k \leq \infty$.

### Proof

Clearly since $z_{pp}(s)$ is prf, it is bounded along the positive real axis, except, perhaps, at the origin or at infinity. Suppose $z_{pp}(k) = 0$ for $k \to \infty$. Constructing the associated impedance function, we get

$$Z(k) = \sum z_{ij} n_i n_j \qquad \text{14.6.5}$$

This quantity must be positive for all values of $n_j$ and $n_i$. Let all the $n$'s be zero except $n_p$ and $n_q$. This yields

$$Z(k) = z_{pp}(k) n_p{}^2 + 2 z_{pq}(k) n_p n_q + z_{qq}(k) n_q{}^2 \qquad \text{14.6.6}$$

Clearly the only way this quantity will be positive for all the $n$'s when $z_{pp}(k)$ is zero is that $z_{pq}(k)$ is also zero. It follows that as $k \to \infty$ at least one row of $[Z(k)]$ is identically zero. Then det. $[Z(k)]$ is zero at infinity and $[Z(s)]^{-1}$ has a pole at the origin. This is a contradiction.

*Proof completed*

## Theorem 14.6.1

If $[Z(s)]$ is a symmetric, nonsingular $PR$ matrix, and

(I). $\operatorname{Re}[Z(j\omega_0)] = [0]$,

(II). $[Z(s)]$ has no poles and zeros on the $j$ axis*

then it is possible to find a constant $k(k > 0)$ such that either $[\zeta]$ (defined in Eq. 14.6.2) and $[\eta]$ (defined in Eq. 14.6.3) or their inverses have a pole at $j\omega_0$.

### Proof

It is observed in Eq. 14.6.2 that $[\zeta]$ may have a pole at $j\omega_0$ if

$$\Delta_1 \equiv |k[Z(k)] - s[Z(s)]| = 0 \qquad \text{14.6.7}$$

---

* This is more restrictive than necessary. It will suffice to remove only poles and zeros at the origin and infinity. However it is basic to remove all $j$ axis poles and zeros a priori—the "chop-chop" technique.

Its inverse may have a pole if

$$\Delta_2 \equiv |k[Z(s)] - s[Z(k)]| = 0 \qquad \text{14.6.8}$$

Note from Eq. 14.6.4 that $[\zeta]$ and $[\eta]$ (or their respective inverses) must have the same poles. Thus to prove the theorem select $k$ such that either $\Delta_1$ or $\Delta_2$ is zero at $j\omega_0$. Expanding $\Delta_1$ and $\Delta_2$ for a $2 \times 2$ matrix we get

$$\Delta_1 = \big(kz_{11}(k) - j\omega_0 z_{11}(j\omega_0)\big)\big(kz_{22}(k) - j\omega_0 z_{22}(j\omega_0)\big)$$
$$- \big(kz_{12}(k) - j\omega_0 z_{12}(j\omega_0)\big)^2 \qquad \text{14.6.9}$$

and

$$\Delta_2 = \big(kz_{11}(j\omega_0) - j\omega_0 z_{11}(k)\big)\big(kz_{22}(j\omega_0) - j\omega_0 z_{22}(k)\big)$$
$$- \big(kz_{12}(j\omega_0) - j\omega_0 z_{12}(k)\big)^2 \qquad \text{14.6.10}$$

Because of condition (I) the quantities $j\omega_0 z_{pq}(j\omega_0)$ and $z_{pq}(j\omega_0)/j\omega_0$ are real. Assuming that $j\omega_0 z_{11}(j\omega_0)$ is positive we may select $k$ such that $[kz_{11}(k) - j\omega_0 z_{11}(j\omega_0)] = 0$. This can always be done since $z_{11}(k)$ is bounded (Lemma 14.6.1), and therefore the quantity $kz_{11}(k)$ may assume any value from zero to infinity. For this value of $k$, $\Delta_1$ becomes

$$\Delta_1 = - [kz_{12}(k) - j\omega_0 z_{12}(j\omega_0)]^2 < 0$$

However if $k$ is made large enough, $\Delta_1$ approaches the positive quantity $k^2|Z(k)|$. This means that as $k$ goes from zero to infinity $\Delta_1$ changes sign and hence goes through zero. If $j\omega_0 z_{11}(j\omega_0)$ is negative, then $z_{11}(j\omega_0)/j\omega_0$ is positive. It follows that $\Delta_2$ goes through zero for some value of $k > 0$. This completes the proof of the theorem for the $2 \times 2$ matrix.

It is observed that both conditions (I) and (II) are sufficient but not necessary. It is possible that in some cases one positive $k$ may force the real and the imaginary parts to go to zero simultaneously without condition (I). Likewise the $z_{pp}(k)$ does not have to be bounded for one of the $\Delta$'s to change sign as $k$ increases.

To continue the proof for a $3 \times 3$ matrix, we shall use the determinant expansion*

$$|a_{pq}| = \frac{(a_{11}a_{22} - a_{12}{}^2)(a_{11}a_{33} - a_{13}{}^2) - (a_{11}a_{23} - a_{12}a_{13})^2}{a_{11}} \qquad \text{14.6.11}$$

The factor $(a_{11}a_{22} - a_{12}{}^2)$ is of the form of Eqs. 14.6.9 and 14.6.10 and therefore can be made zero for either $\Delta_1$ or $\Delta_2$ which means that the respective $\Delta$ will be negative for some $k$. Suppose this happens to $\Delta_1$. As $k$ approaches infinity $\Delta_1$ approaches the positive quantity

---

* See Eq. 13.1.13 where this expansion is developed.

$k^3|Z(k)|$, and thus again it must go through zero. This process may be continued to show that either $\Delta_1$ or $\Delta_2$ always may be made zero for some positive $k$.

*Proof completed*

Now we are in a position to devise a synthesis procedure which is based on the Bott-Duffin synthesis for a 1-port. This requires us to

(1). Tailor $[Z(s)]$ such that it has no poles or zeros on the $j$ axis and Re $[Z(j\omega_0)] = [0]$.

(2). Apply the matrix decomposition given in Eqs. 14.6.2–14.6.3.

(3). Select $k$ such that $[\zeta]$ and $[\eta]$ or their inverses have a pole at $j\omega_0$.

(4). Remove that pole and repeat (1).

We pause to investigate the degree of the termination $[\zeta]$ in the Bott-Duffin $n$-port network after the generated $j\omega_0$ pole has been removed. Recall (Section 14.2) that $[\zeta]$ has the same degree as $[Z(s)]$. Let $[\zeta^1]$ define the remainder matrix and $[K]$ the residue matrix at the pole $j\omega_0$. Then

$$[\zeta] = [\zeta^1] + \frac{2s}{s^2 + \omega_0^2}[K] \qquad\qquad 14.6.12$$

## Theorem 14.6.2

If $[Z(s)]$ is a symmetric $n \times n$ nonsingular $PR$ matrix, and

(I). it has no $j$ axis poles and zeros

(II). Ev $[Z(j\omega_0)] = [0]$

then $[K]$ defined in 14.6.12 is nonsingular.

It is important to note that the above two constraints are precisely the same as in Theorem 14.6.1. Hence the results of the above theorem apply to those of Theorem 14.6.1.

*Proof*

Utilizing the expression Ev $[Y] = [Z(s)]^{-1}$ Ev $[Z(s)][Z(-s)]^{-1}$, we get

$$\text{det. Ev } [\zeta]^{-1} = \frac{(s^2 + \omega_0^2)^{2n}|\text{Ev }[\zeta^1]|}{|(s^2 + \omega_0^2)[\zeta^1] + 2s[K]||(s^2 + \omega_0^2)[\zeta^1] - 2s[K]|} \qquad 14.6.13$$

$$\equiv (s^2 + \omega_0^2)^{2\gamma}f(s)$$

Suppose $[K]$ is singular. At $s = j\omega_0$

$$|(s^2 + \omega_0^2)[\zeta^1] \pm 2s[K]| = \pm 2j\omega_0|K| = 0 \qquad\qquad 14.6.14$$

Then the denominator of Eq. 14.6.13 has the factor $(s^2 + \omega_0{}^2)^2$, and therefore $\gamma$ is less than $n$. Now

$$\text{Ev } [\zeta]^{-1} = \text{Ev } [Z_1(s)]^{-1} \qquad \text{(by 14.6.2)} \qquad \textbf{14.6.15}$$

and furthermore

$$\text{Ev } [Z_1(s)]^{-1} = (k^2 - s^2) \, (k[Z(s)] - s[Z(k)])^{-1} \text{ Ev } [Z(s)] \times \qquad \textbf{14.6.16}$$
$$(k[Z(-s)] + s[Z(k)])^{-1} \qquad \text{(by 14.6.1)}$$

Recall that $[\zeta]$ has a pole at $j\omega_0$ because $k[Z(k)] - s[Z(s)]$ (not $k[Z(s)] - s[Z(k)])$ is made singular at $j\omega_0$. It follows that also det. Ev $[Z(s)]$ $= (s^2 + \omega_0{}^2)^2 \gamma f_1(s)$ ($f_1(s)$ is some even function of $s$). But Ev $[Z(j\omega_0)]$ $= [0]$, which means that each member of the matrix has the factor $(s^2 + \omega_0{}^2)^2$.[*] Thus the determinant $|\text{Ev } [Z(s)]|$ must have the factor $(s^2 + \omega_0{}^2)^{2n}$ unless the denominator has a part of this factor. But then at least one of the members of Ev $[Z(s)]$ has a pole at $j\omega_0$. This, however, is excluded by the first constraint. Then $\gamma = n$ and $[K]$ may not be singular. This completes the proof of the theorem.

### Corollary 14.6.1

The degree of the termination $[\zeta]$ in the Bott-Duffin $n$-port network after the generated $j\omega_0$ is removed is $2n$ less than that of $[Z(s)]$.

*Proof*

By the above theorem, the degree of $\dfrac{s}{s^2 + \omega_0{}^2} \, [K]$ is $2n$. Hence the degree of $[\zeta]$ is $2n$ higher than the degree of $[\zeta^1]$ (see Eq. 14.6.12). But the degree of $[\zeta]$ is the same as that of $[Z(s)]$, and therefore the degree of $[Z(s)]$ is $2n$ higher than the degree of $[\zeta^1]$.

*Proof completed*

### Example 14.6.1

Realize the following impedance matrix:

$$[Z(s)] = \begin{bmatrix} \dfrac{s^2 + s + 2}{2s^2 + s + 1} & \dfrac{1}{2} \dfrac{s^2 + 3s + 4}{4s^2 + 3s + 1} \\[3mm] \dfrac{1}{2} \dfrac{s^2 + 3s + 4}{4s^2 + 3s + 1} & \dfrac{s^2 + 2s + 3}{3s^2 + 2s + 1} \end{bmatrix} \qquad \textbf{14.6.17}$$

*Solution*

This matrix is already in the form Re $[Z(j)] = [0]$. Hence we have to find a positive $k$ such that either $\Delta_1$ or $\Delta_2$ is zero at $s = j$ (see Eqs. 14.6.7 and 14.6.8). It turns out that $k = 1$ makes $\Delta_1 = 0$ at $s = j$. Accordingly, both $[\zeta]$ and $[\eta]$

---

[*] See Lemma B.1 in Appendix B.

will have at least one pole at $s = j$. Calculate $[\zeta]$ and remove this pole (and its conjugate). This gives:

$$[\zeta] = \frac{s}{s^2 + 1} \begin{bmatrix} \dfrac{42}{17} & \dfrac{39}{17} \\[2mm] \dfrac{39}{17} & \dfrac{69}{17} \end{bmatrix}$$

$$+ \begin{bmatrix} \dfrac{128s^4 + \dfrac{3310}{17} s^3 + \dfrac{2246}{17} s^2 + \dfrac{758}{17} s + 6}{58s^4 + 89s^3 + 61s^2 + 21s + 3} & \dfrac{100s^4 + \dfrac{2702}{17} s^3 + \dfrac{1918}{17} s^2 + \dfrac{682}{17} s + 6}{58s^4 + 89s^3 + 61s^2 + 21s + 3} \\[6mm] \dfrac{100s^4 + \dfrac{2702}{17} s^3 + \dfrac{1918}{17} s^2 + \dfrac{682}{17} s + 6}{58s^4 + 89s^3 + 61s^2 + 21s + 3} & \dfrac{176s^4 + \dfrac{4600}{17} s^3 + \dfrac{3158}{17} s^2 + \dfrac{1085}{17} s + 9}{58s^4 + 89s^3 + 61s^2 + 21s + 3} \end{bmatrix} \quad \textbf{14.6.18}$$

Now $[\eta]$ may be calculated directly from the definition 14.6.3, although it probably will be easier to use the congruence transformation $[\eta] = [Z(k)]^{-1}[\zeta][Z(k)]^{-1}$ given in 14.6.4. Having these results permits writing

$$[Z_1(s)]^{-1} = \frac{4s}{3} \begin{bmatrix} 1 & -\tfrac{1}{2} \\ -\tfrac{1}{2} & 1 \end{bmatrix} +$$

$$\begin{bmatrix} \dfrac{s}{s^2 + 1} \begin{bmatrix} \dfrac{42}{17} & \dfrac{39}{17} \\[2mm] \dfrac{39}{17} & \dfrac{69}{17} \end{bmatrix} + \begin{bmatrix} \dfrac{128s^4 + \dfrac{3310}{17} s^3 + \dfrac{2246}{17} s^2 + \dfrac{758}{17} s + 6}{58s^4 + 89s^3 + 61s^2 + 21s + 3} & \dfrac{100s^4 + \dfrac{2702}{17} s^3 + \dfrac{1918}{17} s^2 + \dfrac{682}{17} s + 6}{58s^4 + 89s^3 + 61s^2 + 21s + 3} \\[6mm] \dfrac{100s^4 + \dfrac{2702}{17} s^3 + \dfrac{1918}{17} s^2 + \dfrac{682}{17} s + 6}{58s^4 + 89s^3 + 61s^2 + 21s + 3} & \dfrac{176s^4 + \dfrac{4600}{17} s^3 + \dfrac{3158}{17} s^2 + \dfrac{1085}{17} s + 9}{58s^4 + 89s^3 + 61s^2 + 21s + 3} \end{bmatrix} \end{bmatrix}^{-1}$$

**14.6.19a**

$$[Z_2(s)]^{-1} = \frac{4}{3s} \begin{bmatrix} 1 & -\tfrac{1}{2} \\ -\tfrac{1}{2} & 1 \end{bmatrix} + \frac{s}{s^2 + 1} \begin{bmatrix} \dfrac{36}{17} & \dfrac{-12}{17} \\[2mm] \dfrac{-12}{17} & \dfrac{72}{17} \end{bmatrix} +$$

$$
\begin{bmatrix}
\dfrac{4\left(32s^4 + \dfrac{1740}{51}s^3 + \dfrac{1490}{51}s^2 + \dfrac{463}{51}s + 1\right)}{58s^4 + 89s^3 + 61s^2 + 21s + 3} \\[4ex]
\dfrac{-2\left(24s^3 + \dfrac{1960}{51}s^3 + \dfrac{1232}{51}s^2 + \dfrac{184}{51}s\right)}{58s^4 + 89s^3 + 61s^2 + 21s + 3} \\[4ex]
\dfrac{-2\left(24s^4 + \dfrac{1960}{51}s^3 + \dfrac{1232}{51}s^2 + \dfrac{184}{51}s\right)}{58s^4 + 89s^3 + 61s^2 + 21s + 3} \\[4ex]
\dfrac{4\left(48s^4 + \dfrac{3315}{51}s^3 + \dfrac{2499}{51}s^2 + \dfrac{740}{51}s + 1\right)}{58s^4 + 89s^3 + 61s^2 + 21s + 3}
\end{bmatrix}
$$

14.6.19b

The final network representation of $[Z(s)]$ is shown in Fig. 14.9. Each 1-port element indicated is prf.

The representation is not given in the form of Fig. 14.1 in order to emphasize the fact that no transformers are necessary. The values indicated in the drawing are as follows:

$$a = b = c = \frac{3}{2s}$$

$$d = \frac{3}{17}\frac{s}{s^2 + 1},\ e = \frac{39}{17}\frac{s}{s^2 + 1},\ f = \frac{30}{17}\frac{s}{s^2 + 1}$$

$$g = \frac{28s^4 + \dfrac{608}{17}s^3 + \dfrac{328}{17}s^2 + \dfrac{76}{17}s}{58s^4 + 89s^3 + 61s^2 + 21s + 3},$$

$$h = \frac{100s^4 + \dfrac{2702}{17}s^3 + \dfrac{1918}{17}s^2 + \dfrac{682}{17}s + 6}{58s^4 + 89s^3 + 61s^2 + 21s + 3},$$

$$i = \frac{76s^4 + \dfrac{1898}{17}s^3 + \dfrac{1240}{17}s^2 + \dfrac{403}{17}s + 3}{58s^4 + 89s^3 + 61s^2 + 21s + 3}$$

$$j = k = l = \frac{3s}{2}$$

$$m = \frac{17}{24}\left(\frac{s^2 + 1}{s}\right),\ n = \frac{17}{12}\left(\frac{s^2 + 1}{s}\right),\ o = \frac{17}{60}\left(\frac{s^2 + 1}{s}\right)$$

$$p = \frac{58s^4 + 89s^3 + 61s^2 + 21s + 3}{80s^4 + \dfrac{3040}{51}s^3 + \dfrac{3496}{51}s^2 + \dfrac{1484}{51}s + 4},$$

$$q = \frac{58s^4 + 89s^3 + 61s^2 + 21s + 3}{2\left(24s^4 + \dfrac{1960}{51}s^3 + \dfrac{1232}{51}s^2 + \dfrac{184}{51}s\right)},$$

$$r = \frac{58s^4 + 89s^3 + 61s^2 + 21s + 3}{144s^4 + \dfrac{9340}{51}s^3 + \dfrac{7532}{51}s^2 + \dfrac{2592}{51}s + 4}$$

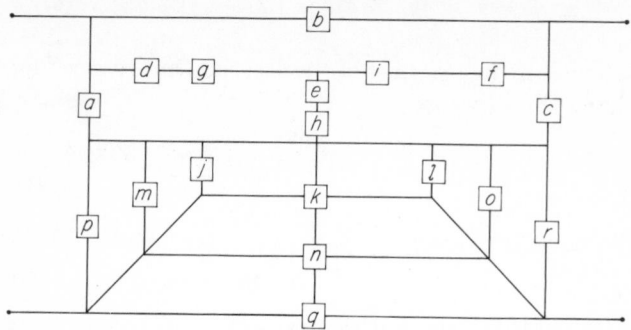

Fig. 14.9. A realization of [Z(s)] in Example 14.6.1. The values indicated
are given in the text

## TAILORING [Z(S)] TO BE MINIMUM RESISTIVE IN THE ABSOLUTE SENSE  14.7

In the previous section it was shown that $[Z(s)]$ may be reduced
in degree by $2n$ by a Bott-Duffin-like $n$-port process if the function
is minimum resistive in the absolute sense $(\text{Re } [Z(j\omega_0)] = [0])$. In
order to tailor $[Z(s)]$ into this form we shall express $[Z(s)]$ in terms
of two other impedance matrices with two "built-in" arbitrary
constants. One of the terms will be of the right form:

$$[Z(s)] = \frac{(s^2 + ab)^2[Z(s)] - (a + b)^2 s(ab[A] + s^2[B])}{s^4 - s^2(a^2 + b^2) + a^2b^2}$$

$$+ (a + b)^2 s \frac{ab[A] + s^2[B] - s[Z(s)]}{s^4 - s^2(a^2 + b^2) + a^2b^2} \equiv [Z_1(s)] + [Z_2(s)]$$

14.7.1

where

$$[A] = \frac{a[Z(b)] - b[Z(a)]}{a^2 - b^2}, \quad [B] = \frac{a[Z(a)] - b[Z(b)]}{a^2 - b^2}$$

$a$ and $b$ are real or complex conjugates in the $r.h.p.$

### Theorem 14.7.1

If $[Z(s)]$ is an $n$ by $n$ symmetric $PR$ matrix, then (1). $[Z_1(s)]$ and
$[Z_2(s)]$ as given in Eq. 14.7.1 are also symmetric $PR$ matrices, and
(2) if $[Z(s)]$ is nonsingular and $a$ and $b$ are roots of det. Ev $[Z(s)] = 0$,
then the degree of $[Z_1(s)]$ and that of $[Z_2(s)]$ are at most $2n - 2$
larger than that of $[Z(s)]$.

### Proof

(1). The matrices $[A]$ and $[B]$ are real as can be verified by setting

$a = x + jy$, $b = x - jy$, $[Z(a)] = [U] + j[V]$, and $[Z(b)] = [U] - j[V]$.

Constructing the real part of the associate impedance functions of $[Z_1(s)]$ and $[Z_2(s)]$ we get

$$[N]_t \text{ Re } [Z_1(s)][N] = \frac{(-\omega^2 + ab)^2}{\omega^4 + \omega^2(a^2 + b^2) + a^2b^2} [N]_t \text{ Re } [Z(s)][N]$$

and 14.7.2

$$[N]_t \text{ Re } [Z_2(s)][N] = \frac{(a + b)^2\omega^2}{\omega^4 + \omega^2(a^2 + b^2) + a^2b^2} [N]_t \text{ Re } [Z(s)][N]$$

$$[N] = \text{real column matrix}$$

on the $j$ axis. It follows that the respective real part of the associate impedance functions is positive on the $j$ axis if $[Z(s)]$ is $PR$. Also note that they have $j$ axis poles only if $[Z(s)]$ has them. Hence all the residues of the $j$ axis poles of the associate impedance functions $Z(s)$, $Z_1(s)$, and $Z_2(s)$ are positive. Furthermore, both matrices have built-in $r.h.p.$ zeros which cancel the only (two) possible $r.h.p.$ poles. Thus both $[Z_1(s)]$ and $[Z_2(s)]$ are analytic in the $r.h.p.$ Application of the minimum real-value theorem shows that the respective real part of the associate impedance functions is positive throughout the $r.h.p.$ and the matrices are $PR$. Note that both matrices are symmetric comprising a sum of symmetric matrices. The proof of (1) is now completed.

(2). It is observed that the denominator of $[Z_1(s)]$ and $[Z_2(s)]$ is apparently $4n$ higher in degree than that of $[Z(s)]$. However each numerator has two built-in zeros lowering the maximum degree to $2n$ higher than that of $[Z(s)]$. Furthermore, by setting $s = -a$ it is seen that a factor $(s + a)$ would also cancel from the numerator and the denominator of det. $[Z_1(s)]$ and of det. $[Z_2(s)]$ if this factor is present in det. Ev $[Z(s)]$. It follows that if $a$ and $b$ are roots of det. Ev $[Z(s)]$, then the degree of $[Z_1(s)]$ and that of $[Z_2(s)]$ are at most $2n - 2$ larger than that of $[Z(s)]$. "At most" is used since additional common factors are present if det. Ev $[Z(s)]$ has higher-order zeros at $s = -a$ and $-b$. This completes the proof of (2) and the theorem.

Perhaps it is interesting to note that $[Z_2(s)]$ equals $(a + b)^2[F(s)]$ of Section 14.4. It may be realized by removing its zeros at the origin and at infinity yielding a matrix which is 2 less in degree than that of $[Z(s)]$. On the other hand $[Z_1(s)]$ is a minimum resistance in the absolute sense. Specifically, Re $[Z(j\sqrt{ab})] = [0]$. It may be realized by the Bott-Duffin $n$-port method outlined in the previous section. It follows that each of the final termination after completion of the first cycle will be at least 2 less in degree than $[Z(s)]$ provided of course that $a$ and $b$ are roots of det. Ev $[Z(s)] = 0$.

## PROBLEMS

14.1. In the following impedance matrix det Ev $Z(s)$ has a real axis zero

$$[Z(s)] = \begin{bmatrix} \dfrac{3s+3}{s+2} & 2\dfrac{2s+1}{s+2} \\[3mm] 2\dfrac{2s+1}{s+2} & 4\dfrac{2s+1}{s+2} \end{bmatrix}$$

Utilize the techniques of zero cancellation as explained in the last part of Section 14.2 to realize $[Z(s)]$ by means of the network of Fig. 14.2. Answer: $k = 1$.

14.2. Obtain a cascade realization of Problem 14.1.

14.3. Realize the following impedance matrix by means of the techniques of zero cancellation as outlined in Section 14.4.

$$[Z(s)] = \begin{bmatrix} 4\dfrac{2s+1}{s+2} & 2\dfrac{2s+1}{s+2} \\[3mm] 2\dfrac{2s+1}{s+2} & 3\dfrac{s^2+3s+3}{s^2+3s+2} \end{bmatrix}$$

14.4. Refer to Fig. 14.2. Show that if the impedance of the $2n$-port buffer is given by:

$$a \left[ \begin{array}{c:c} [0] & [I] \\ \hdashline -[I] & [0] \end{array} \right]$$

then $[Z(s)] = [\zeta]^{-1}a^2$. Hence, here the buffer may be defined as a $2n$-port gyrator.

14.5. Repeat problem 14.4 when the impedance matrix of the buffer is

$$sL \left[ \begin{array}{c:c} [B] & [0] \\ \hdashline [0] & [B]^{-1} \end{array} \right]$$

Further show that $[Z(s)] = [B][\zeta][B]$ when $L$ approaches infinity.

14.6. Fig. P14.6 shows a cascade $2n$-port connection. The first element (marked 1) is a congruence transformer whose index matrix is $[A]$. The second element (marked 2) has the impedance matrix given by

$$\left[ \begin{array}{c:c} [Z_{11}] & [Z_{12}] \\ \hdashline [Z_{21}] & [Z_{22}] \end{array} \right]$$

Show that the impedance matrix of the combination is given by

$$[Z] = \left[ \begin{array}{c:c} [A]_t[Z_{11}][A] & [A]_t[Z_{12}] \\ \hdashline [Z_{21}][A] & [Z_{22}] \end{array} \right]$$

Use these results to show that only two gyrators are necessary to realize Fig. 14.6 if congruence transformers are employed.

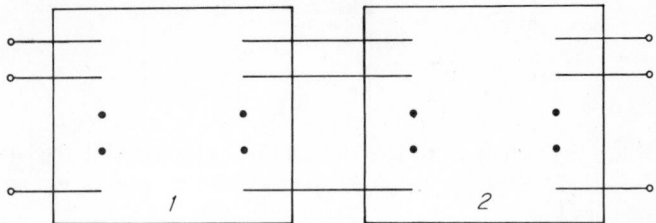

**Fig. P 14.6**

14.7. In the following impedance matrix Ev $[Z(j)] = [0]$. Realize this function by means of the method of Section 14.6.

$$\begin{bmatrix} \dfrac{s^2 + 2s + 3}{3s^2 + 2s + 1} & \dfrac{1}{2}\dfrac{s^2 + 4s + 5}{5s^2 + 4s + 1} \\[4mm] \dfrac{1}{2}\dfrac{s^2 + 4s + 5}{5s^2 + 4s + 1} & \dfrac{s^2 + 3s + 4}{4s^2 + 3s + 1} \end{bmatrix}$$

Hint: The problem is very similar to that in Example 14.6.1. Further $k = 1$.

14.8. Refer back to problem 14.3. Obtain $[Z_1(s)]$ and $[Z_2(s)]$ corresponding to Eq. 14.7.1 with the constants $a$ and $b$ which were selected in problem 14.3. What are the degrees of $[Z(s)]$, $[Z_1(s)]$ and $[Z_2(s)]$ respectively?

## FURTHER READING

14.1. Bayard, M., "Synthesis of $n$-Terminal Pair Networks," Proc. Symposium on Modern Network Synthesis, Polytechnic Institute of Brooklyn (1952).

14.2. Belevitch, V., "On the Brune Process for $n$-Ports," *IRE Trans. on Circuit Theory*, Vol. CT-7, pp. 280–296, Sept. (1960).

14.3. Keitzer, E. E., "Some Problems of Network Analysis and Synthesis," Doctoral Dissertation, College of Engineering and Science, Carnegie Inst. of Tech., Pittsburgh, Pennsylvania, May 1954.

14.4. McMillan, Brockway, "Introduction to Formal Realizability Theory," *The Bell System Technical Journal*, Vol. 31, pp. 217–299 and 541–600 (1952).

14.5. Nain, H. J., "Synthesis of $n$-Port Networks," Ph.D. Dissertation, Engr. Division, Case Institute of Technology, Cleveland, Ohio, June 1962.

14.6. Tellegen, B. D. H., "Synthesis of $2n$-poles by Networks Containing the Minimum Number of Elements," *J. of Math. and Phys.*, Vol. 32, pp. 1–18 (1953).

14.7. Youla, D. C., "Weissfloch Equivalents for Lossless $2n$-ports," *IRE Trans. on Circuit Theory*, Vol. CT-7, pp. 193–199, Sept. (1960).

# Oono's Synthesis* | CHAPTER 15

From a historical point of view, Gewertz's synthesis procedure for 2 port preceded Oono's method. In Chapter 13 we described a method which reduces to the Gewertz synthesis procedure for the 2-port problem. Now we shall discuss another synthesis procedure which is also due to Oono. The method can be used directly on the even part without completing the matrices; this offers computational advantages. Furthermore, the procedure does not require the repeated generation of inverse $PR$ matrices, and thus no question is raised concerning the convergence of the procedure.

Oono's procedure produces a network for each one of the reduced matrices of a previous chapter (Section 13.9). The process is Darlingtonlike in nature. Accordingly, each reduced matrix is realized as an $(n + 1)$-port, lossless network whose one extra port is terminated in a 1-ohm resistance (Fig. 15.1).

The final synthesis is then accomplished by connecting these single terminated $(n + 1)$-port network in series. The total number of matrices which must be synthesized is equal to the rank of the original even part matrix.

With this chapter we terminate the discussion on $n$-port synthesis in this book.

---

* Oono, Y., "Synthesis of a Finite $2n$-Terminal Network by a Group of Networks Each of Which Contains Only One Ohmic Resistance," *Journal of Math. and Phys.*, Vol. 29, pp. 13–26 (1950).

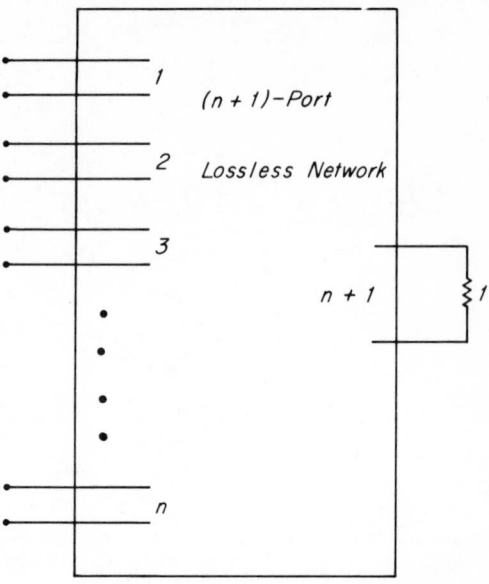

**Fig. 15.1. Oono's realization of a reduced matrix**

## 15.2. DEVELOPMENT

In Fig. 15.1 let the $(n + 1)$-port network equations be given by

$$E_1 = \sum_1^{n+1} z_{1q} I_q$$

$$E_2 = \sum_1^{n+1} z_{2q} I_q$$

$$\cdot \quad \cdot \quad \cdot \quad \cdot \quad \cdot \quad \cdot \quad \quad 15.2.\blacksquare$$

$$E_n = \sum_1^{n+1} z_{nq} I_q$$

$$E_{n+1} = \sum_1^{n+1} z_{(n+1)q} I_q$$

Since the last port is terminated in a 1-ohm resistance, we have

$$E_{n+1} = \sum_1^{n+1} z_{(n+1)q} I_q = -I_{n+1} \qquad \textbf{15.2.2}$$

and therefore

$$-I_{n+1}(1 + z_{(n+1)(n+1)}) = \sum_1^n z_{(n+1)q} I_q \qquad \textbf{15.2.3}$$

Eliminating $I_{n+1}$ from Eqs. 15.2.1, we get

$$E_1 = \sum_1^n z_{1q} I_q + z_{1(n+1)} I_q$$

$$= \sum_1^n \left( z_{1q} - \frac{z_{1(n+1)} z_{(n+1)q}}{1 + z_{(n+1)(n+1)}} \right) I_q$$

$$E_2 = \sum_1^n \left( z_{2q} - \frac{z_{2(n+1)} z_{(n+1)q}}{1 + z_{(n+1)(n+1)}} \right) I_q \qquad \textbf{15.2.4}$$

$$\cdot \quad \cdot \quad \cdot \quad \cdot \quad \cdot \quad \cdot \quad \cdot \quad \cdot \quad \cdot \quad \cdot \quad \cdot$$

$$E_n = \sum_1^n \left( z_{nq} - \frac{z_{n(n+1)} z_{(n+1)q}}{1 + z_{(n+1)(n+1)}} \right) I_q$$

which may be interpreted to mean that in the resultant $n$-port matrix $[Z'(s)]$

$$z'_{pq} = z_{pq} - \frac{z_{p(n+1)} z_{q(n+1)}}{1 + z_{(n+1)(n+1)}}$$

$$\equiv \frac{m_{pq} + n_{pq}}{m_2 + n_2} \quad (m \text{ even, } n \text{ odd; in the reduced matrix}) \qquad \textbf{15.2.5a}$$

Following the Darlington synthesis pattern (Section 7.2), let the $(n + 1)$ port be lossless; henceforth this network will be called Dono's network:

$$z'_{pq} = z_{pq} \frac{1 + (z_{pq} z_{(n+1)(n+1)} - z_{p(n+1)} z_{q(n+1)})/z_{pq}}{1 + z_{(n+1)(n+1)}}$$

$$\equiv \frac{m_{pq} + n_{pq}}{m_2 + n_2} = \frac{m_{pq}}{n_2} \times \frac{1 + n_{pq}/m_{pq}}{1 + m_2/n_2} \qquad Case\ A \quad \textbf{15.2.5b}$$

$$= \frac{n_{pq}}{m_2} \times \frac{1 + m_{pq}/n_{pq}}{1 + n_2/m_2} \qquad Case\ B \quad \textbf{15.2.5c}$$

We may make the following identities:

| Case A | | Case B | |
|---|---|---|---|
| $z_{pq} = \dfrac{m_{pq}}{n_2}$ | | $z_{pq} = \dfrac{n_{pq}}{m_2}$ | 15.2.6 |
| $z_{(n+1)(n+1)} = \dfrac{m_2}{n_2}$ | | $z_{(n+1)(n+1)} = \dfrac{n_2}{m_2}$ | 15.2.7 |

and

$$z_{p(n+1)}z_{q(n+1)} = \frac{m_{pq}m_2 - n_{pq}n_2}{n_2{}^2} \qquad z_{p(n+1)}z_{q(n+1)} = \frac{n_{pq}n_2 - m_{pq}m_2}{m_2{}^2} \qquad 15.2.8$$

Note that the numerator of Eq. 15.2.8 is the numerator of the respective even part. If $p = q$, we have a member of the principal diagonal, and the equation indicates that the term must be a perfect square. Can this be achieved simultaneously for all members of the principal diagonal? The answer is yes.

## Lemma 15.2.1

If all the elements of a reduced matrix are brought into a common denominator and if the numerator of the even part is a perfect square for one member of the principal diagonal, then all members of the principal diagonal have a perfect square numerator.

### Proof

The even-part matrix of a reduced matrix is of rank 1. Hence

$$\text{num. Ev } z'_{pq} = \sqrt{\text{num. Ev } z'_{pp} \times \text{num. Ev } z'_{qq}} \qquad 15.2.9$$

Furthermore, Ev $z'_{pq}$ is rational; if num. Ev $z'_{pp}$ is a perfect square, so is num. Ev. $z'_{qq}$. Then all the principal diagonal elements have this property.

*Proof completed*

This lemma may be interpreted to say that the surplus factor that will make the numerator of one principal diagonal member a perfect square will do the same to the rest of the members.

Thus, in trying to determine all the elements in Oono's matrix, all the $pq$ $(n \times n)$ elements may be obtained from Eq. 15.2.6, whereas the rest of the elements are obtained from Eq. 15.2.7 and 15.2.8. Setting $p = q$ in Eq. 15.2.8, we get

| Case A | | Case B | |
|---|---|---|---|
| $z_{p(n+1)} = \dfrac{\sqrt{m_{pp}m_2 - n_{pp}n_2}}{n_2}$ | | $z_{p(n+1)} = \dfrac{\sqrt{n_{pp}n_2 - m_{pp}m_2}}{m_2}$ | 15.2.10 |

It is important to note that this is the same result as would be obtained if both $z_{p(n+1)}$ and $z_{q(n+1)}$ were obtained directly from Eq. 15.2.8 by use of Eq. 15.2.9. Thus (*Case A*)

$$z_{p(n+1)}z_{q(n+1)} = \frac{m_{pq}m_2 - n_{pq}n_2}{n_2^2} = \frac{\text{num. Ev } z'_{pq}}{n_2^2}$$

$$= \frac{\sqrt{\text{num. Ev } z'_{pp}}}{n_2} \frac{\sqrt{\text{num. Ev } z'_{qq}}}{n_2} \qquad \textbf{15.2.11}$$

permitting the choice of $z_{n(n+1)}$ as in Eq. 15.2.10.

Eqs. 15.2.6, 7, and 8 imply a strong interrelation between the residues at the poles of the individual members. Let $[K^i]$ be the residue matrix of Oono's matrix at the $i^{\text{th}}$ pole.

## Lemma 15.2.2

The $(n + 1) \times (n + 1)$ lossless matrix (Oono's matrix) associated with Oono's realization of a reduced matrix possesses a residue matrix, $[K^i]$, at the $i^{\text{th}}$ pole which is a resistive matrix of rank 1.

### Proof

(1). Note that since the principal diagonal elements are prf $m_{pp} + n_2$ and $m_2 + n_2$ are Hurwitz. Hence (*Case A*) $m_{pp}/n_2$ and $m_2/n_2$ are reactance functions which means that all the principal diagonal elements have positive residues.

(2). Computing the value of the residue $(2 \times 2)$ minor $|K|^{\alpha}$ at a zero $(s = j\omega_i)$ of $n_2$, we have

$$|K|^{\alpha} \equiv k_{pq}{}^i k_{(n+1)(n+1)}{}^i - k_{p(n+1)}{}^i k_{q(n+1)}{}^i \qquad \textbf{15.2.12}$$

where (from Eqs. 15.2.6–7, and 15.2.10)

$$k_{pp}{}^i = \frac{m_{pq}}{\frac{d}{ds} n_2} \bigg|_{s=j\omega_1} , \qquad k_{(n+1)(n+1)}{}^i = \frac{m_2}{\frac{d}{ds} n_2} \bigg|_{s=j\omega_i} ,$$

$$k_{p(n+1)}{}^i = \frac{\sqrt{m_{pp}m_2 - n_{pp}n_2}}{\frac{d}{ds} n_2} \bigg|_{s=j\omega_1} ,$$

$$\text{and } k_{q(n+1)}{}^i = \frac{\sqrt{m_{qq}m_2 - n_{qq}n_2}}{\frac{d}{ds} n_2} \bigg|_{s=j\omega_i}$$

Putting these values in 15.2.12, we get

$$|K|^{\alpha} = \frac{m_{pq}m_2 - \sqrt{m_{pp}m_2 - n_{pp}n_2} \sqrt{m_{qq}m_2 - n_{qq}n_2}}{\left(\frac{d}{ds} n_2\right)} \bigg|_{s=j\omega_i} \qquad \textbf{15.2.13}$$

Because of Eq. 15.2.9, this may be written as

$$|K|^\alpha = \left.\frac{m_{pq}m_2 - (m_{pq}m_2 - n_{pq}n_2)}{\left(\dfrac{d}{ds}\,n_2\right)^2}\right|_{s=j\omega_1} = 0 \qquad \text{15.2.14}$$

Then

$$k_{pq}{}^i k_{(n+1)(n+1)}{}^i = k_{p(n+1)}{}^i k_{q(n+1)}{}^i \qquad \text{15.2.15}$$

This equation contains the truth that the residue matrix is of rank 1. This may be shown as follows. Let $p = r$; then

$$k_{rq}{}^i k_{(n+1)(n+1)}{}^i = k_{r(n+1)}{}^i k_{q(n+1)}{}^i \qquad \text{15.2.16}$$

Dividing by Eq. 15.2.15, we get

$$\frac{k_{rq}{}^i}{k_{pq}{}^i} = \frac{k_{r(n+1)}{}^i}{k_{p(n+1)}{}^i} \qquad \text{15.2.17}$$

Similarly if $q = r$, then

$$\frac{k_{rp}{}^i}{k_{pq}{}^i} = \frac{k_{r(n+1)}{}^i}{k_{q(n+1)}{}^i} \qquad \text{15.2.18}$$

Dividing 15.2.17 by 15.2.18, we get

$$\frac{k_{rq}{}^i}{k_{rp}{}^i} = \frac{k_{q(n+1)}{}^i}{k_{p(n+1)}{}^i} \qquad \text{15.2.19}$$

Similarly we may replace the letter $r$ by $t$ giving

$$\frac{k_{rq}{}^i}{k_{rp}{}^i} = \frac{k_{(n+1)q}{}^i}{k_{(n+1)p}{}^i} = \frac{k_{tq}{}^i}{k_{tp}{}^i} \qquad \text{15.2.20}$$

These equations mean that any 2 by 2 minor of the residue matrix $[K^i]$ is singular. Because all 3 by 3 minors can be expressed as a linear sum of 2 by 2 minors, they are also singular. It follows that all the higher-order minors are zero and $[K^i]$ is of rank 1. Hence the $[K^i]$ matrix is of rank 1 and its principal diagonal elements are positive. This is sufficient to show that it represents a resistive matrix, as evidenced by the fact that it may be realized by means of an ideal transformer (Section 13.4) terminated with a resistor at one of its ports.

*Proof completed*

This means that Oono's matrix may be expanded in a partial fraction expansion (as in Eq. 13.8.8). Since each residue matrix is of rank 1, each member of the expansion may be realized as a perfect capacitive or inductive transformer, or as a perfect inductive transformer, one of whose windings is terminated with a capacitor (see Section 13.4).

The fact that each residue matrix is of rank 1 makes it possible to fill each matrix by completing each 2 by 2 minor, once one column or row is evaluated. With this in mind, investigate the residues of the $(n + 1)$, the end column. The members of this column are obtained from Eqs. 15.2.7 and 15.2.10. There is a slight question concerning the sign because of the square root involved in the operation. Only one sign is arbitrary. This may be shown by computing the even part of Eq. 15.2.5. Recall that the $z_{pq}$ terms are all odd functions of $s$. Thus

$$r_{pq} \equiv \text{Ev } z'_{pq} = 0 - \frac{z_{p(n+1)} z_{q(n+1)}}{1 - z_{(n+1)(n+1)}^2} \qquad 15.2.21$$

$$(r_{pq} = \text{member of the even part of the reduced matrix})$$

At the $i^{\text{th}}$ pole this becomes

$$r_{pq} \equiv \text{Ev } z'_{pq}(j\omega_i) = \frac{k_{p(n+1)}{}^i k_{q(n+1)}{}^i}{(k_{(n+1)(n+1)}{}^i)^2} \qquad 15.2.22$$

Thus once the sign of one of these residues is decided upon [in addition to $k_{(n+1)(n+1)}{}^i$], the rest may be obtained from Eq. 15.2.22. Note also that the left side of Eq. 15.2.22 is given in terms of the even part of $z'_{pq}$. In fact, since $z_{(n+1)(n+1)}$ is obtained readily from the common denominator of any member of the even part of the reduced matrix, and since the rest of the terms in the end column are also obtained directly from the even part (Eq. 15.2.10), there follows:

## Theorem 15.2.1

If the even part of a reduced matrix is brought into a common denominator, the residue matrices (of Oono's matrix) may be completely determined directly from the even part without the necessity of completing the reduced matrix from the even part.

This theorem is only a restatement of the fact that each residue matrix can be completed once the end column is constructed and that this column is obtained from the even part of the reduced matrix.

Please note that Eq. 15.2.22 can be used not only for sign determination but also instead of Eq. 15.2.11 to compute the $(n + 1)$ column in Oono's residue matrices once two terms of the column are available. However, it is perhaps wise to use it only to check the results.

## Example 15.2.1

Realize the impedance matrix

$$[Z(s)] = \begin{bmatrix} \dfrac{s+2}{s+1} & \dfrac{s+1}{s+4} \\[2mm] \dfrac{s+1}{s+4} & \dfrac{s+1}{s+3} \end{bmatrix}$$

15.2.23

by means of Oono's method.

### Solution

Obtaining the reduced matrices as shown in Section 13.9, we get

$$\text{Ev } [Z(s)] = \begin{bmatrix} r_{11} & r_{12} \\[2mm] r_{12} & \dfrac{r_{12}{}^2}{r_{11}} \end{bmatrix} + \begin{bmatrix} 0 & 0 \\[2mm] 0 & \dfrac{r_{11}r_{22} - r_{12}{}^2}{r_{11}} \end{bmatrix} \equiv [R_1{}^0] + [R_2{}^0]$$

15.2.24

$[R_2{}^0]$ is a 1-port network and may be realized by the techniques of Chapter 7 directly from its even part.

Evaluating the terms of $[R_1{}^0]$, we get

$$[R_1{}^0] = \begin{bmatrix} \dfrac{4-s^2}{1-s^2} & \dfrac{4-s^2}{16-s^2} \\[3mm] \dfrac{4-s^2}{16-s^2} & \dfrac{(4-s^2)(1-s^2)}{(16-s^2)^2} \end{bmatrix}$$

15.2.25

Bringing the principal diagonal terms into a common denominator and utilizing the surplus factor $(1 - s^2)$, we get

$$[R_1{}^0] = \begin{bmatrix} \dfrac{(s^4 - 20s^2 + 64)^2}{m_2{}^2 - n_2{}^2} & \dfrac{4-s^2}{16-s^2} \\[3mm] \dfrac{4-s^2}{16-s^2} & \dfrac{(s^4 - 5s^2 + 4)^2}{m_2{}^2 - n_2{}^2} \end{bmatrix}$$

15.2.26

where

$$m_2{}^2 - n_2{}^2 = (1 - s^2)(16 - s^2)^2(4 - s^2)$$

$$= \underbrace{(1 + s)(4 + s)^2(2 + s)}_{m_2 + n_2} \times \underbrace{(1 - s)(4 - s)^2(2 - s)}_{m_2 - n_2}$$

It follows that

$$m_2 + n_2 = (s^4 + 42s^2 + 32) + 11s^3 + 64s$$

15.2.27

Proceeding to construct Oono's matrix, we have

$$[Z]_{(\text{Oono's})} = \begin{bmatrix} z_{11} & z_{12} & z_{13} \\ z_{12} & z_{22} & z_{23} \\ z_{13} & z_{23} & z_{33} \end{bmatrix}$$

15.2.28

where

$$z_{33} = \frac{m_2}{n_2} = \frac{s^4 + 42s^2 + 32}{11s^3 + 64}$$

$$z_{23} = \frac{\sqrt{(s^4 - 5s^2 + 4)^2}}{11s^3 + 64}$$

$$z_{13} = \frac{\sqrt{(s^4 - 20s^2 + 64)^2}}{11s^3 + 64}$$

The selection of a positive sign for both $z_{23}$ and $z_{13}$ after taking the square root turns out to be consistent with Eq. 15.2.22. Hence each term of Eq. 15.2.28 may be expressed as follows:

$$z_{33} = \frac{s}{11} + \frac{1}{2s} + \frac{675}{22} \frac{s}{11s^2 + 64}$$

$$z_{23} = \frac{s}{11} + \frac{1}{16s} - \frac{2025}{176} \frac{s}{11s^2 + 64} \qquad \textbf{15.2.29}$$

$$z_{13} = \frac{s}{11} + \frac{1}{s} - \frac{405}{11} \frac{s}{11s^2 + 64}$$

Completing each residue matrix by making use of the fact that they are of rank 1 and that the principal diagonal elements are positive, we get

$$[Z]_{(Oono's)} = \frac{s}{11} \begin{bmatrix} 1 & 1 & 1 \\ 1 & 1 & 1 \\ 1 & 1 & 1 \end{bmatrix} + \frac{1}{s} \begin{bmatrix} 2 & \dfrac{1}{8} & 1 \\ \dfrac{1}{8} & \dfrac{1}{128} & \dfrac{1}{16} \\ 1 & \dfrac{1}{16} & \dfrac{1}{2} \end{bmatrix}$$

$$+ \frac{135}{121} \frac{s}{s^2 + \dfrac{64}{11}} \begin{bmatrix} \dfrac{18}{5} & \dfrac{9}{8} & -3 \\ \dfrac{9}{8} & \dfrac{45}{128} & -\dfrac{15}{16} \\ -3 & -\dfrac{15}{16} & \dfrac{5}{2} \end{bmatrix} \qquad \textbf{15.2.30}$$

which may be realized as in Fig. 15.2.

## PROBLEMS

15.1. Realize by Oono's method

$$[Z] = \begin{bmatrix} \dfrac{s + \frac{1}{2}}{s + 2} & 1 \\ 1 & \dfrac{s + 4}{s + 1} \end{bmatrix}$$

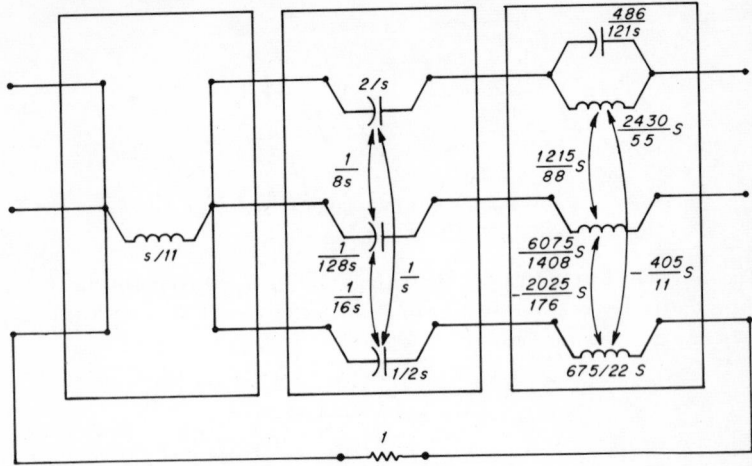

*Fig. 15.2. Oono's network for the reduced matrix* $[R_1]$ *in Example 15.2.1*

## FURTHER READING

RELATED PAPERS

15.1. Oono, Y., "Application of Scattering Matrices to the Synthesis of $n$ Ports," *IRE Trans. on Circuit Theory, PGCT*, Vol. CT-3, No. 2, June (1956).

15.2. Oono, Y., "Formal Realizability of Linear Networks," *Proc. Symposium on Active Network and Feedback Systems, Polytechnic Institute of Brooklyn*, April (1960).

15.3. Oono, Y., "On Pseudo-Scattering Matrices," *Proc. Symposium on Modern Network Synthesis, Polytechnic Institute of Brooklyn*, April (1955).

15.4. Oono, Y., and Yasuura, K., "Synthesis of Finite Passive 2$n$-Terminal Networks with Prescribed Scattering Matrices," *Memoirs of the Faculty of Engineering, Kyushu University*, Vol. 14, No. 2 (1954).

# The Degree of a Rational Matrix Function*

**APPENDIX A**

A rational matrix function $[F(s)]$ is an $n$ by $n$ matrix whose elements are rational functions of the complex variable $s$. Let $[A]$ be an $n$ by $n$ matrix of complex constants and let $|A|$ denote the determinant of such a matrix. Then

$$|[F(s)] + [A]| = \frac{P_A(s)}{Q_A(s)} \qquad \textbf{A.1}$$

where $P_A(s)$ and $Q_A(s)$ are polynomials in $s$ and $P_A(s)$ and $Q_A(s)$ have no common factors. We define the *degree* of $[F(s)]$ to be the maximum degree of $P_A(s)$ for all possible choices of the constant matrix $[A]$. The symbol $\delta[F(s)]$ is used to denote the degree of the matrix $[F(s)]$. The same symbolism is used to denote the degree of a polynomial. With this notation the definition of degree may be expressed by the relation

$$\delta[F(s)] = \max_{[A]} \delta P_A(s) \qquad \textbf{A.2}$$

If $[A]$ is a matrix which yields the maximum we shall say that $[A]$ *uncovers* the degree of $[F(s)]$.

If $n = 1$, then $[F(s)]$ is simply a scalar rational function. In particular $[F(s)]$ might be a polynomial. Then it is seen from A.2 that the new and old definitions of the degree of a polynomial are consistent. More generally, it is seen that A.2 defines the degree of a rational scalar function to be the total number of poles. This pole enumeration includes multiplicity and the pole at infinity.

* The material is based on the paper by Duffin, R. J., and Hazony, D., "The Degree of a Rational Matrix Function," which has been accepted for publication in S.I.A.M. See also Report No. 35, USAF Cambridge Research Center Contract No. AF 19(604)–3997.

### Theorem A.1

If $[B]$ and $[C]$ are $n$ by $n$ matrices of constants, then

$$\delta[B][F(s)][C] = \delta[F(s)] \qquad \text{A.3}$$

provided $[B]$ and $[C]$ are nonsingular.

*Proof*

Multiplying A.1 by $[B]\,|C|$ gives

$$|[B][F(s)][C] + [B][A][C]| = |B|\,|C|\,\frac{P_A(s)}{Q_A(s)}$$

Here $[B][A][C]$ is an arbitrary matrix, so

$$\delta[B][F(s)][C] = \max_{[A]} \delta P_A(s)$$

Comparison of this relation with A.2 yields the proof of A.3.

### Theorem A.2

Let the matrix $[A]$ uncover the degree of $[F(s)]$. Let $[B]$ be an arbitrary $n$ by $n$ matrix of constants and let $t$ be a complex scalar. Then the matrix $[A] + t[B]$ uncovers the degree of $[F(s)]$ except possibly for a finite set of values of $t$.

*Proof*

A standard identity from the theory of determinants gives

$$|[F(s)] + [A] + t[B]| = r_0(s) + tr_1(s) + \cdots + t^n r_n(s) \qquad \text{A.4}$$

Let $q(s)$ be the least common denominator polynomial of the rational functions $r_j(s)$. In order to be definite it is assumed that the leading coefficient of $q(s)$ is unity. Then

$$q(s)|[F(s)] + [A] + t[B]| = p_0(s) + tp_1(s) + \cdots + t^n p_n(s) \qquad \text{A.5}$$

where $p_0(s), \cdots, p_n(s)$ are polynomials in $s$. Thus the right side of A.5 is a polynomial $p(s, t)$ in the variables $s$ and $t$. If $q(s)$ has a factor $s - a$, then by hypothesis there is a $j$ such that $p_j(a) \neq 0$. Thus $p(a, t)$ is a polynomial in $t$ such that the coefficient of $t^j$ does not vanish. Thus $p(a, t) = 0$ for at most $n$ values of $t$. Hence if $q(s)$ has $k$ distinct factors, it follows that $q(s)$ and $p(s, t)$ have no factors in common except possibly for a set of at most $nk$ values of $t$. Let $T$ denote this exceptional set.

From the definition of degree, it follows that

$$\delta[F(s)] \geq \delta p(s, t) \qquad (t \text{ not in } T) \qquad \text{A.6}$$

Let $m$ be the maximum degree of the polynomials $p_j(s)$. Then there is a set $T_0$ of at most $n$ points and such that $\partial^m p(s, t)/\partial s^m = 0$:

$$\delta p(s, t) = m \qquad (t \text{ not in } T_0) \qquad \text{A.7}$$

Moreover by definition of $m$

$$m \geq \delta p_0(s) \qquad \text{A.8}$$

As yet no use has been made of the hypothesis that $[A]$ uncovers the degree of $[F]$. This gives

$$\delta p_0(s) \geq \delta[F(s)] \qquad \text{A.9}$$

Combining relations A.6, 7, 8, and A.9, we get

$$\delta[F(s)] \geq \delta p(s, t) = m \geq \delta p_0(s) \geq \delta[F(s)] \qquad \text{A.10}$$

provided $t$ is not in the finite set $T + T_0$. Evidently A.10 is a set of equalities so $\delta[F(s)] = \delta p(s, t)$. But $p(s, t)$ and $q(s)$ have no common factors if $t$ is not in $T$, so the proof of Theorem A.2 is complete.

## Corollary A.1

There is a nonsingular matrix which uncovers the degree of $[F(s)]$.

### Proof

In Theorem A.2 let $[B]$ be a nonsingular matrix. Then it is easy to show that $[A] + t[B]$ is also nonsingular for all $t$ of large absolute value. In addition, let $t$ be chosen to avoid the finite set $T + T_0$. Then Corollary A.1 follows from Theorem A.2.

## Theorem A.3

There is a polynomial $q(s)$ such that

$$p_C(s) = q(s)|[F(s)] + [C]| \qquad \text{A.11}$$

is a polynomial for an arbitrary $n$ by $n$ constant matrix $[C]$ and $\delta p_C(s) \leq \delta[F(s)]$. Moreover $\delta p_C(s) = \delta[F(s)]$ if $[C]$ uncovers the degree of $[F(s)]$.

### Proof

Such a polynomial $q(s)$ will be termed a *universal denominator* of $[F(s)]$. It is to be shown that the polynomial $q(s)$ defined by relation A.5 is a universal denominator. Take $[B] = [C] - [A]$, then for $t = 1$ we have

$$p(s, 1) = q(s)|[F(s)] + [C]| = p_C(s)$$

and this proves A.11. Note that $\delta p(s, 1) \leq m$, where $m$ is the maximum degree of the polynomials $p_j(s)$. Equation A.10 shows that $m = \delta[F(s)]$, so

$$\delta p(s, 1) \leq \delta[F(s)] \qquad \text{A.12}$$

If it is assumed that $[C]$ uncovers the degree of $[F]$, then $\delta p_C(s) \geq \delta[F(s)]$. This shows that A.12 is an equality, and Theorem A.3 is proved.

### Theorem A.4

If $|F(s)|$ does not vanish identically then $\delta[F(s)]^{-1} = \delta[F(s)]$.

### Proof

By virtue of Corollary A.1 there is a nonsingular matrix $[A]^{-1}$ which uncovers the degree of $[F]^{-1}$. Let $q(s)$ be the universal denominator for $[F(s)]$. Then by Theorem A.3 $p = q|F|$ and $p_A = q|[F] + [A]|$ are polynomials and

$$\delta[F(s)] \geq \delta p_A(s) \qquad \text{A.13}$$

Also

$$|A| \,|[F]^{-1} + [A]^{-1}| = \frac{|[F] + [A]|}{|F|} = \frac{p_A}{p}$$

so it follows that $\delta p_A \geq \delta[F]^{-1}$. Combining this with A.13, we get

$$\delta[F(s)] \geq \delta p_A(s) \geq \delta[F(s)]^{-1} \qquad \text{A.14}$$

But by the symmetry between a matrix and its inverse it follows that

$$\delta[F(s)]^{-1} \geq \delta[F(s)]$$

Thus A.14 is actually an equality, and Theorem A.14 is proved.

Given an $n$ by $n$ matrix $[M]$ there are $\binom{n}{r}^2$ minor determinants of order $r$. Such determinants are obtained by striking out any $n - r$ rows and any $n - r$ columns of $[M]$. The total number of minor determinants is

$$s = \sum_{r=1}^{n} \binom{n}{r}^2$$

Let the minor determinants of $[M]$ be denoted by

$$|M|_i; \quad i = 1, 2, \cdots, s$$

Here $|M|_s$ is taken to be $|M|$. Also define the "empty minor" to be $|M|_0 = 1$.

The *algebraic complement* of the minor $|M|_i$ is denoted by $|M|^i$. Thus $\pm|M|_i$ is the minor determinant formed by the rows and columns which were struck out of $[M]$. The sign is $+$ if an even number of rows and column interchanges brings the minor into leading position. The sign is $-$ if the number of interchanges is odd. Also $|M|^0 = |M|$ and $|M|^s = 1$.

## Lemma A.1

Let $[M]$ and $[N]$ be $n$ by $n$ matrices. Then the determinant of their sum is given by

$$|[M] + [N]| = \sum_0^s |M|_i|N|^i \qquad \text{A.15}$$

### Proof

The demonstration of this lemma is similar to that for the well-known Laplace expansion of a determinant. It is simply necessary to check that the terms occurring on the left occur on the right and vice versa. Details are omitted.

In what follows we shall say that the function $s^{-2}$ has a pole of degree 2 etc.

## Theorem A.5

Let $[A]$ uncover the degree of $[F(s)]$. Then a necessary and sufficient condition that $|[F(s)] + [A]|$ have a pole of degree $h$ is that $|F(s)|$ or some minor determinant of $[F(s)]$ have the same pole of the same degree.

### Proof

Note that the pole at infinity is included in this accounting. Applying the expansion A.15 to $|[F] + [A]|$, we get

$$|[F(s)] + [A]| = \sum_0^s |F(s)|_i|A|^i$$

Let $h$ be a positive integer or zero; let $g$ be a value of $s$ including infinity. Then it is clear from the expansion that if the left side has a pole at $g$ of degree $h$, then at least one term on the right, say $|F(s)|_i|A|^i$, has a pole of degree $h_1$ and $h_1 \geq h$.

Let $|F(s)|_k$ be a minor of the greatest order, say $r$, such that $|F(s)|_k$ has the pole of degree $h_1$. Let $[C]$ be a constant matrix such that all elements are zero except those in the minor $|C|^k$. Moreover, take $|C|^k = 1$. Then again by A.15

$$|[F(s)] + [C]| = \sum_{0}^{s} |F(s)|_i |C|^i \qquad \textbf{A.16}$$

Clearly one term on the right side of A.16 is $|F(s)|_k$, and this term has a pole of degree $h_1$. If some other term of A.16 has $|C|^i \neq 0$ then the order of $|F(s)|_i$ is greater than $r$.

Thus there is only one term on the right side of A.16 with a pole of degree $h_1$. However, it follows from Theorem A.3 that the poles of $|[F(s)] + [C]|$ are of no higher degree than those of $|[F] + [A]|$, so $h_1 \leq h$. Thus $h_1 = h$, and the proof of Theorem A.5 is complete.

The relationships just developed lead to two alternative characterizations of the degree of a rational matrix function. The first alternative characterization is stated as the following theorem.

### Theorem A.6

If $[C]$ is a constant matrix, then

$$\delta \frac{p_C(s)}{q(s)} \equiv \delta |[F(s)] + [C]| \leq \delta[F(s)] \qquad \textbf{A.17}$$

This is an equality if $[C]$ uncovers the degree of $[F(s)]$.

### Proof

Referring to relation A.5, one sees that $p_n(s) = |B|q(s)$. Then if $[B]$ is nonsingular, $\delta q(s) = \delta p_n(s)$. But it was shown that $\delta p_n(s) \leq m = \delta[F(s)]$. This shows that the universal denominator satisfies

$$\delta q(s) \leq \delta[F(s)] \qquad \textbf{A.18}$$

Now refer to Eq. A.11 of Theorem A.3. Consider the two cases: (a). $\delta p_C(s) \geq \delta q(s)$ and (b). $\delta p_C(s) < \delta q(s)$. In case (a)

$$\delta |[F(s)] + [C]| \leq \delta p_C(s) \leq \delta[F(s)] \qquad \textbf{A.19}$$

The second inequality follows from Theorem A.3. In case (b)

$$\delta |[F(s)] + [C]| \leq \delta q(s) \leq \delta[F(s)]$$

The second inequality follows from A.18. This establishes A.17 in all cases.

Now suppose that $[C]$ uncovers the degree of $[F(s)]$. Then by Eq. A.18 and Theorem A.3

$$\delta q(s) \leq \delta[F(s)] = \delta p_C(s)$$

This shows that only case (a) occurs. Moreover, since $p_C(s)$ and $q(s)$ have no common factors, it is seen that A.19 is an equality, and the proof of Theorem A.6 is complete.

It is worth noting that the relationship A.17 may be an equality even if $[C]$ does not uncover the degree. This is seen from the scalar example: $F(s) = s^{-1}$ and $C = 0$. On the other hand, it must not be supposed that relationship A.17 is always an equality. This is clear from the example

$$[F(s)] = \begin{bmatrix} s & 0 \\ 0 & s^{-1} \end{bmatrix}, \qquad [C] = \begin{bmatrix} 0 & 0 \\ 0 & 0 \end{bmatrix}$$

The second alternative characterization of the degree of a rational matrix function is stated as a corollary.

### Corollary A.2

Let $k$ be the number of distinct poles of the rational matrix function $[F(s)]$. Then the degree of $[F(s)]$ may be defined to be

$$\delta[F(s)] = h_1 + h_2 + \cdots + h_k \qquad \text{A.20}$$

Here $h_j$ is the maximum degree to which the $j^{\text{th}}$ pole occurs in the determinant or minor determinants of $[F(s)]$.

### Proof

Equation A.20 is seen to be a direct corollary of Theorems A.5 and A.6.

Thus, three different characterizations of the degree have been given here. The definition given by Corollary A.2 is perhaps the most direct for use in numerical evaluation.

### Corollary A.3

The degree of a minor matrix cannot exceed the degree of the whole matrix.

### Proof

This is a direct consequence of Corollary A.2.

### Theorem A.7

Let $[F(s)]$ and $[G(s)]$ be $n$ by $n$ matrices with rational matrix elements. Then

$$\delta\big([F(s)] + [G(s)]\big) \leq \delta[F(s)] + \delta[G(s)] \qquad \text{A.21}$$

*Proof*

Consider the minor $|[F(s)] + [G(s)]|_k$. It can be expanded in sub-minors by a formula analoguous to A.15. Employing a similar notation to that used in A.15, we get

$$|[F(s)] + [G(s)]|_k = \sum_{0}^{s'} |F(s)|_{ki}|G(s)|_k{}^i \qquad \text{A.22}$$

Suppose that the left side has a pole at $g$ of degree $h$. Then some single term on the right side of A.22 has a pole of at least this degree. But this term on the right is a product of a minor of $[F]$ and a minor of $[G]$. Thus if $h_F$ is the greatest degree of the pole in any minor of $[F]$, $h_G$ is the greatest degree of the pole in any minor of $[G]$. Then

$$h \leq h_F + h_G$$

This relation together with Corollary A.2 proves Theorem A.7.

## Theorem A.8

If $[F(s)]$ is finite at the poles of $[G(s)]$ and $[G(s)]$ is finite at the poles of $[F(s)]$, then

$$\delta\big([F(s)] + [G(s)]\big) = \delta[F(s)] + \delta[G(s)] \qquad \text{A.23}$$

*Proof*

Suppose that $[F(s)]$ has a pole at $g$. Then it may be assumed that there is a minor $|F(s)|_k$ with a pole of degree $h$, and no other minor has a pole of greater degree. In addition it may be supposed that any minor of lower order has a pole of lower degree. Consider then the expansion of $|[F(s)] + [G(s)]|_k$ by sub-minors according to formula A.22. One term in the right side of A.22 is precisely the minor $|F(s)|_k$, and other terms are minors $|F(s)|_i$ of lower order multiplied by minors of $G$. Thus $|[F(s)] + [G(s)]|_k$ has a pole of degree $h$. Taking account in this way of all poles of $[F]$ and then of all poles of $[G]$ and using Corollary A.2, we get

$$\delta\big([F(s)] + [G(s)]\big) \geq \delta[F(s)] + \delta[G(s)]$$

This relation together with Theorem A.7 gives Eq. A.23 and so completes the proof.

The following result is a corollary of Theorem A.3.

## Corollary A.4

Let $[B]$, $[C]$, and $[D]$ be arbitrary $n$ by $n$ matrices of constants. Let $q(s)$ be the universal denominator of $[F(s)]$. Then

$$q(s)|[B][F(s)][C] + [D]| = u(s) \qquad \text{A.24}$$

is a polynomial and $\delta u(s) \le \delta[F(s)]$. Consequently $\delta[B][F(s)][C] \le \delta[F(s)]$.

### Proof

Let $[B_t] = [B] + t[I]$ and $[C_t] = [C] + t[I]$ when $[I]$ is the identity matrix. Then it is easy to show that if the parameter $t$ has small absolute value but $t \ne 0$, then $[B_t]$ and $[C_t]$ are nonsingular. It follows from Theorem A.3 that

$$q(s)|[F(s)] + [B_t]^{-1}[D][C_t]^{-1}|$$

is a polynomial. Multiplying this polynomial by $|B_t| \, |C_t|$, we get

$$q(s)|[B_t][F(s)][C_t] + [D]| = u_t(s) \qquad \text{A.25}$$

which is a polynomial. Moreover, $\delta u_t(s) \le \delta[F(s)]$. Now allow $t$ to approach zero. Then in any finite region excluding the poles of $[F(s)]$ it is clear that $u_t(s)$ converges uniformly to a function $u(s)$. Hence $u(s)$ is a polynomial and $\delta u(s) \le \delta[F(s)]$. Also Eq. A.24 is the limit of Eq. A.25, and the proof of the corollary is complete.

### Theorem A.9

Let $[F(s)]$ and $[G(s)]$ be $n$ by $n$ matrices with rational matrix elements. Then

$$\delta([F(s)][G(s)]) \le \delta[F(s)] + \delta[G(s)] \qquad \text{A.26}$$

### Proof

Let $[A]$ uncover the degree of $[F(s)][G(s)]$. Let $s$ and $w$ denote two independent complex variables, $q(s)$ be the universal denominator for $[F(s)]$, and $r(w)$ be the universal denominator for $[G(w)]$. Then let

$$u(s, w) = q(s)r(w)|[F(s)][G(w)] + [A]| \qquad \text{A.27}$$

According to Corollary A.4, if $w$ is held constant, $u(s, w)$ is a polynomial in $\delta$ of degree not exceeding $\delta[F(s)]$. For the same reason if $s$ is held constant, then $u(s, w)$ is a polynomial in $w$ of degree not exceeding $\delta[G(w)]$. It is clear, therefore, that $u(s, w)$ is a polynomial in $s$ and $w$ together. Moreover

$$\delta u(s, s) \le \delta[G(s)] + \delta[F(s)] \qquad \text{A.28}$$

But if $w = s$, Eq. A.27 gives

$$\delta([F(s)][G(s)]) \le \delta u(s, s) \qquad \text{A.29}$$

and the substitution of this in A.28 yields A.26 and the proof is complete.

## Theorem A.10

Let $[F(s)]$ and $[G(s)]$ be $n$ by $n$ matrices with rational matrix elements. Then there are constant matrices $[C]$ and $[D]$ such that

$$\delta([F(s)] + [C])([G(s)] + [D]) = \delta[F(s)] + \delta[G(s)] \qquad \text{A.30}$$

### Proof

Let $q(s)$ and $r(s)$ be the universal denominators of $[F(s)]$ and $[G(s)]$, respectively. Let $[A]$ uncover the degree of $[F(s)]$ and let $[B]$ be nonsingular. Let $p(s, t)$ be the polynomial defined by Eq. A.5. Since $[A]$ uncovers the degree of $[F(s)]$, it follows that $p_0(s)$ and $q(s)$ do not have a common factor. Since $p_n(s) = |B|q(s)$, and since $|B| \neq 0$, it follows that $p_n(s)$ does not vanish identically. These considerations show that $p_0(s)$ and $p_n(s)$ do not have common factors.

Let $r(s)$ have a factor $s - b$. Then $p(b, t) = 0$ for at most $n$ values of $t$ because $p_0(b)$ and $p_n(b)$ are not both zero. Hence if $r(s)$ has $K$ distinct factors, there is a set $T_1$ of at most $nK$ values such that $r(s)$ and $p(s, t)$ have no common factors if $t$ is not in $T_1$. Let $T$ and $T_0$ be the sets defined in the proof of Theorem A.2. Choose a value of $t$ not in $T + T_0 + T_1$ and let $[C] = [A] + t[B]$. Then

$$q(s)|[F(s)] + [C]| = p_C(s)$$

and $\delta p_C(s) = \delta[F(s)]$. Moreover, $p_C(s)$ has no factor in common with $q(s)r(s)$. Likewise there is a $[D]$ such that

$$r(s)|[G(s)] + [D]| = z_D(s)$$

is a polynomial such that $\delta z_D(s) = \delta[G(s)]$, and $z_D(s)$ has no factors in common with $q(s)r(s)$. Then

$$q(s)r(s)|([F(s)] + [C])([G(s)] + [D])| = p_C(s)z_D(s)$$

From this it follows that

$$\delta[([F(s)] + [C])([G(s)] + [D])] \geq \delta[F(s)] + \delta[G(s)]$$

This together with Eq. A.26 of Theorem A.9 implies Eq. A.30, and the proof is complete.

## FURTHER READING

RELATED PAPERS

A.1. Duffin, R., "Elementary Operations Which Generate Network Matrices," *Amer. Math. Soc.*, Vol. 6, pp. 335–359 (1955).

A.2. Leroy, R., "Sur la Synthese Der Reseaux Passifs a $n$ Paires de Bornes," *Cables and Transmission*, Vol. 4, pp. 234–247 (1950).

A.3. McMillan, Brockway, "Introduction to Formal Realizability Theory," *Bell System Technical Journal*, Vol. 31, pp. 217–299 and 541–600 (1952). Especially see Part II, Sections II and V.

A.4. Tellegen, B. D. H., "Synthesis of 2m-Poles by Networks Containing the Minimum Number of Elements," *Jour. of Math. and Phys.*, Vol. 32 pp. 1–18 (1953).

# Proof of Theorem 14.5.1: Part 2

### Lemma B.1

If $[Z(s)]$ is $PR$ and if Ev $[Z(j\omega_0)] = [0]$, $(\omega_0 \neq 0, \infty)$. Then

$$\frac{d}{d\omega_0} \text{Ev} [Z(j\omega_0)] = [0]$$

*Proof*

Constructing the associate impedance function $[N]_t[Z(s)][N]$ ($[N]$ = real column matrix) and letting all the $n$'s be zero except $n_p$ and $n_q$ we get

$$[N]_t \text{ Ev} [Z(s)][N] = n_p^2 \text{ Ev } z_{pp} + 2n_p n_q \text{ Ev } z_{pq} + n_q^2 \text{ Ev } z_{qq} \geq 0 \text{ on } j \text{ axis}$$

B.1

This is identically zero at $s = j\omega_0$, since Ev $[Z(j\omega_0)] = [0]$. Further-more, $z_{pp}$ and $z_{qq}$ are prf, their respective even part numerator must have the factor $(s^2 + \omega_0^2)^2$. Hence $\frac{d}{ds} \text{ Ev } z_{pp} = 0 = \frac{d}{ds} \text{ Ev } z_{qq}$ at $s = j\omega_0$.

Setting $s = j\omega_0 + \epsilon$, $(\epsilon \to 0^+)$, in B.1 we get

$$[N]_t \text{ Ev} [Z(j\omega_0 + \epsilon)][N] = 2n_p n_q \epsilon \frac{d}{dj\omega_0} \text{ Ev } z_{pq}(j\omega_0) \geq 0$$

The only way this term will be nonnegative for all possible $n$'s is that $\frac{d}{dj\omega_0} \text{ Ev } z_{pq}(j\omega_0) = 0$. It follows that $\frac{d}{ds} \text{ Ev } [Z(s)] = [0]$, $s = j\omega_0$.

*Proof complete*

Please note that $\frac{d}{ds} \text{ Ev } [Z(s)] = [0] = \frac{d}{dj\omega_0} \text{ Ev } [Z(j\omega_0)]$ at $s = j\omega_0$.

In what follows we shall use the following theorem, proven in Section 8.5.

## Theorem 8.5.1

If $Z(s)$ is prf with no $j$ axis poles or zeros, and if Re $Z(j\omega_0) = 0$, then

$$\frac{d}{d\omega_0} \text{Im } Z(j\omega_0) \pm \frac{\text{Im } Z(j\omega_0)}{\omega_0} > 0$$

$$\text{(strict inequality)}$$

The theorem extends to matrices:

## Lemma B.2

If $[Z(s)]$ is $PR$, nonsingular, and it has no poles and zeros on the $j$ axis, and if Re $[Z(j\omega_0)] = [0]$, then $[A]$ and $[B]$

$$[A] = \frac{a[Z(b)] - b[Z(a)]}{a^2 - b^2}$$

$$[B] = \frac{a[Z(a)] - b[Z(b)]}{a^2 - b^2}$$

B.2

are finite and nonsingular ($a = \bar{b} = j\omega_0$).

### Proof

Let $a = \bar{b} = j\omega_0 + \epsilon$ and proceed to evaluate $[A]$ and $[B]$. Ignoring higher order terms in $\epsilon$, we get

$$[A] = \frac{1}{2\epsilon} \left\{ \text{Ev } [Z(j\omega_0)] + \epsilon \left( \text{Ev } \frac{d}{dj\omega_0} [Z(j\omega_0)] - \frac{\text{Im } [Z(j\omega_0)]}{\omega_0} \right) \right\}$$

$$= \frac{1}{2} \left( \frac{d}{d\omega_0} \text{Im } [Z(j\omega_0)] - \frac{\text{Im } [Z(j\omega_0)]}{\omega_0} \right) \quad \text{(by Lemma B-1)}$$

B.3

Similarly

$$[B] = \frac{1}{2} \left( \frac{d}{d\omega_0} \text{Im } [Z(j\omega_0)] + \frac{\text{Im } [Z(j\omega_0)]}{\omega_0} \right)$$

B.4

Hence $[A]$ and $[B]$ are finite. It is yet to show that they are nonsingular. Suppose $[A]$ is singular, then by means of a nonsingular transformation $[A^1] = [C]_t[A][C]$ is a diagonal matrix and at least one of its members is zero, say $a_{pp}^1 = 0$. Applying this transformation to $[Z(s)]$, we get $[Z^1] = [C]_t[Z][C]$. Evaluating $[A^1]$ from $[Z^1]$ gives

$$a_{pp}^1 = \frac{1}{2} \left( \frac{d}{d\omega_0} \text{Im } z_{pp}^1(j\omega_0) - \frac{\text{Im } z_{pp}^1(j\omega_0)}{\omega_0} \right)$$

B.5

But $z_{pp}^1$ is prf and Re $z_{pp}^1(j\omega_0) = 0$. Hence (by Theorem 8.5.1) $a_{pp}^1$ is nonzero. Then $[A]$ and similarly $[B]$ are nonsingular.

*Proof completed*

### Lemma B.3

If $[Z(s)]$ is a nonsingular $PR$ matrix without $j$ axis poles and zeros, but det. Ev $[Z(j\omega_0)] = 0$, then $[A]^{-1}$ and $[B]^{-1}$

$$[A]^{-1} = \left( \frac{a[Z(b)] - b[Z(a)]}{a^2 - b^2} \right)^{-1}, \quad [B]^{-1} = \left( \frac{a[Z(a)] - b[Z(b)]}{a^2 - b^2} \right)^{-1}$$

are finite for $a = \bar{b} = j\omega_0$.

### Proof

Because det. Ev $[Z(j\omega_0)] = 0$, diagonalization of Ev $[Z(j\omega_0)]$ will produce some zero elements on the principal diagonal. Rearrange the rows and columns so that all the zero diagonal elements occupy the first $n - r$ positions on the diagonal ($r$ denotes the rank of Ev $[Z(j\omega_0)]$). Then

$$\text{Ev} [Z^1(j\omega_0)] = [C]_t \, \text{Ev} [Z(j\omega_0][C] = \begin{bmatrix} 0 & & & & & \\ & \cdot & & & & \\ & & \cdot & & & \\ & & & 0 & & \\ & & & & \text{Ev } z_{(n-r+1)(n-r+1)}^1(j\omega_0) & \\ & & & & & \cdot \\ & & & & & \text{Ev } z_{nn}^1(j\omega_0) \end{bmatrix}$$

B.6

Let $a = \bar{b} = j\omega_0 + \epsilon \; (\epsilon \to 0^+)$; hence $[A^1] = [C]_t[A][C]$ is defined. Thus

$$[A^1] = \frac{1}{2\epsilon} \times \begin{bmatrix} 0 & & & & \\ & \cdot & & & \\ & & 0 & & \\ & & & \text{Ev } z_{(n-r+1)(n-r+1)}^1(j\omega_0) & \\ & & & & \cdot \\ & & & & & \cdot \\ & & & & & \text{Ev } z_{nn}^1(j\omega_0) \end{bmatrix} + \begin{bmatrix} a_{11}^1 & \cdots & a_{1(n-r)}^1 & \cdots \\ \cdot & & & \\ \cdot & & & \\ a_{(n-r)1}^1 & \cdot & a_{(n-r)(n-r)}^1 & \cdot \\ \cdot & & & \\ \cdot & & & \\ & & & \cdot \; a_{n,n} \end{bmatrix}$$

B.7

where $a_{pq}^1 = \frac{1}{2} \left( \text{Ev} \frac{d}{dj\omega_0} z_{pq}^1(j\omega_0) - \frac{\text{Od } z_{pq}^1(j\omega_0)}{j\omega_0} \right)$.

Note that the first $(n - r)$ by $(n - r)$ principal matrix minor of $[Z^1]$ is a $PR$ matrix and that its real part at $j\omega_0$ is identically zero. Hence if we calculate the terms in $[A^1]$ corresponding to this minor we have

$$[A_{11}{}^1] = \begin{bmatrix} a_{11}{}^1 & \cdots & a_{1(n-r)}{}^1 \\ \cdot & & \\ \cdot & & \\ a_{(n-r)1}{}^1 & \cdots & a_{(n-r)(n-r)}{}^1 \end{bmatrix} \qquad \text{B.8}$$

Furthermore, by Lemma B.2 this matrix is finite and has an inverse, $[A_{11}{}^1]^{-1}$.

Evaluating $[A^1]^{-1}$ from Eq. B.7 and letting $\epsilon \to 0$, we get

$$A^1]^{-1} = \begin{bmatrix} \begin{bmatrix} a_{11}{}^1 & \cdot & \cdot & a_{1(n-r)}{}^1 \\ \cdot & & & \\ \cdot & & & \\ a_{(n-r)1}{}^1 & \cdot & \cdot & a_{(n-r)(n-r)}{}^1 \end{bmatrix}^{-1} & \begin{matrix} 0 & 0 & \cdot & \cdot \\ & 0 & & \end{matrix} \\ \begin{matrix} 0 \\ 0 \\ \cdot \\ \cdot \end{matrix} & \begin{matrix} \cdot \\ \cdot \\ \cdot & \cdot & 0 \end{matrix} \end{bmatrix} \equiv \begin{bmatrix} [A_{11}{}^1]^{-1} & [0] \\ \hline [0] & [0] \end{bmatrix}$$

$$\text{B.9}$$

Hence $[A^1]^{-1}$ is finite. To complete the proof of the Lemma note that $A]^{-1} = [C][A^1]^{-1}[C]_t$. Similarly $[B]^{-1}$ is also finite.

*Proof completed*

## Lemma B.4

If $[Z(s)]$ is $PR$, nonsingular, without $j$ axis poles or zeros, but det. Ev $[Z(j\omega_0)] = 0$, then $[F(s)]^{-1}$

$$[F(s)]^{-1} = \left( \frac{s}{s^4 - s^2(a^2 + b^2) + a^2 b^2} (ab[A] + s2[B] - s[Z(s)]) \right)^{-1}$$

exists for $a = \bar{b} = j\omega_0$.

*Proof*

Let $a = \bar{b} = j\omega_0 + \epsilon$ $(\epsilon \to 0^+)$ and proceed to evaluate $[F(s)]$ for

$[Z^1(s)] = [C]_t[Z(s)][C]$. The congruence transformation is chosen to diagonalize $[C]_t$ Ev $[Z(j\omega_0)][C]$ (see Lemma B.3). Then

$$[F^1(s)] = \frac{1}{2\epsilon} \times \frac{s}{(s^2 + \omega_0^2)^2} \left\{ \omega_0^2 \begin{bmatrix} 0 & & & & & \\ & \ddots & & & & \\ & & 0 & & & \\ & & & \text{Ev } z_{(n-r+1)(n-r+1)}^1(j\omega_0) & & \\ & & & & \ddots & \\ & & & & & \text{Ev } z_{nn}^1(j\omega_0) \end{bmatrix} + \right.$$

$$\omega_0^2\epsilon \begin{bmatrix} a_{11}^1 & \cdots & \cdots & a_{1(n-r)}^1 & \cdots & \cdots \\ \vdots & & & & & \\ \vdots & & & & & \\ a_{(n-r)1}^1 & & & & & \\ \vdots & & & & & \\ \vdots & & & & & a_{nn}^1 \end{bmatrix} +$$

$$s^2 \begin{bmatrix} 0 & & & & & \\ & \ddots & & & & \\ & & 0 & & & \\ & & & \text{Ev } z_{(n-r+1)(n-r+1)}^1(j\omega_0) & & \\ & & & & \ddots & \\ & & & & & \text{Ev } z_{nn}^1(j\omega_0) \end{bmatrix} +$$

$$\epsilon s^2 \begin{bmatrix} b_{11}^1 & \cdots & \cdots & b_{1(n-r)}^1 & \cdots & \cdots \\ \vdots & & & & & \\ \vdots & & & & & \\ \vdots & & & & & \\ b_{(n-r)1}^1 & & & & & \\ \vdots & & & & & \\ \vdots & & & & & b_{nn}^1 \end{bmatrix} \left. \right\} - \epsilon s[Z^1(s)]$$

B.10

Evaluating the inverse of this expression and letting $\epsilon \to 0$, we get

$$[F^1(s)]^{-1} = 2\frac{(s^2 + \omega_0^2)^2}{s}\left[\begin{array}{c|c} (\omega_0^2[A_{11}{}^1] + s^2[B_{11}{}^1] - s[Z_{11}{}^1])^{-1} & [0] \\ \hline [0] & [0] \end{array}\right] \quad \text{B.11}$$

Hence, essentially, it remains to be shown

$$\omega_0^2[A_{11}{}^1] + s^2[B_{11}{}^1] - s[Z_{11}{}^1] \qquad \text{B.12}$$

is not identically singular. This is indeed the case. The proof is the same as the proof that $[F(s)]$ is not singular in Theorem 14.4.1 (page 300).

*Proof completed*

# INDEX